Electricity
and Electronics

TEACHES MODERN CONCEPTS

by
HOWARD H. GERRISH

Professor, Industrial Arts
San Jose State College, San Jose California
Member of Institute of Electrical and Electronics
Engineers
WA6DBM
(Formerly W8USB and XEIWE)

South Holland, Illinois
THE GOODHEART-WILLCOX CO., Inc.
Publishers

INTRODUCTION

It is the purpose of this text to provide an easy-to-understand source of information on basic fundamentals, for the student who is interested in the rapidly progressing field of Electricity and Electronics. These fundamentals are applicable regardless of changes in circuit concepts.

ELECTRICITY AND ELECTRONICS employs a dual approach to learning:

1. Experimentation and demonstration to assure thorough understanding of principles. The instructional material is arranged to provide continuity in learning, and learning situations which are challenging to the student.

2. Practical application of the principles and skills developed, by constructing inexpensive, professional appearing take-home projects. The projects have proven student appeal and have been thoroughly shop and laboratory tested.

Every effort has been made to relate the principles and projects to actual applications in home and industry.

Upon completion of this course, the student should have a thorough understanding of the modern concepts of Electronics.

Today, broad horizons in Electronics offer a myriad of opportunities for a specialized education, and a lifetime of challenging and personally rewarding employment.

Tape controlled equipment in Warner and Swasey plant being checked by technician.

CONTENTS

Contents

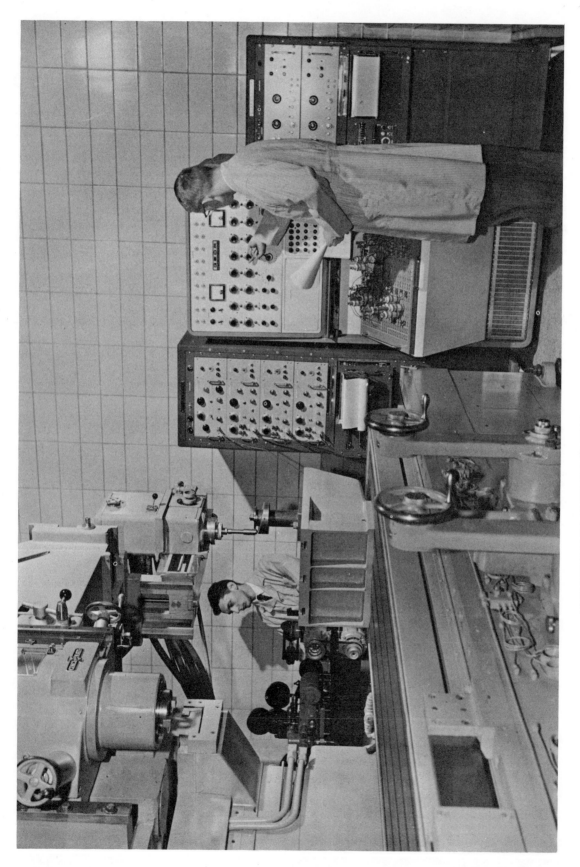

APPLICATION OF ELECTRONIC EQUIPMENT IN INDUSTRY--Computer and electronic equipment being used in modern laboratory.

8

PROJECTS AND ACTIVITIES

1. Static Electricity Experiments
2. Electricity from a Grapefruit
3. Electricity from Nickels and Pennies
4. Voltaic Cell
5. Series and Parallel Cells
6. Photo Electric Control
7. Thermocouple
8. Electricity from Light
9. Series and Parallel Circuits
10. Electric Stove
11. Hot-dog Roaster
12. Magnetic Lines of Force
13. Laws of Magnetism
14. Electromagnets
15. Solenoid Sucking Coil
16. Door Chime
17. Relay
18. Circuit Breaker
19. Buzzer
20. Magnetic Putting Green
21. Faraday's Discovery
22. RPM Meter
23. Inductance Dimmer
24. Transformer Experiments
25. Induction Coil and Shocker
26. Hooty-Hoot, The Wise Owl
27. Automatic Garage Light Control
28. Using a Nomograph
29. Series DC Motor
30. Shunt DC Motor
31. DC Motor with Permanent Magnetic Fields
32. Controlled Speed
    DC Motor
33. Universal Motor
34. AC Motor
35. The Applause Meter
36. Characteristics of the Diode
37. Triode Characteristics
38. Half-wave Rectifier
39. Full-wave Rectifier
40. Metallic Rectifiers
41. Power Supply
42. Voltage Doublers
43. AC-DC Power Supply
44. Audio Amplifier
45. Telephone Amplifier
46. The Paging Amplifier
47. A CW Transmitter
48. The Squawker Hot Rod Horn
49. Code Oscillator
50. Superheterodyne Receiver
51. Alignment
52. Pentagrid Converter
53. IF Amplifier
54. Diode Detector
55. Audio Power Amplifier
56. A Crystal Radio
57. Four Transistor Radio
58. Electroluminescent Night Light
59. Safety Flasher
60. Electronic Timer - DC
61. Electronic Timer - AC
62. Radio Control Transmitter
63. Radio Control Receiver
64. Oscilloscope Familiarization
65. Using the Signal Generator

KITS ARE AVAILABLE

The Electrodemonstrator, components and parts, required to conduct experiments in electronics, described in this text, are available from the Lab-Volt Division, Buck Engineering Co., Inc., P. O. Box 686, Farmingdale, N. J., 07727. Full information may be obtained without obligation.

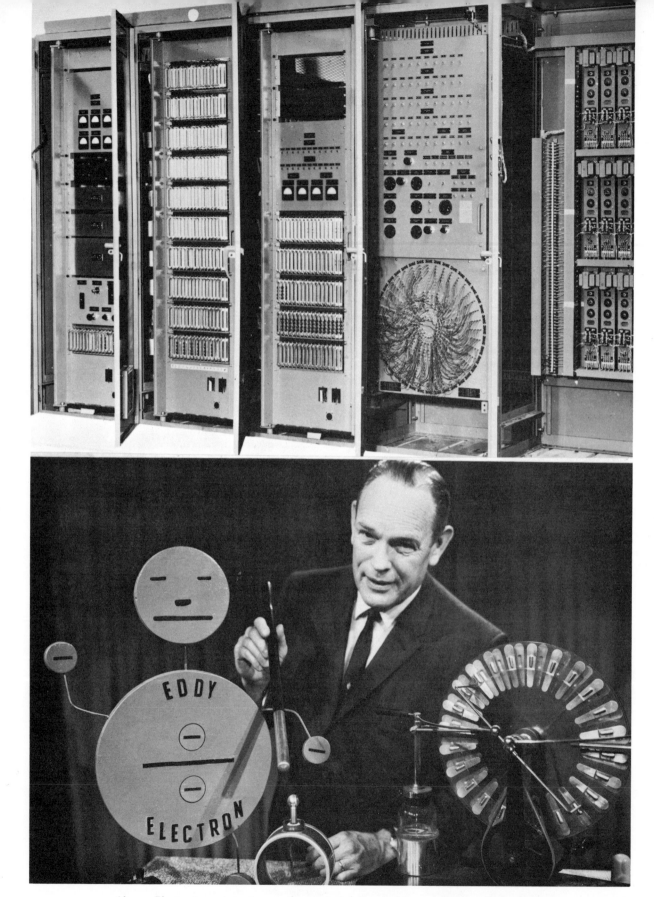

Above. Electronic equipment as used to control delivery of ingots, Fairless Works, U. S. Steel Corporation. Below. Howard Gerrish demonstrating static electricity on Electronic World TV program.

Chapter 1

SCIENCE OF ELECTRONICS

You are fortunate to live in an age in which the opportunity exists to study the electron. New discoveries, developments, and applications in electronics almost daily open a promising vista of unlimited opportunities for the creative scientist, as well as for the skilled technician. We are living in a truly scientific age.

THE NATURE OF MATTER

The scientist tells us that everything is made up of matter. Matter may be defined as anything which occupies space or has mass. Also some matter differs from other matter by frequent observable characteristics or properties. It may differ in color, taste or hardness. These characteristics permit us to identify the various forms of matter. Sometimes observable characteristics will not permit identification of a substance and it is necessary to make a chemical analysis to determine its nature and behavior. Most materials we use are made of a combination of various kinds of matter or mixtures of matter.

LESSON IN SAFETY: The experimenter, the technician, the scientist, the engineer, must respect the power of electricity. Although voltages used in projects and experiments described in this book are not dangerous to the normal, healthy individual, there is never an excuse to be careless.

In the basic study of the electron theory, it must be understood that some types of elementary matter exist which are neither mixtures nor compounds and that further

effort to break this matter into parts by chemical decomposition will produce no further change in the characteristics of the matter. These simple forms of material have been called ELEMENTS. Scientists have made further subdivisions of the elements by physical forces, such as those generated in the "atom smasher." Our concern is the nature of an element. There are many of them. Some familiar elements are iron, copper, gold, aluminum, carbon, and oxygen. Chemists have isolated over ninety different kinds of elements existing in nature and several more found in their laboratories.

MOLECULE AND THE ATOM

If you were to take a crystal of table salt and cut it in half, you would have two parts, but both would be common salt. Salt is a chemical compound of sodium (Na) and chlorine (Cl) or NaCl. In your imagination you might conceive the further division of the crystal of salt until it could not be divided again. This question has disturbed scientists and philosophers for hundreds of years. Can a particle of matter be divided to the point that if it is divided again it will disappear?

In science the smallest particle that can exist and still retain the properties of the original compound or element is called a MOLECULE. Referring again to the crystal of salt, even though the salt has been divided to the smallest particle that can exist by itself, it is still a compound of sodium and chlorine. So this tiny particle must consist of two parts; one of sodium and one of chlorine. The molecule of salt would no longer be salt if it were divided. However, if a molecule of an element were subdivided, the parts would be all alike. These tiny particles of an element are named ATOMS. The smallness of just one molecule will stagger your imagination. If you could start filling a small match box with molecules at the rate of ten million per second, it would take you over a billion years to fill the box!

The word atom is derived from the Greek word meaning "indivisible." It was not until recent years that the atom was divided into parts. It is not within the scope of this text

The structure of the atom may be compared to the solar system, where the sun is at the center, or nucleus. The planets (Earth, Venus, Mars, etc.) revolving around the sun may be compared to the whirling electrons in orbit. The whirling electrons or planetary electrons are kept from falling into the center by centrifugal force. Normally for each proton in the nucleus there is one electron in orbit. The positive and negative charges cancel, leaving the atom electrically neutral. The atomic structure of each element may be described as having a fixed number of electrons in orbit. Examples of the atomic structure of

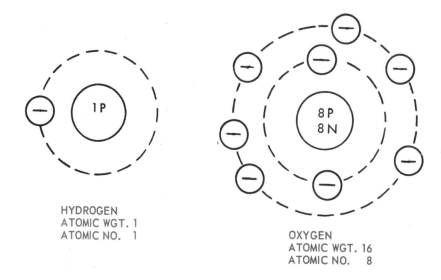

HYDROGEN
ATOMIC WGT. 1
ATOMIC NO. 1

OXYGEN
ATOMIC WGT. 16
ATOMIC NO.   8

Fig. 1-1. The atomic structure of hydrogen and oxygen.

to describe the chemical and physical reactions that take place when an atom is "split." However, it *is* important to learn some things about the structure of an atom.

ELECTRONS - PROTONS - NEUTRONS

Physicists have discovered that atoms are composed of minute particles of electricity. The center of each atom or NUCLEUS contains positively charged particles of electricity called PROTONS, and also neutral (neither positive or negative) particles. Most of the mass or weight of the atom is in its nucleus. Surrounding the nucleus, in rapidly revolving orbits, are negatively charged particles of electricity called ELECTRONS.

two common elements are displayed in Fig. 1-1. All elements are arranged in order in the Periodic Table of Elements according to their ATOMIC NUMBER, which is the number of electrons in the orbits. Or they may be arranged by their atomic weights, which is approximately the number of protons and neutrons in the nucleus. Referring again to Fig. I-1, the atomic weight of hydrogen is one, (scientifically 1.008), and its atomic number is one. The atomic weight of oxygen is sixteen and its atomic number is eight.

IONIZATION

Usually an atom remains in its normal state unless energy is added to the atom by some exterior force such as heat, friction or bombardment by other electrons. When energy is thus added to the atom, it will become excited and electrons which are loosely bound to the atom in the outer rings or orbits may leave the atom. If electrons leave the balanced or neutral atom, then there is a deficiency of electrons and the atom is no longer in electrical balance. The atom is then said to be IONIZED. If the atom has lost electrons, which are negative particles of electricity, the atom then would be a positively charged or positive ion. If the atom gained

Fig. 1-2. An electroscope. The gold leaves in the glass enclosure will indicate an electric charge.
(Welch Scientific Co.)

some electrons, then the atom would be negatively charged or a negative ion. This is an important lesson in electronic theory.

STATIC ELECTRICITY - LAW OF CHARGES

The word static means "at rest." Electricity can be at rest. The generation of static electricity may be demonstrated in many ways. By stroking the fur of a cat, you will notice that its fur will tend to be attracted to your hand as you bring your hand back over the cat. If this is done at night, you may see tiny sparks and hear a crackling sound which is caused by the discharge of static electricity. Actually the friction between your hand and the cat is exciting the atoms and they are becoming unbalanced. The sparks are created when the atoms attempt to neutralize themselves. You may have experienced the building-up of a static charge in your body while walking across a carpet or sliding across the seats of your car. Sometimes a spark discharge may result when you touch another person or the door handle of a car.

One of the fundamental laws in the study of electricity is the Law of Charges.

LIKE CHARGES REPEL EACH OTHER

UNLIKE CHARGES ATTRACT EACH OTHER

This law will be used many times in experiments described in this text. It is important to remember that ONE ELECTRON WILL REPEL ANOTHER ELECTRON. A negatively charged mass will be attracted by a positively charged mass. The Law of Charges may be demonstrated in the electrical laboratory by means of an electroscope or pith balls, Fig. 1-2.

Materials needed:

1. Electroscope
2. Vulcanite Rod and Cat Fur
3. Glass Rod and Silk
4. Single and Double Pith Balls on Stands

EXPERIMENT I. Rub the vulcanite rod vigorously with the cat fur. You now have a negative charge on the rod as electrons were transferred to the rod from the fur by friction. Bring the charged rod close to the ball on top of the electroscope. You will notice that the gold leaves in the electroscope will expand. Remove the rod and the leaves will close. The electroscope is used in this case to show the presence of an electrical charge. The negatively charged rod repels the electrons on the ball of the electroscope and forces them down to the leaves. The leaves being both negatively charged will repel each other and expand. Fig. 1-3.

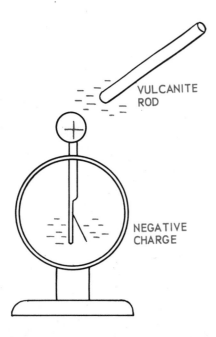

Fig. 1-3. *The negatively charged rod forces electrons down to the leaves of the electroscope. The leaves expand because they are both negative and repel each other.*

EXPERIMENT II. Once again rub the vulcanite rod in order to charge it. Now touch the ball on the electroscope with the rod. You will notice that the leaves expand and remain in this manner after the rod is removed. The rod has shared its charge with the electroscope and the electroscope remains charged, Fig. 1-4. Now touch the ball with your finger and the leaves will close, showing that the electroscope has been discharged through your body.

EXPERIMENT III. Repeat experiments 1 and 2, using the glass rod and the silk. The glass rod will charge positively; however the results will be the same, with opposite polarity.

EXPERIMENT IV. Repeat experiment I by bringing the charged rod close to, but not

touching, the electroscope. In this position, touch the electroscope with your other hand. Remove your hand and then the rod. You will observe that the electroscope will remain charged. As no actual contact was made between the rod and the electroscope, the electroscope was charged by induction. The nearness of the negative rod forced the electrons on the electroscope to travel away, through your hand. Of course, when your hand was removed, there was no way for the electroscope to regain its lost electrons so it must remain positively charged as indicated by the expanded leaves.

Fig. 1-4. *The electroscope becomes charged when the rod touches the ball, and will remain charged.*

EXPERIMENT V. Once again, rub the vulcanite rod and charge it negatively. Bring the rod close to a hanging pith ball, Fig. 1-5. The ball will at first be attracted to the rod due to unlike charges. When the pith ball touches the rod, it assumes the charge of the rod and is immediately repelled. Now both the ball and rod are negative. Try once again to touch the ball with the rod. Notice that the ball is always repelled.

EXPERIMENT VI. Using a second pith ball, charge it in the same manner as Experiment V. You will now have two pith balls charged

Fig. 1-5. The pith ball is attracted, and then repelled, by the charged rod.

negatively. Try to bring the balls close together and notice that they will not touch. There is a repulsive force existing between them. Fig. 1-6.

EXPERIMENT VII. Leaving one pith ball negative, charge the second pith ball positively by using the glass rod and the silk. As you bring the two balls close to each other, you will notice that they are attracted to each other. Fig. 1-7.

These experiments prove the laws of charges. It will be difficult for you to understand lessons in electricity, if these laws are not thoroughly understood.

THE COULOMB

In the earlier part of this lesson it was indicated that the atom and parts of the atom must be infinitesimal particles. It would not

Fig. 1-6. The like charged pith balls repel each other.

Fig. 1-7. Unlike charged pith balls attract each other.

be practical to assume that the charge on a body is one or even a dozen more or less electrons. A larger quantity would be more convenient to use. A quantity of electricity is known as a COULOMB and represents 6.28×10^{18} electrons or 6,280,000,000,000,000,000 electrons. The French scientist, Charles A. Coulomb, discovered many of the principles and laws of electrical charges. The Coulomb was named in his memory.

ELECTROSTATIC FIELDS

Once again perform Experiment IV and ask this question. When the vulcanite rod was brought close to, but not touching the electroscope, why did it affect the electroscope? This is so because of the invisible lines of force existing around a charged body. These lines of force are called the ELECTROSTATIC FIELD or DIELECTRIC FIELD. The field is strongest very close to the charged body. It diminishes at a distance inversely proportional to the square of the distance. Referring to Fig. 1-8, two charged balls are

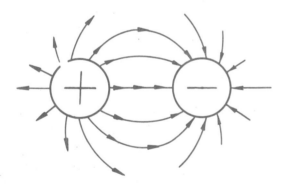

Fig. 1-8. The electrostatic fields of unlike charged bodies, showing attractive force.

shown with lines representing the electrostatic fields of opposite polarity and the attractive force existing between them. In Fig. 1-9, two charged balls are shown with like polarities and the repulsive force existing between the balls due to electrostatic fields. Once again, the electrostatic fields add further proof to the law of charges. Like charges repel. Unlike charges attract.

LESSON IN SAFETY: Horseplay has no place in the electricity shop, nor in any shop where machinery is operating and men are working with tools. Do not pay the penalty for poor working habits. It may be very expensive.

ELECTRIC CURRENT

At this point, you should have a thorough understanding of static electricity and the

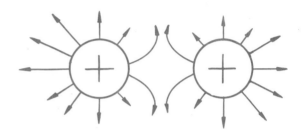

Fig. 1-9. The electrostatic fields of like charged bodies, showing repulsive force.

electrostatic fields existing around charged bodies. Consider the illustration in Fig. 1-10 which is very similar to previous Fig. 1-8, except that a short piece of copper wire has been connected between the balls, A and B. Again, you should realize what is meant by a negatively charged body such as ball A. It actually has an excess of negative charges or electrons. In the case of ball B, it will have a deficiency of electrons because of its

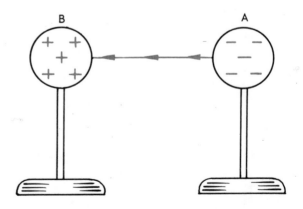

Fig. 1-10. Electrons flow from the negatively charged ball to the positive ball.

positive charge. When the wire or CONDUCTOR is connected between the two balls, then the excess electrons on ball A

CONDUCTOR

Fig. 1-11. Current through a conductor is a result of the transfer of energy between atoms.

will follow along the conductor to ball B. Electrons will continue to flow until the electrons on <u>both balls are equal.</u> Then there is no difference in electrons between them. The force which caused these electrons to move is called <u>electromotive force</u> or <u>difference in potential.</u> It is known as VOLTAGE.

Voltage is the electrical pressure or force which causes the flow of electrons. It is measured in VOLTS.

This flow of electrons is called an <u>electric current.</u> It is necessary for the technician to measure the flow of electrons or current in a circuit, so units of measurements have been standardized. Comparing the electrical circuit to a water pipe, one would measure the flow of water as so many gallons per minute. Electric current is measured by the number of electrons flowing per second past a given point in the conductor. The term coulomb is useful as a representation of a quantity of electrons. The standard unit for the measurement of electric current is the <u>ampere.</u> This represents the flow of one coulomb per second past a fixed point in the circuit. Mathematically,

$$I = \frac{Q}{t} \quad \text{or} \quad Q = It$$

where Q = coulombs

I = current in amperes

t = time in seconds

Example: If 40 coulombs of electrons passed a given point in 10 seconds, then a current of 4 amperes would flow.

$$I = \frac{40 \text{ coulombs}}{10 \text{ seconds}} = 4 \text{ amperes}$$

DIRECTION OF CURRENT FLOW

It is apparent that the flow of electrons then constitutes an electric current. But <u>electrons are negative charges of electricity,</u> and therefore are attracted to the positively charged body. One may assume that electron flow is in the direction of negative to positive. This may cause some misunderstanding because many older texts describe electric current as flowing from positive to negative. This stems from an early belief that electricity was some kind of "liquid" or "juice" flowing in the wires. Frequently one will still hear an electrician say, "Turn on the juice." For the purposes of this text and this study of electronics, current <u>will always be considered as flowing from negative to positive.</u> Any exceptions will be clearly stated.

CONDUCTORS AND INSULATORS

If a source of electrical potential is connected to a device, such as a lamp, by means of copper wires, the electrons will flow or be conducted from the negative terminal of the source, through the lamp, and back to the positive terminal of the source. These copper wires are the path or road along which will flow the electric current. The wire is called a <u>conductor.</u> Some materials are good conductors of electricity. Materials which have a large number of free electrons are considered good conductors. The actual conduction is accomplished by transferring electrons from one atom to the next in the conductor. One may visualize this flow by assuming that a piece of copper wire is neutral. If an electron is forced onto one end of the wire, an electron is forced off from the other end, as illustrated in Fig. 1-11. The original electron did not flow through the conductor, yet the energy was transferred by the interaction between the electrons in the conductor. The actual transfer of electrical energy has been accurately measured and approaches the speed of light or 186,000 miles per second or 300,000,000 meters per second.

Copper conductors are used in most electrical circuits. Copper is an excellent conductor. Silver is even better than copper, but it is too expensive for general use. Many high power lines use aluminum for added strength and light weight. Brass, zinc and iron are also fair conductors.

Materials which have only a few free electrons do not readily conduct electrons and are called insulators. Insulation is used on wires to protect personnel from accidental contact with circuits and to avoid electrical contact between wires and supporting devices. Common materials used for insulation are rubber, glass, air, bakelite, mica and asbestos. It is apparent then, that some materials resist the flow of electrons, while others have less resistance to the flow of electrons. This is true and resistance must always be considered as an important characteristic of electrical circuits. Resistance will be studied in detail in Chapter 3.

TEST YOUR KNOWLEDGE

Write your answers to these questions on a separate sheet of paper. Do not write in this book.

1. A negative charge of electricity is called an _____; a positive charge, a _____; a neutral particle, a _____.
2. A unit of measurement for a quantity of electricity is a _____ and represents _____ x 10 ^{18} electrons.
3. What are the two laws of electrostatic charges?
4. A negative rod will charge an electroscope by contact. The leaves will both be _____.
5. A positive rod will charge an electroscope by induction. The leaves will be _____.
6. Electricity moves at the speed of light which is _____ miles per second or _____ meters per second.
7. Name four insulators. Why are insulators used?
8. When a charged rod is brought close to a pith ball, explain the action. Why?
9. Electromotive force or potential difference is measured in _____.
10. Current is measured in _____ and represents the flow of _____ per _____.
11. Check in a reference book in your library and discover the atomic weight and atomic number of:

	weight	number
Cu Copper	_____	_____
Al Aluminum	_____	_____
Ge Germanium	_____	_____
As Arsenic	_____	_____

12. A charged body will be surrounded by an _____.

FOR DISCUSSION:

1. How do lightning rods protect a building during a storm?
2. Which great scientist discovered the relationship between lightning and electricity? Describe his experiments.
3. A police car seems to have some unusual radio interference while driving along the highway. This interference was not present when the car was not moving. Suggest a possible cause and explain.
4. Electrostatic fields are used in industry to reclaim by-products and prevent air pollution from smoke. Explain.

Chapter 2

SOURCES OF ELECTRICITY

Every young man is familiar with the story of Benjamin Franklin and his kite. For centuries before Franklin, scientists and philosophers had observed the supernatural manifestations of lightning. It was through the experimentation and research of Dr. Franklin that the relationship between lightning and static electricity was confirmed. What is this phenomena known as electricity and where does it come from? Years before the discovery of the electron theory by J. J. Thomson, it was suggested by Dr. Franklin that electricity consisted of many tiny particles or electric charges. He further theorized that electrical charges were created by the distribution of electrical particles in nature.

In the previous lesson, we learned that a potential difference or electromotive force (emf) was created when electrons were redistributed. A body might assume a charge; its polarity is determined by the deficiency or excess of electrons. Man since has bent his scientific interests and research on the development of machines and processes which will cause an electrical unbalance and an electrical pressure.

THE BATTERY

One of the more familiar sources of an electrical potential or voltage is the battery. In 1790, the Italian scientist, Galvani, observed a strange phenomena during the dissection of a frog which was supported on copper wires. Each time he touched the frog with his steel scalpel, its leg would twitch. Galvani reasoned that the frog's leg

contained electricity. As a result of these experiments, Alesandra Volta, another Italian scientist, invented the electric cell, named in his honor, called the Voltaic Cell. The unit of electrical pressure, the volt, is also named in his honor. Volta discovered that when two dissimilar elements were placed in a chemical which acted upon them, an electrical potential was built up between them.

The student may construct several voltaic cells to demonstrate this action. Cut a one inch square of blotting paper and soak it in a strong salt solution. Place the wet paper between a penny and a nickel as shown in Fig. 2-1. If a sensitive meter is connected to the

Fig. 2-1. A simple cell is produced by a nickel, a penny and a salt solution.

coins, it will indicate that a small voltage is present. In Fig. 2-2 electricity is created by a grapefruit. Small cuts are made in the skin of the grapefruit. In one cut, place the penny;

in the other, the nickel. Once again a meter will indicate a voltage. A better cell may be made by placing a carbon rod (these may be removed from an old dry cell) and a strip of

Fig. 2-2. *A grapefruit will produce enough electricity to operate a small transistor radio.*

Fig. 2-3. *An experimental cell made by zinc, carbon and acid.*

zinc in a glass jar containing an acid and water as illustrated in Fig. 2-3.

LESSON IN SAFETY: When mixing acid and water, always pour acid into water. Never pour water into acid. Acid will burn your hands and eat holes in your clothing. Wash your hands at once with clear water if you have spilled some acid on them. Acid may be neutralized with baking soda. See your instructor for first aid treatment!

If the polarity of the carbon rod is tested, it will be found to be positive. The zinc will be negative. If a wire is connected between these elements or underlineelectrodes, a current will flow. A voltaic cell may be described as a means of converting chemical energy into electrical energy.

The student in electronics also needs a basic knowledge of chemistry. In the above mentioned example of a voltaic cell, sulfuric acid, (H_2SO_4) and water (H_2O) may be used as the liquid or electrolyte. When the electrodes are placed in this acid electrolyte, a chemical action takes place. The sulfuric acid breaks down into positive ions (H_2) and negative ions (SO_4). The negative ions move toward the zinc electrode, and combine with it by making zinc sulfate ($ZnSO_4$) and the positive ions move toward the carbon electrode. This action creates a potential difference between the electrodes. The zinc will have an excess of electrons and will be negative. The carbon will be positive. Such a cell will develop about 1.5 volts.

If a load, such as a light, is connected to the cell, a current will flow and the light will glow, as shown in Fig. 2-3. As the cell is used, the chemical action continues until the zinc electrode is consumed. The chemical equation for this action would be·

$$Zn + H_2SO_4 + H_2O \rightarrow ZnSO_4 + H_2O + H_2 \uparrow$$

Zinc plus sulfuric acid plus water chemically reacts to form zinc sulfate and water and free hydrogen gas. This cell cannot be recharged because the zinc has been consumed. It is called a PRIMARY CELL. The chemical action cannot be reversed.

DEFECTS IN PRIMARY CELLS

One might think that the chemical action of the voltaic cell would continue to develop a voltage as long as the active ingredients of the cell were present. In studying the equation for the discharge of the cell, you will observe the formation of free hydrogen gas. Since the carbon electrode does not enter into chemical action, the hydrogen forms bubbles of gas which collect around the carbon electrode. As the cell continues to discharge, an effective insulating blanket of bubbles will form around the carbon, which reduces the output and terminal voltage of the cell. The cell is said to be POLARIZED. The action is called POLARIZATION. To overcome this defect in the simple voltaic cell a DEPOLARIZING AGENT may be added. Compounds which are rich in oxygen, such as manganese dioxide (MnO_2), are used for this purpose. The oxygen in the depolarizer combines with the hydrogen bubbles and forms water. This chemical action appears as:

$$2\ MnO_2 + H_2 \rightarrow Mn_2O_3 + H_2O$$

The free hydrogen has been removed, so the cell will continue to produce a voltage.

One might assume that when current is not being used from the cell, the chemical action would also stop. However, during the smelting of zinc ore, not all impurities are removed. Small particles of carbon, iron and other elements remain. These impurities act as the positive electrode for many small cells within the large cell, but this chemical action adds nothing to the electrical energy produced at the cell terminals. This action is called LOCAL ACTION. It may be reduced by using pure zinc for the negative electrode, or by a process called amalgamation. A small quantity of mercury is added to the zinc during manufacturing. As mercury is a heavy liquid, any impurities in the zinc will float on the surface of the mercury, causing them to leave the zinc surface. This process increases, to a great extent, the life of a primary cell.

THE DRY CELL

Although the action of the primary cell has been described as a liquid cell or wet cell, it is not in common use. It is more convenient to make the primary cell a DRY CELL. This avoids the danger of spilling liquid acids. The common dry cell known as the LeClanche cell, is shown in Fig. 2-4. The dry cell consists of a zinc container which acts as the negative electrode. In the center is a carbon rod which is the positive electrode. Surrounding the carbon rod is a paste of ground carbon, manganese dioxide and sal ammoniac, (ammonium chloride), mixed with water. The

depolarizer is the MnO_2. The ground carbon increases the effectiveness of the cell by reducing its internal resistance. During discharge of the cell, water is formed. You may recall having difficulty removing dead cells from a flashlight. The water caused them to expand. Although this complaint has been removed by improved manufacturing techniques, it is still not advisable to leave cells in your flashlight for long periods of time. You should keep fresh cells in your flashlight, so it will be ready for emergency use.

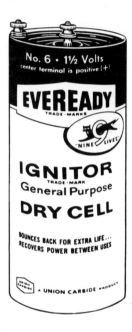

Fig. 2-4. The popular dry cell still serves many purposes in home and industry. (Union Carbide Co.)

THE MERCURY CELL

A relatively new development in the dry cell is shown in Fig. 2-5. It is called a Mercury Cell. It develops a voltage of 1.34 volts by the chemical action between zinc and mercuric oxide. It is expensive to manufacture, but has a decided advantage of producing approximately five times more current than the conventional dry cell. It also maintains its terminal voltage under load for longer periods of operation. The Mercury Cell has found wide application in powering field instruments and portable communications systems.

Nickel Plated Steel
Outer Top

Tin Plated Steel
Inner Top

Sealing and
Insulating
Gasket

Inner Steel
Case

Depolarizer
Cylinders (3)

Safety
Absorbent
Sleeve

Electrolyte
Absorbent
Material

Anode
Cylinders (4)

Barrier

Outer Steel
Case

Insulator
Spacer

Vent Area

Fig. 2-5. Mercury cell battery which develops voltage
by chemical action between zinc and mercuric oxide.

NICKEL-CADMIUM RECHARGEABLE CELL

Another new development in the field of
dry cells is the rechargeable cell. These are
essentially Nickel-Cadmium alkaline batteries using a paste rather than a liquid for
the electrolyte. One brand uses plates of
perforated nickel-plated steel on which a
porous body of nickel had been sintered. The
plates are impregnated with nickel hydrate
for the positive and Cadmium hydrate for the
negative plates. Among the many advantages
of these cells is their ability to be recharged.
Several of these rechargeable cells are illustrated in Fig. 2-6. Other advantages include long life, high efficiency, compactness
and light weight. This Nickel-Cadmium Cell
will produce a high discharge current due
to its low internal resistance. A flashlight
using one of these rechargeable cells is

Fig. 2-6. Rechargeable cells using nickel and cadmium hydrate are becoming quite popular.
(Gulton Industries, Inc.)

shown in Fig. 2-7. Other uses include the powering of transistor radios, burglar alarm systems, photo-flashers, missiles and aircraft instruments.

THE BATTERY

Frequently a single cell is called a battery. By strict definition, a battery consists of two or more cells connected together. These cells are enclosed in one case. In the

Fig. 2-7. This battery powered flashlight may be recharged by plugging into any 117-volt receptacle in your home. (Gulton Industries, Inc.)

study of electricity it is important to understand the purpose and results of connecting cells in groups. First, consider the series connection. In this method the positive terminal of one cell is connected to the negative terminal of the second cell. In Fig. 2-8, four cells are connected in series. The output voltage will equal,

$$E_{out} = E_{one\ cell} \times n,$$

when n equals the number of cells, so

$$E_{out} = 1.5\ volts \times 4 = 6\ volts$$

Notice that the voltage has increased four times, however the capacity of the battery to supply a current is the same as one cell. Cells are connected in this manner to supply higher voltages for many applications. Your

flashlight may use two or more cells in series. B-Batteries for portable radios have many cells in series to produce 22 1/2, 45 or 90 volts.

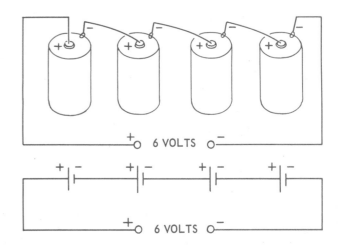

Fig. 2-8. The pictorial and schematic diagram of four cells connected in series.

In Fig. 2-9, the positive terminals have been connected together, and the negative terminals have been connected together. These cells are connected in parallel. The total voltage across the terminals of the battery is the same as <u>one cell only</u>. Although

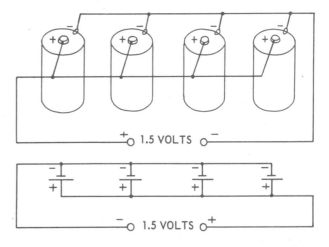

Fig. 2-9. The pictorial and schematic diagram of four cells connected in parallel.

the voltage has not increased, the life of the battery has been increased because the current is drawn from all cells instead of one.

Which method, then, would be the most economical to use? Generally speaking, if the load applied to the battery is a low resistance load, it is better to use the parallel connection. For a high resistance load, use the series connection.

It is also possible to connect cells in a mixed grouping. In Fig. 2-10, two series batteries with 6 volts terminal voltage are

Fig. 2-10. The pictorial and schematic diagram of two groups of cells connected in series and the groups connected in parallel.

connected in parallel. The total voltage is still 6 volts, but the capacity has been increased. This is called a SERIES-PARALLEL method of connecting cells.

SECONDARY CELLS

The secondary cell may be recharged or restored. Chemically speaking, the reaction which occurs on discharge may be reversed

by forcing a current through the battery in the opposite direction. This charging current must be supplied from another source, which may be a generator or the power company. Fig. 2-11 shows one type of battery charger used by garages and filling stations for recharging automobile batteries. An alternating current, which will be studied in a later lesson, must be rectified to a direct current for charging the battery.

THE LEAD ACID CELL

The more familiar example of the lead-acid cell is the automotive storage battery. A storage battery does not store electricity. It stores chemical energy which produces electrical energy. The active ingredients in a

Fig. 2-11. A quick charger for the automotive battery found in many service stations.
(Exide Sales, Electric Storage Battery Co.)

fully charged lead-acid cell consist of lead peroxide (PbO_2) which acts as the positive plate, and pure spongy lead (Pb) for the negative plate. The liquid electrolyte is sulfuric acid (H_2SO_4) and water (H_2O). One may distinguish the positive plates by their reddish-brown color. The negative plates are gray.

Although the chemical reaction is rather involved, the student may study the following equation, with the purpose of better understanding;

Spongy Lead + Lead Peroxide + Sulfuric Acid $\leftrightarrows$ Lead Sulfate + Water

or

$$Pb + PbO_2 + 2\,H_2SO_4 \leftrightarrows 2PbSO_4 + 2\,H_2O$$

CHARGED   DISCHARGED

Notice that during discharge, both the spongy lead and the lead peroxide plates are being changed to lead sulfate and the electrolyte is being changed to water. When the cell is recharged, the reverse action occurs. The lead sulfate changes back to spongy lead and the lead peroxide. The electrolyte changes to sulfuric acid.

LESSON IN SAFETY: During the charging process of a storage battery, highly explosive hydrogen gas may be present. Do not light matches near charging batteries. Charge only in a well ventilated room. Batteries should be first connected to the charger, before the power is applied. Otherwise, the sparks made during connection might ignite the hydrogen gas and cause an explosion.

The electrolyte of a fully charged battery is a solution of sulfuric acid and water. The weight of pure sulfuric acid is 1.835 times heavier than water. This is called its specific gravity. The specific gravity of water is 1.000. The acid and water mixture in a fully charged battery has a specific gravity of approximately 1.300 or less. As the electrolyte changes to water when the

Fig. 2-12. At your garage or service station, the mechanic will use the hydrometer to check the state of charge of your car battery. (Exide Sales, Electric Storage Battery Co.)

cell discharges, the specific gravity becomes approximately 1.100 to 1.150. Therefore, the specific gravity of the electrolyte may be used to determine the state of charge of a cell. The instrument used to measure

the specific gravity is a HYDROMETER, as shown in Fig. 2-12. Readings may be taken from the floating bulb and scale. The principle of the hydrometer is based on Archimedes principle in physics, which states that a floating body will displace an amount of liquid equal to its own weight. If the cell is in a fully charged state, the electrolyte

Fig. 2-13. A phantom view of the construction of the lead-acid storage battery. (Delco-Remy)

liquid is heavier, so the float in the hydrometer will not sink so far. The distance that it does sink, is calibrated in specific gravity on the scale, and can be read directly as the state of charge of the cell.

Referring to Fig. 2-13, the plates of the modern lead-acid cell are made of a grid of special lead-antimony alloy upon which is pressed a paste of the chemically active material. The grid holds the material in place and adds mechanical strength. When the paste on the plate grids is hard and dry, each plate is formed to its correct chemical material by placing it in an electrolyte, and passing a current through it in the proper direction. One direction makes a positive plate; the opposite direction, a negative plate. In Fig. 2-13 is shown the construction of a cell, which consists of alternate negative and positive plates grouped together. All negative plates are connected together and all positive plates are connected together by a lead plate strap at the top. The plates are insulated from each other by means of separators. These separators must be thin, porous layers of insulation and are usually made of wood, rubber or spun glass.

LESSON IN SAFETY: Sulfuric acid used in automotive storage batteries will burn your hands, eat holes in your clothes and generally destroy other materials which it contacts. When testing a cell with a hydrometer, be certain that small drops of acid at the end of the rubber tube do not drip on you or on nearby objects of value. Hold the hydrometer over the battery filler hole while taking readings. Store hydrometer in hanging position in glass or rubber jar.

LESSON IN SAFETY: Expensive storage batteries may be destroyed by excessive vibration and rough handling. Chemicals may break off from the plates, and cause internal short circuits and dead cells. Handle a battery gently and be sure it is securely clamped and bolted in your car.

In the 12 volt automotive battery, six of these cells are placed in a molded hard-rubber case. Each cell has its own individual compartment. At the bottom of each compartment a space sediment chamber is provided, so that particles of chemicals broken from the plates due to chemical action or vibration, may collect. Otherwise, these particles might short-out the plates and make a dead cell.

The individual cells are connected in series by lead alloy connectors. The entire battery is then sealed with a battery-sealing compound. Each cell is provided with a filler-cap, so that distilled water may be added to the electrolyte as it evaporates. Special care

of a battery includes a periodic check of the liquid level in each cell. It should be maintained at about 1/4 in. above the top edges of the plates. If the electrolyte does not completely cover the plates, the ends of the plates exposed to air will become seriously sulfated or coated with a hard inactive chemical compound. Badly sulfated batteries have a short life, so protect your investment by giving your battery good care.

LESSON IN SAFETY: Storage batteries are heavy. Use the proper carrying strap when moving a battery. Get help from your fellow worker when lifting a battery into a car. Do not strain yourself by improper and thoughtless lifting.

BATTERY CAPACITY

So that batteries may be purchased and used more intelligently, you should understand the term "capacity." The capacity of a battery is its ability to produce a current over a certain period of time. It is equal to the product of amperes supplied by the battery and the time. Capacity is measured in ampere-hours. The description of an automotive battery might indicate a capacity of 100 ampere-hours. This would mean that the battery theoretically would supply,

100 amps for 1 hour   100 x 1 = 100 amp hours
50 amps for 2 hours   50 x 2 = 100 amp hours
10 amps for 10 hours   10 x 10 = 100 amp hours
1 amp for 100 hours   1 x 100 = 100 amp hours

A battery will not perform exactly by this theoretical schedule, as the rate of discharge must always be considered. A rapidly discharged battery will not give its maximum ampere-hour rating. A slowly discharged battery may exceed its rated capacity. The Society of Automotive Engineers (SAE) has set standards for the rating of automotive batteries. A manufacturer must meet these standards in order to advertise a battery as a specific ampere-hour capacity.

Several factors determine the capacity of a storage battery. 1). The number of plates in each cell. An increased number of plates

Fig. 2-14. *Typical cell structure of a photovoltaic cell.*
(International Rectifier Corp.)

provides more square inches of surface area for chemical action. Automotive batteries are commonly made with 13, 15, and 17 plates per cell. The number of plates is a determination of the life and quality of a battery. 2). The kind of separators used will have some effect on the capacity and life of a battery. 3). The general condition of the battery in respect to its state of charge, age and care will influence the capacity rating of any given battery.

ELECTRICAL ENERGY FROM LIGHT

For many years scientists have attempted to transform the light energy from the sun into useful quantities of electrical power. Although certain experimental equipment has been successful, general utilization of sun-power is still in its infancy. Just as light may be produced by an electric current running through a resistance or filament in a light bulb, light may also produce an electric current. The photo voltaic cell is one device which will make this conversion. This may be described as a device which will develop an electrical potential between its terminals, when the surface of the cell is exposed to light. Referring to Fig. 2-14, a selenium photo voltaic cell is constructed of a layer of selenium compound, a barrier layer, and transparent front electrode. When light strikes the surface, electrons from the selenium compound cross the barrier, caus-

ing a potential difference between the base plate and the front electrode. The electrons cannot return to the selenium compound because the barrier permits conduction in one direction only. It is a unidirectional conductor.

Fig. 2-15 shows a sun battery used by experimenters. This battery will generate a 2 milliampere current through a 10 ohm load

Fig. 2-15. *A photocell. A popular device for the experimenter, but it also has many industrial uses.*

when exposed to bright sunlight. The batteries may be connected in series and parallel for higher power requirements.

Other interesting applications of photo

cells include the familiar light meter used in photography. In this application, a sensitive meter responds to the current generated by the cell. The brighter the scene, the greater deflection of the meter. In Fig. 2-16 a photo sensitive cell is used to control the amount of light reaching the film. Photo cells are used in industry for operations of counting, sorting and automatic inspection. Technical personnel are shown in Fig. 2-17 completing the final soldering and cleaning of solar cell modules on the hemisphere shell of the Courier Communication Satellite. Each module consists of 84 solar cells. They combine to supply the required electrical energy derived from the sun.

PHOTO ELECTRIC CONTROL

As a student of electronics, you should build several devices which utilize the phenomenon of electrical energy from light. Fig. 2-18 shows a photo electric control device using a phototube. When light shines on the tube, electrons are emitted from the cathode. This is described as photo electric effect. The electrons are attracted to the plate in the tube which has a positive charge. As a result, a current will flow through the tube and this current will vary according to the intensity of the light. Further discussion on the principles of the vacuum tube is included in a later chapter of this text. Photo-

Fig. 2-16. An exploded view of the photoelectric cell used in the Brownie Starmatic camera.
(Eastman Kodak Co.)

Fig. 2-17. Workmen are installing solar cells on the Courier Communications Satellite.
(Philco Corp.)

electric tubes are used in counting operations, burglar alarms, door opening mechanisms and in many other devices. The circuit may be arranged so it will operate if a light shining on the tube is interrupted. It may also be triggered by a beam or flashing light.

Fig. 2-18. A photo electrically controlled relay.

Parts List - Photo Relay

K_1 - Relay SPDT - 5000 Ω, 6.3 ma, Advance GHE/1C, 5000 D.

R_1 - Potentiometer, 1 meg Ω, 1/2 w

R_2 - 18 K Ω, 1/2 w

V_1 - GL930 Photo Tube

V_2 - 6J5 Tube

ELECTRICAL ENERGY FROM HEAT

A simple device used to indicate and control the heat of electric ovens and furnaces is shown in Fig. 2-19. This is called a thermocouple. When two dissimilar metals in contact with each other are heated, a potential difference will develop between the metals.

This simple experiment will demonstrate the electrical principle. Take a piece of iron stove pipe wire and a piece of copper wire. Twist the ends of the wire tightly together and connect the other ends to a sensitive galvanometer. Light a match and hold the flame under the twisted joint. As the joint becomes hot, you will notice that a small voltage will indicate on the meter. The output voltage of the thermocouple may be amplified

and used to activate large motors, valves, controls and recording devices. Commercial types of thermocouples employ various kinds of dissimilar metals and alloys such as Nickel-Platinum, Chromel-Alumel and Iron-Constantan. These unfamiliar names apply to special alloys developed for thermocouples. The combination indicating device including meter and thermocouple is called a pyrometer. For an instrument which must be extremely sensitive to temperature change, a larger number of thermocouples may be

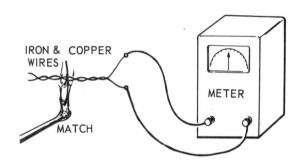

Fig. 2-19. The basic principle of the thermocouple may be demonstrated by heating two dissimilar wires twisted together.

joined in series. Such a group is known as a thermopile.

ELECTRICAL ENERGY FROM MECHANICAL PRESSURE

Many crystalline substances such as Quartz, Tourmaline and Rochelle Salts have a peculiar characteristic. When a voltage is applied to the surfaces of the crystal, the crystal will become distorted. The opposite is also true. If a mechanical pressure or force is applied to the crystal surfaces, a voltage will be developed. The crystal microphone, Fig. 2-20, is a familiar example. Sound waves striking a diaphragm, which is mechanically linked to the crystal surfaces, cause distortion in the crystal which in turn develops a voltage across its surfaces. Thus, sound waves are converted to electrical energy. Another familiar application is the phono cartridge which is installed in the pick-up arm on the record player. The phonograph needle is caused to move by the sound grooves in the record. The moving needle applies

Fig. 2-20. Crystal microphone which converts sound waves to electrical energy.

mechanical pressure to the crystal in the cartridge and an electrical potential is developed. The potential will vary in frequency and magnitude according to the movement of the needle. The varying potential is amplified and connected to a speaker. You hear the voice or music. This electrical phenomenon of creating electricity by the mechanical distortion of a crystal is known as PIEZO-ELECTRIC EFFECT. Crystals may be cut for particular operating characteristics. In a later chapter, the use of crystals as frequency controls for radio transmitters will be discussed.

ELECTRICITY FROM MAGNETISM

The most important sources of electrical energy today are the dynamo and generator. The importance of this source requires detailed study and Chapter V in this text will be devoted to the subject.

ACTIVITIES

I. Construct a cell using a penny, a nickel and blotting paper soaked in salt solution. Measure the voltage with a multimeter.

II. Construct a thermocouple by twisting the ends of a copper and an iron wire together. Connect the wires to a voltmeter. Then heat the junction with a match. Observe the voltage developed.

III. Secure this material from the supply room.

　　　4 flashlight cells
　　　4 cell holders
　　　Voltmeter.

A. Connect the cells in series as per diagram.

What is the voltage between A and B? A and C? A and D? A and E?

What conclusion do you draw from this experiment?

B. Connect the cells in parallel as per diagram.

What is the voltage between A and B?

Remove cell #4. Measure voltage from A to B.

Remove cells #3 and 4. Measure the voltage from A to B.

Remove cells #2, 3, and 4. Measure the voltage from A to B.

What conclusion do you draw from this experiment?

IV. Secure a sun battery from supply.

A. Connect terminals to a voltmeter. Observe meter reading. Now shine a flashlight on the cell or place it in sunshine and observe the meter reading.

TEST YOUR KNOWLEDGE

1. Name five sources of electricity.

2. What safety precaution should be observed when mixing acid and water?

3. Draw a diagram of four 1.5 v cells in series. What is the terminal voltage?

4. Draw a diagram of four 1.5 v cells in parallel. What is the terminal voltage?

5. Using six 1.5 v cells, connect in series-parallel to produce a terminal voltage of 3 volts.

6. What are the chemical compositions of the plates of a storage battery?

7. What is the composition of the electrolyte in a lead-acid storage battery?

8. What is meant by the "specific gravity" of a liquid?

9. Name and explain two common defects of the primary voltaic cell.

10. Name the materials and draw a rough sketch of a dry cell.

11. What is the major advantage of the nickel-cadmium cell?

12. What precautions should be observed when lifting or carrying a storage battery?

13. Name several factors which determine the capacity of a storage battery.

14. Name several applications using piezoelectric effect.

Section of Stanford University electron accelerator, in which 240 klyston amplifier tubes are installed. Each amplifier tube is capable of producing 24 million watt bursts of microwave power.

Chapter 3

CIRCUITS AND POWER

Electrical circuits usually consist of a source of voltage, and one or more devices or components connected to this source by means of wires or conductors. Also, a means to turn the flow of electricity on or off is provided, by using a device called a <u>switch</u>. A diagram showing the various connections to components, devices and switches is called a <u>schematic diagram</u>. As the architect draws a plan for constructing a home, the technician or engineer will draw a schematic plan for the connections of a circuit. The student may consider the conductors as a means of dis-

SUPER HI-WAY

CARS

COUNTRY ROAD

Fig. 3-1. A superhighway will carry more traffic than a country road. It has less resistance to the flow of automobiles.

tributing, or directing, the electrons around the circuit. They are the roads to accommodate the electron traffic.

The flow of electron traffic can more easily be understood by comparison to automobile traffic. Consider the size of the road. A large, smooth, four lane highway will carry more traffic than a narrow and rough country road, as illustrated in Fig. 3-1. This is also true of the electrical conductor. A large wire can carry more electrons than a

small wire. It has less resistance to the flow, because of its larger size. Fig. 3-2.

LESSON IN SAFETY: Your body is a good conductor of electricity. An electric current flowing from one hand across your chest and heart and out of your other hand can be dangerous, if not fatal. The wise technician uses only one hand when he is required to work on high voltage circuits. Keep one hand in your pocket! The operators of switchboards and power stations stand on insulated platforms so that there is no direct path to ground in case of accidental contact with a high voltage wire.

Conductors are conveniently arranged according to their size by the American Wire Gauge System. The larger the gauge number, the smaller its diameter and cross sectional area. For example, a No. 14 wire is larger than a No. 20 wire.

Fig. 3-2. A large conductor has less resistance than a small conductor and can carry a larger current.

The standard unit of measure for the cross sectional area of a wire is the CIRCULAR MIL. A mil represents one thousandth of an inch. It is a convenient method of expressing the diameter of a conductor, rather than using fractions of an inch. THE CIRCULAR MIL IS THE CROSS SECTIONAL AREA OF A WIRE WHICH IS ONE MIL IN DIAMETER. A wire having a diameter of 50 mils would have a cross sectional area of 2500 circular mils. For purposes of comparison, simple rules of geometry may be applied. The area of a circle is equal to πR^2. Computing the area in square inches of a wire fifty thousandths (.050") of an inch in diameter or .025 inches in radius,

$$\begin{aligned} \text{Cross Sectional Area} &= 3.14 \times (.025)^2 \\ &= 3.14 \times .000625 \\ &= .00196 \text{ sq. inches.} \end{aligned}$$

Notice that in the above formula $R = \dfrac{D}{2}$ or $\dfrac{.050}{2}$ or the radius is equal to one half the diameter.

The cross sectional area could be represented by:

$$A = \pi \left(\frac{D}{2}\right)^2 \quad \text{or} \quad \pi \frac{D^2}{4} \quad \text{or}$$

$$\frac{3.14}{4} D^2 = .7854 D^2$$

and if D is in mils, A would equal $.7854D^2$ sq. mils. Now the circular mil was defined as the area of a wire having the diameter of one mil which would equal:

$$A = .7854 \times (1^2) = .7854 \text{ sq. mils}$$

Therefore, in order to find the <u>circular mil</u> area of a conductor, it is necessary to divide its square mil area by .7854 which is the square mils area in one circular mil. To simplify these mathematics, note that:

$$A = \frac{.7854\ D^2 \ (\text{sq. mil. area})}{.7854 \ (\text{area of circular mil})}$$

$$= D^2 \text{ circular mils.}$$

THE CIRCULAR MIL CROSS SECTIONAL AREA OF A CONDUCTOR IS EQUAL TO THE SQUARE OF ITS DIAMETER IN MILS.

To change the size of a wire from square mils to circular mils, it would be necessary to divide by .7854. To change a wire size given in circular mils to square mils, one would multiply by .7854. This information is important when comparing the current carrying capacity of round and square wires.

Summarizing the above discussion, one should remember that the RESISTANCE TO THE FLOW OF ELECTRICITY BY A WIRE OR CONDUCTOR WILL VARY INVERSELY WITH ITS SIZE OR CROSS-SECTIONAL AREA.

A LESSON IN SAFETY: The wires used to conduct electricity around your home have been selected with sufficient size to take care of your needs. Most circuits for lighting purposes use either No. 12 or No. 14 wire rated at 15 amperes. The wires for your range or water heater may be No. 6 to No. 10. Always use wires of the correct size and avoid trouble.

It was mentioned in Chapter I, that some materials are good conductors of electricity and others are poor conductors. So, THE KIND OF MATERIAL USED IN THE MANUFACTURING OF WIRE ALSO AFFECTS ITS ABILITY TO CONDUCT OR ITS RESISTANCE.

In the selection of the material for a particular application, it would be necessary to consider its cost, its resistance, its weight and strength. An accepted method of comparing materials is by the amount of resistance offered by one circular-mil-foot of the material. This is a wire one mil in diameter and one foot long. Fig. 3-3.

Fig. 3-3. This diagram shows the dimensions of a circular-mil-foot.

LENGTH OF WIRE AND RESISTANCE

A third consideration in the selection of a conductor is its length. If one foot of wire has a certain resistance, then ten feet of the same wire will have ten times more resistance and fifty feet will have fifty times more. This you should remember, because this resistance uses power and creates losses in the line. Devices connected to long conductors may have insufficient voltage for proper operation due to line losses.

A LESSON IN SAFETY: When using long extension cords to operate lights and tools, be sure that they have sufficient size so that there will be little line loss or voltage drop. Small wire extension cords may heat up and burn. Motor driven tools at the end of a small, long extension cord will heat and operate inefficiently. Also, it is very wise to equip all your tools with a three wire cord. The third wire is a ground and is connected to the case and handle of the tool. This precaution has saved many lives.

RESISTANCE
varies with

1. SIZE OF WIRE
2. LENGTH OF WIRE
3. KIND OF WIRE
4. TEMPERATURE

Table 3-1

RESISTANCE
IS MEASURED IN <u>OHMS</u>
OHMS IS REPRESENTED BY Ω
ITS LETTER SYMBOL IS R
ITS SCHEMATIC SYMBOL IS ‑⋀⋀‑
KILOHM MEANS 1,000 OHMS
MEGOHM MEANS 1,000,000 OHMS

Table 3-2

TEMPERATURE AND RESISTANCE

A fourth consideration is temperature. Most metals used in conductors, such as copper and aluminum, increase in resistance as the temperature increases. In many electronic circuits careful design is necessary to insure proper ventilation and radiation of heat from current carrying devices. When wires are enclosed in metallic coverings or conduit, the National Electric Code will specify that larger wires should be used so that heat, due to losses in the line, will not change the current carrying ability of the conductors.

The factors affecting resistance are summarized in Table 3-1. MEMORIZE THEM!

STRANDED WIRES

Not every conductor is a solid wire. Frequently it is necessary to use several smaller wires twisted together to form a cable. This method allows greater flexibility and ease of installation. If a wire is subject to movement or vibration, such as occurs in a lamp cord, a stranded wire produces greater strength and less danger of breaking. Stranded wires are usually made up of 7, 19, or 37 separate wires twisted together. A further improvement is made by twisting several stranded wires into one cable. Fig. 3-4. Do not confuse

Fig. 3-4. A. Stranded hookup wire used in electronic circuits. B. Power cable, (a) Three stranded conductors, (b) Insulation and jute fillers, (c) Tough, flexible jacket, (d) Bronze protective armor. C. Wire for a telephone switchboard. This has numerous conductors which are insulated from each other and are color coded.

this stranded cable with the multi-wire conductor used in many electronic applications. The multi-conductor has several wires, each insulated from the other. These wires are color-coded so that correct connections may be made.

A LESSON IN SAFETY: When making connections with stranded wires, the stranded ends should be tightly twisted together and coated with solder. This is called tinning. Fine wires separated from the connection is a mark of poor workmanship and may cause dangerous short circuits.

OHM'S LAW

One of the fundamental laws of electrical circuits was derived from experimentation done by George Simon Ohm, the German scientist and philosopher, during the 19th century. To honor the achievements of Mr. Ohm, the standard unit of measurement for resistance is called the OHM. It is frequently represented by the Greek letter "omega" as Ω. If you see on a diagram 1000 Ω, it means 1000 ohms. In electronic circuits the use of the kilohm and megohm is very common. The Greek prefix "kilo" means 1000. The prefix "meg" means one million. These are summarized in Table 3-2.

Ohm's Law is stated as: The current in amperes in a circuit is equal to the applied voltage divided by the resistance, or,

$$I \text{ (in amperes)} = \frac{E \text{ (in volts)}}{R \text{ (in ohms)}}$$

Notice the letter symbols used in this equation:

I = intensity of the current in amperes
E = electromotive force in volts
R = resistance in ohms

In non-mathematical language this formula means:

As voltage is increased - current increases
As voltage is decreased - current decreases
As resistance is increased - current decreases
As resistance is decreased - current increases

A mathematical explanation: A certain device which has a resistance of 100 ohms is connected to a 100 v. source of electricity. How much current will flow in the circuit? Fig. 3-5.

Fig. 3-5. E = 100 V, R = 100 Ω, I = 1 amp.

Solution:

$$I = \frac{E}{R} \quad \text{or} \quad I = \frac{100 \text{ v}}{100 \, \Omega} = 1 \text{ ampere}$$

If the voltage is increased to 200 volts, how much current will flow? Fig. 3-6.

Fig. 3-6. E = 200 V, R = 100 Ω, I = 2 amps.

Circuits and Power

Solution:

$$I = \frac{200\,v}{100\,\Omega} = 2 \text{ amperes}$$

Returning the voltage to 100 volts, but increasing the resistance to 200 ohms, then: Fig. 3-7.

E = 100 V   R = 200 Ω

METER

A

I = .5 AMPS

Fig. 3-7. E = 100 V, R = 200 Ω, I = .5 amps.

$$I = \frac{E}{R} \quad \text{or} \quad I = \frac{100\,v}{200\,\Omega} = .5 \text{ amperes}$$

Finally, decrease the resistance to 50 ohms, then Fig. 3-8,

E = 100 V   R = 50 Ω

METER

A

I = 2 AMPS

Fig. 3-8. E = 100 V, R = 50 Ω, I = 2 amps.

$$I = \frac{E}{R} \quad \text{or} \quad I = \frac{100\,v}{50\,\Omega} = 2 \text{ amps.}$$

Compare this computation to the previous discussion, and notice that these statements have been proved true. By simple transposition of symbols in the Ohm's Law equation, it is possible to solve for any one unknown quantity, if the other two are known.

Ohm's Law may be written three ways.

$$I = \frac{E}{R}$$
$$E = IR$$
$$R = \frac{E}{I}$$

Problem: A current of .5 amperes is flowing in a circuit which has 100 ohms resistance. What is the applied voltage? Fig. 3-9.

E = ?   R = 100 Ω

A

I = .5 AMPS

Fig. 3-9. R = 100 Ω, I = .5 amps., E = 50 V.

$$E = IR = .5 \times 100 = 50 \text{ volts}$$

Problem: A circuit has an applied voltage of 50 volts and the current is measured at .5 amp. What is the resistance of the circuit? Fig. 3-10.

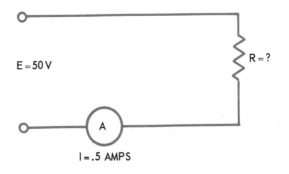

E = 50 V   R = ?

A

I = .5 AMPS

Fig. 3-10. E = 50 V, I = .5 amps., R = 100 Ω.

$$R = \frac{E}{I} \quad \text{or} \quad R = \frac{50}{.5} = 100 \,\Omega$$

Practice with problems is the best way to become thoroughly acquainted with Ohm's Law. A device to help you solve Ohm's Law problems is illustrated in Fig. 3-11.

Fig. 3-11. A memory device to help you solve Ohm's Law problems. Cover the unknown quantity with your finger and the remaining letters give the correct equation. For example, E is unknown. Cover E, and I x R remains.

Caution: When working problems involving Ohm's Law, be certain that all quantities are in their fundamental form, that is, volts in volts, current in amperes, and resistance in ohms. If one or more of these quantities appears with a prefix such as kilo, mega, or milli, a conversion must be made before solving the equation.

Problem: A circuit has a resistance of 10 kilohms and the current is measured as 100 milliamperes. What is the applied voltage?

$$E = I \times R \text{ or } E = .1 \text{ amps} \times 10,000 = 1,000 \text{ v}$$

For methods of making conversions, see Appendix 3.

POWER

In any electrical circuit, the only component in the circuit that uses electrical power is resistance. Power is the time rate of doing work. In the physics of machines it is discovered that when a force moves through a distance, work is done. For example, if a 10 lb. weight is lifted one foot, the work done equals,

F (force) x D (distance) or
10 x 1 = 10 ft. lbs. of work.

See Fig. 3-12. No reference is made to time in this equation. One might take five seconds or 10 minutes to lift the 10 lb. weight. However, if one lifted the 10 pound weight at the rate of once each second, then the power expended would be 10 ft. lbs. per second. To carry the example one step further, if one lifted the 10 pound weight in one-half or .5 second, then the power expended would equal:

$$\frac{10}{.5} \text{ or } 20 \text{ ft. lbs. per second.}$$

A machine that works at a rate of 550 ft. lbs./sec. is equivalent to one horsepower. Also 33,000 ft. lbs./min. equals one horse-power.

In electricity the unit of power is the watt, named in honor of James Watt, who is credited with the invention of the steam en-

F x D = 10 FT. LBS. OF WORK

Fig. 3-12. When a 10 lb. weight is lifted one foot, 10 foot-pounds of work is done.

gine. When one volt of electrical pressure moves one coulomb of electricity in one second, the work accomplished is equal to one watt of power. Recall the definition of one ampere: When one coulomb of electrons moves past a given point in a circuit in one second. So power in an electrical circuit is equal to:

P (watts) = E (volts) x I (amperes)

Comparing electrical power to mechanical power,

746 watts = 1 horsepower

The power formula, sometimes called Watt's Law, can be arranged algebraically, so that if two quantities are known, the third unknown

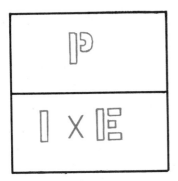

Fig. 3-13. A memory device to help you solve power problems. Cover the unknown quantity with your finger and the remaining letters give the correct equation.

may be found. Use the device in Fig. 3-13 to help you.

$$P = I \times E$$
$$I = \frac{P}{E}$$
$$E = \frac{P}{I}$$

Example: A circuit with an unknown load has an applied voltage of 100 volts. The measured current is 2 amperes. How much power is consumed?

$$P = I \times E \text{ or } 2 \text{ amps} \times 100 \text{ v} = 200 \text{ w}$$

Example: An electric toaster rated at 550 watts is connected to a 110 volt source. How much current will this appliance use?

$$I = \frac{P}{E} \quad \text{or} \quad \frac{550 \text{ w}}{110 \text{ v}} = 5 \text{ amps}$$

A LESSON IN SAFETY: An electric current produces heat when it passes through a resistance. Heaters and resistors will remain hot for some time after the power is removed. Handle them carefully. Burns should be treated immediately. See your instructor.

OHM'S LAW AND THE POWER LAW

It is possible to combine these laws to produce simple formulas which will permit you to solve any unknown, if two quantities are known. In Table 3-3, these equations are given and the explanation of each. Refer to the numbers of these equations.

Fig. 3-14. A memory device combining Ohm's Law and Power Laws. Use it to help you solve your problems.

---

1. $E = I \times R$ Ohm's Law

---

2. $E = \dfrac{P}{I}$ Watt's Law

---

3. $E = \sqrt{PR}$ By transposing equation 12 and taking the square root.

---

4. $I = \dfrac{E}{R}$ Ohm's Law

---

5. $I = \dfrac{P}{E}$ Watt's Law

---

6. $I = \sqrt{\dfrac{P}{R}}$ By transposing equation 9 and taking the square root.

---

7. $R = \dfrac{E}{I}$ Ohm's Law

---

8. $R = \dfrac{E^2}{P}$ By transposing equation 12

---

9. $R = \dfrac{P}{I^2}$ By transposing equation 11

10.	$P = I \times E$	Watt's Law
11.	$P = I^2 \times R$	By substituting $I \times R$ from equation 1, for E.
12.	$P = \dfrac{E^2}{R}$	By substituting $\dfrac{E}{R}$ from equation 4, for I.

Table 3-3

These formulas are conveniently arranged in a wheel-shaped memory device for ready reference. Refer to Fig. 3-14. To use the device, find the equation that uses the two known quantities in your circuit.

For example: If current and resistance are known and power is unknown, use equation 11. If power and voltage are known and current is unknown, use equation 5.

RESISTORS

Resistance units permit the design engineer to use electricity in many interesting and profitable ways. Because the resistance is the only component of a circuit that uses power, most of the useful effects and labor saving devices provided by electrical power use some form of resistance. Resistance may purposely be introduced into a circuit to reduce voltages and limit current flow in electronic devices. Fig. 3-15, shows several forms of the common molded composition type resistors. They are manufactured in a variety of shapes and sizes. The chemical composition, which causes the resistance, is accurately controlled in the industrial laboratory. They are made in many ohmic values from one ohm to several million ohms. Also the physical size of the resistor is rated in watts, which means its ability to dissipate the heat caused by the resistance. The larger sizes provide a greater radiation surface to dissipate ·this heat. Common sizes used in electronic work are the 1/2 watt and one watt size. One may purchase, for example, a 1,000 ohm resistor in a 1/2 watt, 1 watt or 2 watt size. In each size the resistance would be the same.

For higher current applications, resistance units are wirewound. On a ceramic core is wound a wire which has a specific resistance. The whole resistance component is insulated by a coat of vitreous enamel. Sev-

Fig. 3-15. Composition Resistors. 1/10, 1/4, 1/2 and 1 and 2 w. sizes.
(Ohmite Mfg. Co.)

Fig. 3-16. Resistors are made in many types, shapes and sizes to meet specific circuit requirements.

eral of these resistors are illustrated in Fig. 3-16. These are manufactured in sizes from 5 watts to 200 watts, depending upon the heat dissipation required during operation.

A variation to the wire wound resistor provides an exposed surface to the resistance wire on one side to which is attached an adjustable third terminal. Such resistors, sometimes with two or more adjustable taps, are used extensively as voltage dividers in power supplies and other apparatus. These adjustable resistors are shown in Fig. 3-17.

Most electronic equipment requires variable resistance components which can be controlled by a knob on the front panel. The volume control on a radio is an example of this type of control. These are generally the rotary type. The variation in resistance is provided by a sliding contact arm on a molded composition ring as the resistive element.

Fig. 3-17. These adjustable resistors provide a sliding tap for voltage divider applications.

This type is shown in Fig. 3-18. Connections may be made through terminals to both ends of the resistance as well as to the sliding contact arms. This component is called a POTENTIOMETER. For higher current and power applications, these potentiometers may be wire-wound resistance wire instead of the molded composition. The wire wound types are shown in Fig. 3-19.

There are, also, many types and sizes of resistors designed for specific applications. These include extremely accurate precision resistors, and heavy and rugged types for high power applications. In your television set there may be a TV Fuse Resistor. This is a special 7 1/2 ohm resistor which acts as a slow-blow fuse or protective device

constructed that as the temperature increases, their resistance will decrease. Advanced studies in semiconductor characteristics will include detailed explanations of thermistor theory and application.

SERIES CIRCUITS

If a circuit is so arranged that all of the current flowing in the circuit will pass through all components, these components are con-

Fig. 3-18. Potentiometers used in electronic circuitry for fixed and variable resistance.
(Centralab)

in televisions which have series connected filaments. Series string tube filaments will be discussed in a later chapter on Power Supplies.

One relatively new form of resistor, which is rapidly becoming popular in transistor circuitry, is the THERMISTOR. These components are used to offset the effect of temperature change in a circuit. They are so

Fig. 3-20. The schematic diagram of three resistors in series.

nected in SERIES. The components are connected "in-line" or "end-to-end." In Fig. 3-20 three resistors are connected in series. Other components, which will be studied later, may also be connected in series. (In the following discussions, the resistance of the connecting wires in the circuits will be neglected.) If resistors are connected in series, the total resistance of the circuit is equal to the sum of the resistors. In Fig. 3-20, $R_1 = 100\,\Omega$, $R_2 = 400\,\Omega$, and $R_3 = 500\,\Omega$. Then, $R_T = R_1 + R_2 + R_3$ or

Fig. 3-19. A wire-wound potentiometer for higher current applications.
(Ohmite Mfg. Co.)

$$100 + 400 + 500 = 1000 \ \Omega$$

If 100 volts were applied to the terminals of this circuit, the current flowing in the circuit would equal,

Ohm's Law: $I = \dfrac{E}{R}$ or $I = \dfrac{100\,v}{1000\,\Omega} = .1$ amp.

As current passes through a resistor, a certain amount of energy is used and a certain amount of pressure or voltage is lost. The voltage loss across each resistor may be calculated by Ohm's Law, using formula, $E = I \times R$. Fig. 3-21.

Fig. 3-21. *The voltage loss or drop across each resistor may be computed by the formula, $E = I \times R$.*

For R_1,	E_{R_1}	$= .1 \times 100 = 10\,v$
For R_2,	E_{R_2}	$= .1 \times 400 = 40\,v$
For R_3,	E_{R_3}	$= .1 \times 500 = 50\,v$

The symbol such as E_{R_1} means the voltage across resistor R_1. One should particularly note that the sum of the voltage losses or voltage drops is equal to the source voltage. In this example,

$$E_{R_1} + E_{R_2} + E_{R_3} = E_{\text{source}} \text{ or}$$
$$10\,v + 40\,v + 50\,v = 100\,v$$

Because the voltage drop or loss across a resistor is computed by using Ohm's Law, $E = I \times R$, the technician will frequently

refer to this loss as the <u>IR drop</u>, which means the same as the <u>voltage drop.</u>

Since these resistors are connected in series, all the current flowing in the circuit must pass through each resistor. So, therefore, the current must be the same in all parts of the circuit. Fig. 3-22.

Fig. 3-22. *The current measured at any point in the series circuit is the same.*

The above facts concerning series circuits may be summarized in laws known as KIRCHHOFF'S LAWS.

1. The sum of the voltage drops around a series circuit will equal the source voltage.

2. The current is the same when measured at any point in the series circuit.

POWER IN A SERIES CIRCUIT

As the voltage overcomes the resistance, work is done and power is the time rate of doing work. Referring to the section on power, earlier in this chapter, you will discover that in electricity, $P = I \times E$. The energy lost in overcoming the resistance takes the form of heat and must be dissipated by the resistor into the surrounding air. This explains why some resistors are larger than others. They must be large enough to provide radiation surface for heat dissipation.

Referring to Fig. 3-23, the total power

used in this circuit would equal:

$$P = I \times E \text{ or } .1 \times 100\,v \text{ or } 10\,w.$$

To calculate the power consumed by indi-

$R_1 = 100\,\Omega$

$P_{R_1} = 1\,W$

$R_2 = 400\,\Omega$

$P_{R_2} = 4\,W$

$R_3 = 500\,\Omega$

.1 AMP

$P_{R_3} = 5\,W$

$P_T = 10\,W$

Fig. 3-23. The power used by each resistor may be computed by the formula, P = I x E.

vidual resistors, the formula $P = I^2R$ may be used:

For R_1, $P = (.1)^2 \times 100 = 1\,w$

For R_2, $P = (.1)^2 \times 400 = 4\,w$

For R_3, $P = (.1)^2 \times 500 = 5\,w$

For R_T, $P = (.1)^2 \times 1000 = 10\,w$

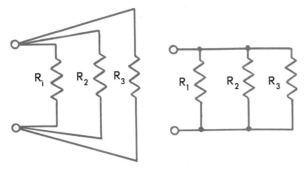

R_1 R_2 R_3 R_1 R_2 R_3

Fig. 3-24. The schematic diagram of three resistors in parallel.

Notice that the sum of the individual powers used by each resistor is equal to the total power used by the circuit.

PARALLEL CIRCUITS

When several components are connected

to the same voltage source, the components are connected in parallel or "side by side." Multiple paths for current flow are provided by a parallel circuit, because each resistor constitutes a path of its own. In Fig. 3-24, three separate paths for electricity are provided by R_1, R_2 and R_3. One must realize, that when components are connected in this manner, the total resistance of the circuit is <u>decreased</u> every time another component is added. Compare a parallel circuit to a system of pipes carrying water. Two pipes will carry more water than one pipe. If a third pipe is

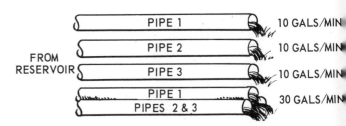

FROM RESERVOIR

PIPE 1	10 GALS/MIN
PIPE 2	10 GALS/MIN
PIPE 3	10 GALS/MIN
PIPE 1 PIPES 2 & 3	30 GALS/MIN

Fig. 3-25. Electricity may be compared to the flow of water. Increasing the number of pipes will decrease the resistance to water flow.

$E_S = 6\,V$ $R_1 = 30\,\Omega$ $R_2 = 30\,\Omega$ $R_3 = 30\,\Omega$

.2 AMP   .2 AMP   .2 AMP

$R_T = 10\,\Omega$ $I_T = .6$ AMPS

Fig. 3-26. The total current equals the sum of the branch currents.

added, the three pipes will carry more water than two pipes. As more pipes are added, the total resistance to the flow of water is <u>decreased</u>. Fig. 3-25.

In Fig. 3-26, resistor $R_1 = R_2 = R_3$ so each resistor will carry the same amount of current, and the three resistors together will carry three times more current than only one. Therefore, the total resistance of the circuit must be one-third of the resistance of a single resistance. Assigning values to $R_1 = 30\,\Omega$, $R_2 = 30\,\Omega$, and $R_3 = 30\,\Omega$, then:

$$R_T = \frac{30\,\Omega}{3} \text{ or } 10\,\Omega$$

When equal resistors are connected in parallel, the total resistance of the parallel group or network is equal to any one resistor divided by the number of resistors in the network.

Total resistance R_T

$$= \frac{R}{N} \frac{\text{value of one resistor}}{\text{number of resistors in network}}$$

The applied voltage is the same for each resistor, because each is connected across the same voltage source.

Therefore, the currents are, using Ohm's Law:

For R_1, $\qquad I = \dfrac{6\,v}{30\,\Omega} = .2$ amps

R_2, $\qquad I = \dfrac{6\,v}{30\,\Omega} = .2$ amps

R_3, $\qquad I = \dfrac{6\,v}{30\,\Omega} = .2$ amps

The total current flowing through the network would be the sum of the individual branch currents or:

$$I_{R_1} + I_{R_2} + I_{R_3} = I_T$$
$$\text{or}$$
$$.2 + .2 + .2 = .6 \text{ amps}$$

This may be proved by applying Ohm's Law, using the total resistance,

$$I_T = \frac{E}{R_T} \text{ or } I_T = \frac{6\,v}{10\,\Omega} = .6 \text{ amps}$$

Summarizing again, there are these laws concerning parallel circuits.

1. The voltage across all branches of a parallel network is the same.

2. The total current is equal to the sum of the individual branch currents.

The differences between these laws and those which apply to series circuits should be compared.

It is not unusual to find two unequal resistors connected in parallel. In this case, the total resistance may be found by using the formula,

$$R_T = \frac{R_1 R_2}{R_1 + R_2}$$

In Fig. 3-27, resistance $R_1 = 20\,\Omega$ and $R_2 = 30\,\Omega$. Applying the formula,

$$R_T = \frac{20 \times 30}{20 + 30} \text{ or } \frac{600}{50} = 12\,\Omega$$

With an applied voltage $E_s = 6\,v$, then the total current in the circuit will be,

$$I_T = \frac{E}{R_T} \text{ or } \frac{6}{12} \text{ or } .5 \text{ amps}$$

This equation may be proved by finding the sum of individual branch current,

For R_1, $\qquad I = \dfrac{6\,v}{20\,\Omega} = .3$ amps

R_2, $\qquad I = \dfrac{6\,v}{30\,\Omega} = .2$ amps

$$I_1 + I_2 = .3 + .2 = .5 \text{ amps or } I_T$$

Two observations should be carefully studied.

1. The total resistance of any parallel circuit must always be less than the value of any resistor in the network. Note in Fig. 3-27. $R_T = 12\,\Omega$ which is less than R_1 which is $20\,\Omega$.

Fig. 3-27. The schematic diagram for two unequal resistors in parallel.

2. The branch of the circuit containing the greatest resistance conducts the least current.

When three or more resistors are connected in parallel, it is convenient to use the conductance method of finding the total resistance. As resistance in ohms is the ability to resist the flow of current, its opposite is conductance, which is the ability of a component to conduct. Resistance is measured in OHMS; Conductance is measured in MHOS (ohm spelled backwards). The symbol representing conductance is G and is equal to the reciprocal of resistance.

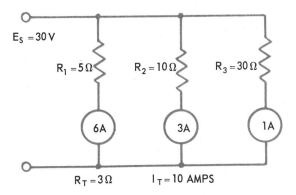

Fig. 3-28. *Three unequal resistors connected in parallel.*

$$G = \frac{1}{R}$$

To illustrate: A resistance of 100 Ω is equal to conductance of $\frac{1}{100}$ or .01 mhos.

Ohm's Law states that $R = \frac{E}{I}$, then $\frac{1}{R} = \frac{I}{E}$ or $G = \frac{I}{E}$ and may be defined as amperes-per-volt, or

$$I = GE$$

Current in a circuit is equal to its voltage times its conductance in mhos.

For example: A circuit has an applied voltage of E = 100 v and a resistance of 50 Ω.

By Ohm's Law: $I = \frac{100}{50} = 2$ amps

By conductance method:

$$G = \frac{1}{R} = \frac{1}{50} = .02 \text{ mhos}$$
$$I = GE \quad \text{or} \quad .02 \times 100 = 2 \text{ amps}$$

Referring to Fig. 3-28, three unequal resistors are connected in parallel. $R_1 = 5\ \Omega$, $R_2 = 10\ \Omega$ and $R_3 = 30\ \Omega$. To find the total resistance: find the sum of the individual branch currents. Assuming a voltage of 30 volts then:

For Branch R_1, $\quad I_1 = \frac{E}{R_1} = \frac{30}{5} = 6$ amps

For Branch R_2, $\quad I_2 = \frac{E}{R_2} = \frac{30}{10} = 3$ amps

For Branch R_3, $\quad I_3 = \frac{E}{R_3} = \frac{30}{30} = 1$ amp

$\quad I_T = I_1 + I_2 + I_3 = 6 + 3 + 1 = 10$ amps

By Ohm's Law:

$$R_T = \frac{E}{I} \quad \text{so} \quad R_T = \frac{30}{10} = 3\ \Omega$$

As I_T is the sum of all of the currents, and is equal to $\frac{E}{R_T}$ (Ohm's Law) then,

$$\frac{E}{R_T} = \frac{E}{R_1} + \frac{E}{R_2} + \frac{E}{R_3}$$

Divide both sides of the equation by E, then

$$\frac{1}{R_T} = \frac{1}{R_1} + \frac{1}{R_2} + \frac{1}{R_3}$$

This equation shows that the conductance of a circuit is equal to the sum of the conductances of the branch circuits. To solve for the total resistance of a circuit in Fig. 3-28.

Fig. 3-29. *Combination circuit of series and parallel resistors.*

$$\frac{1}{R_T} = \frac{1}{5} + \frac{1}{10} + \frac{1}{30} = \frac{10}{30}$$

Inverting both sides of the equation,

$$R_T = \frac{30}{10} = 3\ \Omega$$

This conductance formula is used in the computation of the total resistance of parallel circuits. You should practice using it by completing the problems at the end of this chapter.

SERIES AND PARALLEL COMBINATION CIRCUITS

The technician is frequently required to compute the total resistance of combination series and parallel circuits. This total resistance is referred to as the <u>equivalent resistance</u> of the circuit. It is only necessary to solve in logical order by using the series and parallel resistance formulas of the previous discussion. Referring to Fig. 3-29, $R_1 = 7\ \Omega$, $R_2 = 5\ \Omega$, $R_3 = 10\ \Omega$, $R_4 = 20\ \Omega$, $R_5 = 10\ \Omega$. The applied voltage $E_s = 30$ volts.

Step I. Combined R_4 and R_5. Fig. 3-30. They are in series, so $R_4 + R_5 = 20 + 10 = 30\ \Omega$.

Fig. 3-30. *Two series resistors in one branch of the parallel network have been combined.*

Step II. Find the total resistance of the parallel circuit, Fig. 3-31.

$$\frac{1}{R_T} = \frac{1}{R_2} + \frac{1}{R_3} + \frac{1}{R_{4\&5}} \text{ or } \frac{1}{5} + \frac{1}{10} + \frac{1}{30} = \frac{10}{30}$$

$$R_T = \frac{30}{10} \text{ or } 3\ \Omega$$

Fig. 3-31. *The parallel network is combined to the single equivalent resistance.*

Step III. This equivalent resistance or 3 ohms is in series with R_1 of 7 ohms. Fig. 3-32. So the R_T of the circuit equals 3 ohms + 7 ohms or 10 ohms.

Fig. 3-32. *The combination circuit is equivalent to a single resistance.*

The current flowing in the total circuit is;

$$I_T = \frac{E}{R_T} = \frac{30}{10} = 3 \text{ amps}$$

The voltage drop across R_1 is,

$$E_{R_1} = IR \text{ or } 3 \times 7 = 21 \text{ v}$$

If 21 volts is lost by R_1, then the remaining part of the applied voltage appears across the network of parallel resistors or 9 v.

The current through the three branches must equal the total current of 3 amps in the circuit, Fig. 3-33.

$$I_{R_2} = \frac{E}{R_2} = \frac{9\ v}{5\ \Omega} = 1.8 \text{ amps}$$

$$I_{R_3} = \frac{E}{R_3} = \frac{9\ v}{10\ \Omega} = .9 \text{ amps}$$

$$I_{R_{4\&5}} = \frac{E}{R_{4\&5}} = \frac{9\ v}{30\ \Omega} = .3 \text{ amps}$$

$$I_T = I_{R_2} + I_{R_3} + I_{R_{4\&5}} = 1.8 + .9 + .3 = 3 \text{ amps}$$

Fig. 3-33. *The complete analysis of the combination circuit, showing voltages and currents.*

Knowing the current and voltage of this circuit, the power consumed would be:

$$P = I \times E \quad \text{or} \quad 3 \text{ amps} \times 30 \text{ v} = 90 \text{ w}$$

The sum of the powers dissipated by the individual resistors should equal 90 watts. Using the formula $P = I^2 R$ then:

$$P_{R_1} = (3)^2 \quad \times \quad 7 \quad = \quad 63.0 \text{ w}$$
$$P_{R_2} = (1.8)^2 \quad \times \quad 5 \quad = \quad 16.2 \text{ w}$$
$$P_{R_3} = (.9)^2 \quad \times \quad 10 \quad = \quad 8.1 \text{ w}$$
$$P_{R_4} = (.3)^2 \quad \times \quad 20 \quad = \quad 1.8 \text{ w}$$

$$P_{R_5} = (.3)^2 \quad \times \quad 10 \quad = \quad .9 \text{ w}$$
$$\overline{\phantom{P_{R_5} = (.3)^2 \times 10 = .9}}$$
$$P_T \quad = \quad 90.0 \text{ w}$$

To the beginning student in electronics the solution of series and parallel circuits involving the use of Ohm's and Watt's Laws requires considerable practice. Practice is the only way to assure understanding. Quick recognition of known and unknown quantities and a logical approach to the solution will assure accurate results. Always prove your answer by using other forms of Ohm's Law as has been demonstrated in previous examples.

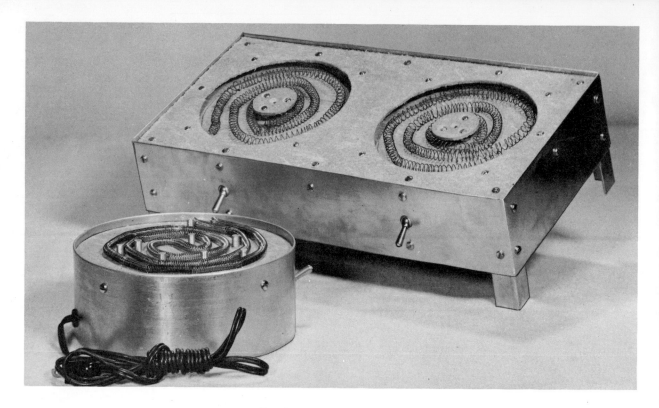

Fig. 3-34. Two electric stoves.

ACTIVITY AND EXPERIMENTATION

ELECTRIC STOVES

1. In Fig. 3-34 two simple electric stoves are illustrated which are satisfactory projects to demonstrate the heat produced by a current flowing through resistance. The little stoves are quite satisfactory for coffee and food warmers. The bases are made of 20 gage aluminum and can be shaped according to your own design. They have been fastened together with sheet metal screws. The top must be constructed of insulating non-inflammable material. In this project, asbestos board was used.

The line cord enters the stove through a 3/8 inch rubber grommet and is secured on the inside with a knot. The heating elements are connected to the line through single pole toggle switches.

Selecting the proper length of nickel-chrome resistance wire is a problem for you to solve. This wire is supplied in a number of gauge sizes, each with a specified ohm's re-sistance per foot. A 330 watt stove operating on 110 volts would require,

$$I = \frac{P}{E} \quad \text{or} \quad \frac{330}{110} = 3 \text{ amps current}$$

and

$$R = \frac{E}{I} \quad \text{or} \quad \frac{110}{3} = 36.6 \, \Omega \text{ resistance}$$

If a nickel chrome wire having a resistance of 3 ohms per ft. were used, a length of $\frac{36.6}{3}$ or 12.2 ft. is required. The wire, cut to length, is then tightly wound into a spring and fastened to the stove top as the heating element. If nickel-chrome wire is not readily available, elements may be purchased in appliance repair shops.

After the stove is operating, measure the actual power being used with a watt-meter and compare the meter reading with your own computation.

HOT DOG ROASTER

2. A HOT DOG roaster is illustrated in Fig. 3-35. It is fun to entertain your friends with this appliance. In this project, the wiener is suspended between two pointed aluminum pins. The pins are connected directly to the 115* volt power source. The wiener is cooked by heat produced from its own internal resistance.

CAUTION: This cooker is in the form of a box with an interlock switch. Observe the photograph carefully. Power cannot be applied to the wieners unless the cover of the box is closed. Do not attempt to construct this project without the interlock as someone unfamiliar with its operation may get a shock.

Some experimentation with the distance the pointed pins are inserted in the wieners may be necessary for real fast cooking.

CAUTION: Be certain that no electrical connections are made to the metal box. It is wiser to use a plastic box if available. It is also easier to clean.

Fig. 3-35. Hot dog roaster.

Exact voltage may vary from 110 to 120 depending on city and locality.

NOTE: Information on the Electrodemonstrator, will be found in Appendix 6, page 313.

Fig. 3-36. Above. Electrodemonstrator, wired to show series circuit.

Fig. 3-37. Below. Lights are connected in parallel.

ELECTRODEMONSTRATOR

3. In Fig. 3-36, an electrodemonstrator is used to show a series circuit. Each light bulb is a resistance unit. A small 6 volt bell transformer is used as a power source.

Procedure:

A. Connect one light only to transformer and observe its brilliance.

B. Connect two lights in series and observe their brilliance. Why are they dimmer?

C. Connect the three lights in series and observe that all lights are now quite dim.

D. Remove one light from the socket. Do the other lights continue to glow?

E. Measure the source voltage with a voltmeter. Measure the voltages across each light. Does the sum of these voltages equal the source voltage?

4. In Fig. 3-37 the lights from the electrodemonstrator are connected in parallel across the 6 volt transformer.

Procedure:

A. Connect two lights in parallel and observe their brilliance.

B. Connect three lights in parallel and observe their brilliance. Is there a difference? Compare to the three lights in series.

C. Unscrew one light bulb. Do the others continue to glow?

D. Using a voltmeter, measure voltage across the terminals of each light and compare to the source voltage.

E. Which circuit uses the most power? The three light series circuit or the three light parallel circuit? Explain.

Circuits and Power

5. Using the PIRE wheel in Fig. 3-14, solve the following problems:

1. E = 100 v, I = 2 amps, R = _____.

2. E = 50 v, R = 1000 ohms, I = _____.

3. I = .5 amps, R = 50 ohms, E = _____.

4. E = 10 v, I = .001 amps, R = _____.

5. I = .05 amps, R = 1000 ohms, E = _____.

6. P = 10 w, I = 2 amps, E = _____.

7. E = 100 v, I = .5 amps, P = _____.

8. P = 500 w, E = 250 v, I = _____.

9. I = .01 amps, R = 100 ohms, E = _____.

10. P = 100 w, I = 2 amps, R = _____.

11. E = 10 v, P = 10 w, R = _____.

12. E = 500 v, I = 2 amps, R = _____.

13. E = 100 v, R = 1000 ohms, P = _____.

14. I = .5 amps, R = 50 ohms, P = _____.

15. I = 4 amps, R = 10 ohms, P = _____.

16. I = 10 ma, E = 50 v, P = _____.

17. I = 20 ma, E = 100 v, R = _____.

18. P = 10 w, I = 1 amp, R = _____.

19. E = 1000 v, R = 1000 ohms, I = _____.

20. I = 100 ma, R = 100 ohms, E = _____.

21. I = 100 ma, R = 100 ohms, P = _____.

22. P = 500 w, E = 100 v, I = _____.

23. E = 100 v, R = 100 ohms, P = _____.

24. E = 50 v, R = 10 kilohms, I = _____.

25. P = 10 w, R = 10 ohms, E = _____.

26. P = 50 w, R = 2 ohms, I = _____.

TEST YOUR KNOWLEDGE

1. State Ohm's Law three ways.

2. State Watt's Law three ways.

3. In a series circuit,

    R_T =

4. What do you know about voltages and current in a series circuit?

5. In a parallel circuit of several equal resistors,

    R_T =

6. In a parallel circuit of two unequal resistors,

    R_T =

7. In a circuit of several unequal resistors in parallel,

    R_T =

8. What do you know about the voltages and currents in a parallel circuit?

9. In a series circuit,

    P_T =

10. In a parallel circuit,

    P_T =

Fig. 3-38. ELECTRONICS IN INDUSTRY. Electricity is used to heat the water in this **HOT SPRAY** painting equipment. Note the thermostatic control which provides uniform temperatures during operation.
(DeVilbiss Co.)

Chapter 4

MAGNETISM

For centuries the mystery of magnetism has baffled the scientist. Shepherds, tending their flocks in ancient days, were mystified by small pieces of stone, which attracted the iron tip on the shepherd's staff. The ancient Chinese navigators discovered that a small piece of this peculiar stone attached to a string would always turn in a northerly direction. These small stones were iron ore. They were called Magnetite by the Greeks, because they were found near Magnesia in Asia Minor. Since mariners used these stones in the navigation of their ships, the stones became known as "leading stones" or LODE-STONES. These were the first forms of natural magnets.

Today, a magnet may be defined as a material or substance which has the power to attract iron, steel and other magnetic materials. By laboratory experiments, it was discovered that the greatest attractive force appeared at the ends of a magnet. These concentrations of magnetic force are called magnetic poles; each magnet has a NORTH POLE and a SOUTH POLE. Further experimentation revealed that existing between the North and South Pole were many invisible lines of magnetic force. Each line was an independent line and not crossing or touching its adjacent line. The photo, Fig. 4-1, shows the magnetic lines of force. This field picture was created by placing a bar magnet beneath a sheet of paper, upon which was sprinkled some fine iron filings. Note the pattern of lines existing between the poles. Note the concentration of lines at each end of the magnet or its poles. Each line of force from the north pole goes to the south pole through space and returns to the north pole through the magnet. These closed loops of the magnetic field may be described as magnetic circuits. You may compare the magnetic circuit to the electrical circuit, where the magnetizing force may be compared to voltage, and the magnetic lines may be compared to current.

Further scientific investigation has proved that the EARTH acts as one enormous magnet, with its poles close to the North and South geographical poles. In early days the scientist assumed that the compass was point-

Fig. 4-1. The electrodemonstrator is used to show the magnetic field of two permanent magnets. See Activities at the end of this chapter, page 66.

ing in a northerly direction so therefore called this direction magnetic north. More recently it was discovered that the north pole of the compass needle was attracted to the south pole of the EARTH. So magnetic south of the EARTH magnet is in the vicinity of the geographic North Pole. Referring to Fig. 4-2, you will observe that magnetic north and the North Pole do not coincide and a compass would not necessarily point toward true north.

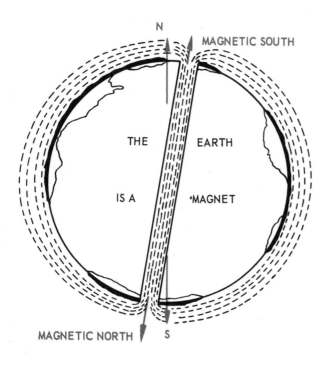

Fig. 4-2. *The earth is an enormous magnet and is surrounded by a magnetic field.*

This angle between true and magnetic north is called the angle of declination or variation. There is, however, an imaginary line around the earth where the angle of declination is zero. When standing on this line your compass would point to true north as well as magnetic north. At all other locations on the surface of the earth, a correction must be applied to the compass reading to find true north.

LAWS OF MAGNETISM

The power of a magnet to attract iron has already been discussed. In Fig. 4-3, two bar magnets have been hung in wire saddles and are free to turn. The student will notice that

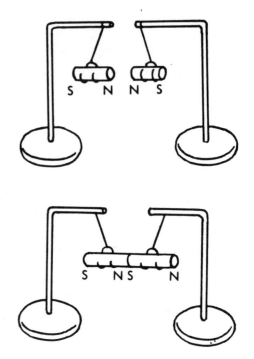

Fig. 4-3. *These permanent magnets demonstrate the Laws of Magnetism.*

when the N pole of one magnet is close to the S pole of the other that an attractive force will bring the two magnets together. On the other hand, if the magnets are turned so that two N poles or two S poles are close to each other, there will be a repulsive force between the two magnets. This proves the Law of Magnetism.

UNLIKE POLES ATTRACT EACH OTHER LIKE POLES REPEL EACH OTHER

By placing the magnets under a sheet of paper and using the iron filings to detect the invisible fields, you will observe in Fig. 4-4, that in the attractive position (N and S together) the invisible field is very strong between the two poles. However, when the magnets are placed with like poles together, the repulsive force is indicated by no invisible lines between the poles.

CAUTION: Certain precautions should be observed in the handling and storage of permanent magnets. Since the magnetism is a result of the molecular alignment, any rough handling such as dropping and

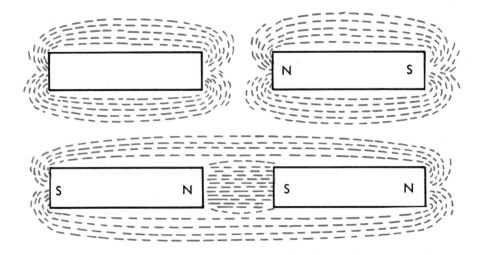

*Fig. 4-4. These sketches show the magnetic fields
of attracting and repelling magnets.*

pounding would upset the molecular alignment and destroy the magnet.

What causes a substance to become magnetized? An acceptable theory states that the molecules in an iron bar act as tiny magnets, and are arranged in-line so that their North and South poles are together. When the iron is demagnetized, the molecules are in random positions. This is illustrated in Fig. 4-5. This

Fig. 4-5. In a permanent magnet the molecules are in line.

conclusion is substantiated by breaking a piece of magnetized iron into several pieces. Then each piece is a separate magnet. Fig. 4-6 shows a broken magnet. The conclusion is

*Fig. 4-6. A long magnet may be broken into several
smaller magnets.*

further justified by the way a magnet is made. For example, take an unmagnetized bar, and rub it several times in the same direction with a permanent magnet. A test will show that the

bar is now magnetized. The rubbing with the magnet lined-up the molecules and caused the iron to become magnetized. Commercially, magnets are made by placing the material to be magnetized in a very strong magnetic field.

CAUTION: Magnets should be stored in pairs with north and south poles together to insure long life. A single horseshoe magnet may be preserved by placing a small piece of soft iron called a "keeper" across its poles.

Permanent magnets are manufactured in a variety of shapes and sizes for particular applications. Horseshoe and bar types are shown in Fig. 4-7. Very small magnets may

*Fig. 4-7. Magnets are manufactured in a variety of styles,
shapes and sizes.*

HORSESHOE
MAGNET

BAR MAGNET

be used to temporarily attach letters and figures to a bulletin board. A visual aid for teaching electrical circuits is illustrated in Fig. 4-8. The resistance symbols have small magnets glued to their backs. They are held in place on a sheet iron bulletin board by magnetism. Many useful home projects may be developed by using these magnets. Industry uses this type of bulletin board for traffic

Fig. 4-8. Small magnets are used to attach symbols to the metal board. This idea has hundreds of applications in home and industry.

control, production flow, temporary notices and a multitude of other labor saving charts.

CAUTION: Heat will destroy a magnet. Heat energy causes an increase in molecular activity and expansion which permits the molecules to return to their random positions of the unmagnetized piece of steel.

MAGNETIC FLUX

The many invisible lines of magnetic force surrounding a magnet are called the magnetic flux. If it is a strong magnet, the lines will be more dense. So the strength of a magnetic field may be determined by its flux density, or the number of lines per square inch or per square centimeter. Flux density is expressed by the equation,

$$B = \frac{\Phi}{A}$$

where B equals flux density, Φ (phi) represents the number of lines and A is the cross-sectional area in either square inches, or square centimeters. If A is measured in

square centimeters, then B is the number of lines per square centimeter or gauss.

THIRD LAW OF MAGNETISM

A simple experiment will demonstrate the third law of magnetism. Place one bar magnet on a table then slowly approach it with a second bar magnet. If the polarities are opposite, they will attract each other when close enough together. This experiment proves that the attractive force increases as the distance between the magnets decreases. Actually this magnetic force, either attractive or repelling, varies inversely as the square of the distance between the poles. For example, if the distance between two magnets with like poles is increased to twice the distance, the repulsive force reduces to one-quarter of its former value. This is valuable information. It explains the reason for accurately setting the gap in magnetic relays and switches. The term gap is the distance between the core of the electromagnet and its armature.

ELECTRIC CURRENT AND MAGNETISM

Scientists, during the eighteenth and nineteenth centuries, directed much of their research to the relationship between electricity and magnetism. The Danish physicist, Hans Christian Oersted, discovered that a magnetic field existed around a conductor carrying an electric current. The proof of this statement is seen in Fig. 4-9, where a current carrying

Fig. 4-9. Compasses line up to show circular pattern of magnetic field around current carrying conductor.

conductor is passed through a sheet of cardboard. Small compasses placed close to the conductor, point in the direction of the magnetic lines of force. Reversing the current will also reverse the direction of the compasses by 180 deg. This shows that the direction of the magnetic field depends upon the direction of current flow. The left hand rule for a conductor may be used to discover the direction of the field. Grasp the conductor with your left hand, extending your thumb in the direction of current flow. Your fingers around the conductor will indicate the circular direction of the magnetic field. In Fig. 4-10

Fig. 4-10. These conventions are used to show the relationship between current flow and the magnetic field.

the conventional method of showing a conductor and its field is displayed. The dot in the center of the conductor is the point of an arrow, showing that the current is flowing toward you. The magnetic field direction is represented by the circular arrows. An awareness of this principle in electrical circuits is particularly important when wires are carrying alternating currents. Then the placement of wires or "lead dress" has certain influence on the behavior of a circuit.

THE SOLENOID

When a current carrying conductor is wound into a coil or SOLENOID, the individual magnetic fields encircling the conductors tend to merge or join together. A solenoid will appear as a magnetic field with a N pole at one end, and a S pole at the opposite end. This solenoid is shown in Fig. 4-11. The LEFT HAND RULE FOR A COIL may be used to determine the polarity of the coil. Grasp the coil with your left hand in such a manner that your fingers encircle the coil in the

direction of current flow. Your extended thumb will point to the N pole of the coil.

The strength of the magnetic field of the solenoid depends upon the number of turns of wire in the coil and the current in amperes flowing through the coil. The product of the amperes and turns is called the AMPERE-TURNS of a coil and is the unit of measurement of field strength. If, for example, a coil of 500 ampere-turns will produce a required field strength, any combination of turns and

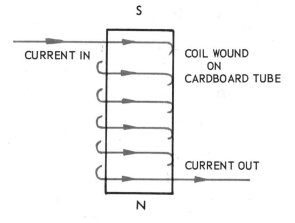

Fig. 4-11. A wire wound into a coil is a solenoid and has a polarity determined by the direction of current flow.

amperes whose product is 500 will be satisfactory, such as,

50 turns x 10 amps = 500 amp-turns

100 turns x 5 amps = 500 amp-turns

500 turns x 1 amp   = 500 amp-turns

MAGNETIC CIRCUITS

Although a detailed study of magnetic circuits is beyond the scope of this text, you should be familiar with the terms used to describe quantities and characteristics of magnetic circuits. It has already been mentioned that a similarity exists between magnetic circuits and electrical circuits. Comparing circuits, it is found that the number of lines of magnetic flux, Φ (in electricity this is current, I) is in direct proportion to the force producing them. This force (F) is in units of magnetomotive force called GILBERTS. (In electricity this is voltage, E.) Also there is resistance in a magnetic circuit which is called RELUCTANCE and its unit of measurement is the REL ($\mathcal{R}$). The equation then becomes,

$$\Phi = \frac{F}{\mathcal{R}} \text{ (Rowland's Law)}$$

where,

Φ = total number of lines of magnetic force

F = force which produces the field in gilberts

$\mathcal{R}$ = resistance to the passage of lines of force

The relationship between F and ampere-turns is,

F = 1.257 IN

where,

F = gilberts, I is the current and N = the number of turns.

Other terms encountered in the study of magnetism are as follows,

H = Intensity of a magnetizing force through a unit of length and is usually expressed in gilberts per centimeter. Mathematically,

$$H = \frac{F}{\ell} \text{ or } \frac{1.257 \text{ IN}}{\ell}$$

The term ℓ is expressed in centimeters.

The term reluctance has been mentioned as the unit of measurement of the resistance to the passage of magnetic lines of force. This may be further defined as the resistance offered by one cubic centimeter of air. Experimentation proves that as the flux path increases in length, the reluctance increases, and as the cross-sectional area of the flux

path decreases, then the reluctance increases. The reluctance is also dependent upon the material used as the path. The ability of a material or substance to conduct magnetic lines of force is called PERMEABILITY. The permeability of air is considered as 1. The term is expressed by the Greek letter μ , pronounced mu. The factors determining the resistance in a magnetic circuit may be compared to the factors affecting the resistance of electron flow in a conductor. Refer to Chapter III. For the magnetic circuit:

$$\mathcal{R} = \frac{\ell}{\mu A} \quad \text{where,}$$

$\mathcal{R}$ equals rels, ℓ equals length of path, μ equals the permeability of the material in the path, and A equals the cross sectional area of the path.

There is a definite relationship between the density of a magnetic field, the force producing the field, and the permeability of

IRON CORE

ELECTROMAGNET

Fig. 4-12. The coil with an iron core is described as an electromagnet.

the material in which the field is produced. Mathematically,

$$\text{Permeability} \mu = \frac{B \text{ Flux lines per Cm}^2 \text{ or gauss}}{H \text{ gilberts per Cm of length}}$$

The B, H and μ of common magnetic materials may be found in an electricity handbook.

ELECTROMAGNETS

The construction of a solenoid coil has already been discussed. The student should realize that in the case of the solenoid, air only is the conductor in the magnetic circuit. Other substances will conduct magnetic lines of force better than air. These materials would be described as having greater <u>permeability</u>. To prove this, a soft iron core may be inserted in the solenoid coil, Fig. 4-12. The strength of the magnetic field will be greatly increased. Two reasons may be given. First, the magnetic lines have been confined or concentrated into the smaller cross-sectional area of the core and secondly, the iron provides a far better path (greater permeability) for the magnetic lines. Such a device is known as an ELECTROMAGNET. The rules for the determination of the polarity of an electromagnet are the same as those for the solenoid. Use the left hand rule. You may wish to construct a simple electromagnet as illustrated in Fig. 4-13.

Fig. 4-13. The electrodemonstrator is used to show the principles of an electromagnet.

The electromagnet is made by selecting a prewound solenoid coil and inserting the soft iron core in the center. Wire according to the diagram. Experiment with this coil by using a compass. Connect the ends of the coil to a 6-volt battery and notice the polarity of the coil. Reverse the connections to the battery and observe the compass action. Remembering the direction of electron flow in a circuit, does this experiment prove the Left Hand Rule?

Continue this experiment by using the electromagnet to pick up several small nails. As the nails are held by the magnetic force, open the switch. The nails will fall. Leaving the switch still open, try to pick up some fine iron filings. Notice that some filings will be attracted to the core. In other words, the core has retained a small amount of its magnetism. This is called RESIDUAL MAGNETISM. As very little magnetism remained, the core would be considered as having LOW RETENTIVITY. Now replace the core of the magnet with a steel core and repeat the experiment. Once the steel is magnetized by the coil, it will be found that it retains its magnetism. A permanent magnet has been made. Steel has a <u>high retentivity</u>.

SOLENOID SUCKING COIL

Referring to Fig. 4-14, the experimentation is continued to demonstrate the sucking action of the solenoid. First, energize the

TO SOURCE VOLTAGE

Fig. 4-14. When the solenoid is energized, the core is sucked into the center.

solenoid coil by closing the switch, then bring the iron core close to one end of the coil. Notice the pulling magnetic force. Release the

Fig. 4-15. Using the electrodemonstrator as a door chime. The same principles and construction may be used for a worthwhile and useful project.

core from your fingers and it will be sucked into the center of the coil and come to rest at the center of the coil. Is this not converting magnetism into mechanical motion? The solenoid sucking coil has numerous applications in industry for the electrical control of mechanical action.

A simple and practical door chime may be built by arranging the coil and parts as in the photo, Fig. 4-15. The door chime uses the sucking coil principle. When the coil is energized, the core is sucked into the coil and strikes the chime.

THE RELAY

The relay is a device used to control a large flow of current by means of a low voltage low current circuit. It is a magnetic switch. Assemble the relay, as shown by the diagram, Fig. 4-16. A flashlight cell is used to energize the electromagnet and this circuit is controlled by the switch. When the coil is magnetized, its attractive force pulls the

Fig. 4-16. Using the electrodemonstrator as a relay.

lever arm, called an <u>armature</u>, toward the coil. The contact points on the armature will open or close depending upon the arrangement, and control the larger high voltage circuit. In this circuit a light bulb is used which is connected to a 115 volt power source. The advantages of this device are apparent.

1. From the safety point of view, the operator touches only a harmless low-voltage circuit, yet controls perhaps several hundred volts by means of the relay.

relay is used in the current voltage regulator, in controlling the starting motor, the horn and the headlights, Fig. 4-17. The low voltage control of lights in the home is becoming common. The low voltage switching system provides greater convenience and safety at a lower cost. In electronic equipment and radio transmitters a relay is used in numerous high voltage circuits and provides a sensitive, positive means of control. Relays of this type are shown in Fig. 4-18. By consulting a radio parts catalog, you will notice a

Fig. 4-17. Relays are used in the current-voltage regulator of your car.
(Delco-Remy)

2. Heavy current machines may be controlled from a remote location without the necessity of running heavy wires to the controlling switch.

3. Switching action by means of relays may be very rapid and positive.

There are hundreds of applications of relays at home and in industry to control motors and machines. In the automobile the

large variety of relays designed for specific applications. In the selection of a relay for a special purpose, consideration should be given to the number of switching contacts required and the current carrying ability of these contacts. Well designed relays have points made of silver, silver alloys, tungsten and other alloys. A relay may be selected for either opening or closing a circuit and its "at rest" position would be "normally closed" or "normally open." The coil is probably the most important specification. Relays are designed with coils which operate on a direct current, or an alternating current. Some are very sensitive and require a milliampere or less to energize. The coil should be selected that will produce sufficient magnetic field at

ture parts as in Fig. 4-19. Compare this device to the relay and notice that in the circuit

Fig. 4-18. Basic circuit using low-voltage relay, as used to control lighting circuit in the home.

its rated voltage to insure positive contact of switch points at all times.

CIRCUIT BREAKER

In reference to electromagnets, the strength of a magnetic field is dependent upon the ampere-turns. If a coil is made with a fixed number of turns, then its field strength may be varied by controlling the current in the coil. Upon this principle is devised the Circuit Breaker. Assemble the coil and armature parts as in Fig. 4-19. Compare this device to the relay and notice that in the circuit

Fig. 4-19. Above. Electrodemonstrator assembled as a circuit breaker. Below. Circuit breaker circuit.

Fig. 4-18A. Relays such as used in electronic control circuits.

breaker, the coil and armature points are in series and the whole device is connected in series in the line carrying the load. If the line current exceeds a predetermined value, the coil will build up sufficient magnetic force to overcome the spring tension of the armature. The armature releases the points and will open and "break" the circuit. The contact points must be "reset" or closed manually. This is a protective device and prevents a circuit from being overloaded beyond the safe carrying capacity of the wires. Modern homes and industry use the circuit breaker in place of the fuse.

energizes the coil and opens the contacts. This action continues as long as a voltage is applied. The device "buzzes" due to vibration of the armature. An extension may be placed on the vibrating armature on which a striker is attached. The striker hits a bell. This is the principle of the doorbell.

Specific examples of electromagnetic applications will be discussed in the later chapters of this text. You must thoroughly understand the action of magnetic fields. Upon these principles are based many electrical and electronic phenomena.

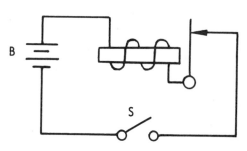

Fig. 4-20. Left. Electrodemonstrator assembled as a buzzer. Right. Buzzer circuit.

LESSON IN SAFETY: The circuit breaker is installed in the home for protection. It prevents the overloading of circuits and the danger of fire. The breaker should never be disabled. If the breaker repeatedly opens the circuit, discover the reason at once and take immediate steps to remedy it.

DOOR BELL AND BUZZER

Probably the most familiar of all devices using electromagnets is the buzzer. Arrange the coils and armature as in Fig. 4-20. Notice that the coil and the contact points are again connected in series. When the coil is energized, the armature is attracted toward the coil and the contact points open and "break" the circuit. The attraction of the coil falls to zero and the armature spring pulls the contact points closed. This once again

MAGNETIC SHIELDS

A magnetic field has no boundaries. To the beginning student, it is difficult to understand that the force of the magnet will pass through any kind of material whether it be a concrete wall, glass, wood or any material one might mention. It is, nevertheless, true. However, an instrument or a circuit may be shielded from magnetic lines of force. This is possible by the application of the permeability of some materials. If a piece of iron is placed in a magnetic field, the lines of force will follow through the iron rather than through the air, because iron has a much greater permeability. The iron acts as a low resistance path for the magnetic lines. In Fig. 4-21, this action may be observed. By this method, magnetic lines may be conducted around an instrument. This is called "shielding." Many shields are used in electronic equipment to prevent magnetic fields from affecting the operation of circuits.

Fig. 4-21. Magnetic lines of force may be conducted around device by a low permeability material used as a shield.

ACTIVITIES

I. The electrodemonstrator is set-up as in Fig. 4-1. The coils are used in this experiment only as a holding device for the two permanent magnets. The cardboard is suspended over the magnets on the long bolts fastened to the base. The magnets may be fixed in the coils by wedging with a pointed match stick or toothpick.

    A. Place magnets so that poles attract. Sprinkle iron filings on cardboard and observe pattern.

    B. Place magnets so that poles repel. Observe pattern.

    C. Place magnets so that ends touch and observe pattern. What conclusions can you draw from these observations?

II. Make two wire saddles as shown in Fig. 4-3, and suspend permanent magnets in free space.

    A. Place so that north poles are next to each other. Observe.
    B. Place so that south poles are next to each other. Observe.
    C. Place so that unlike poles are next to each other. Observe.

Make your conclusions and state the Laws of Magnetism in your own words.

III. Construct and operate the electromagnet, the buzzer, the door chime and the circuit breaker. Use your electrodemonstrator. Ask your instructor to check each activity BEFORE power is applied.

MAGNETIC PUTTING GREEN

Here is an inexpensive and practical project which demonstrates several principles of electrical theory. It will also give you an opportunity to develop some other skills including the bending and shaping of metals, using taps and dies, working with wood, winding coils and following a blueprint. This project, Fig. 4-22, is a wintertime putting green. When the snow is deep and the weather cold, the putting green may be placed on the living room carpet. Here you may develop those golfing skills which will help your game next summer. If you make your "putt," the ball will be magnetically returned to you.

The plans given should be used only as a general guide to construction. The putting green shown in the photo and drawings represents a satisfactory working model, but you are encouraged to change the overall appearance of the device. You may wish to use other materials. You may wish to devise other mechanical arrangements for the activation of the solenoid.

These suggestions may help.

1. The coil is mounted on adjustable brackets. The proper setting will require some experimentation, so the solenoid will kick the ball back to you at the proper moment.

2. The length of the plunger and the tension of the spring will determine the force of the return of the ball. You may want the ball to return several feet.

3. The spring brass contact in the switch must be so adjusted that the weight of a golf ball will close the switch and trigger the solenoid. Actual movement of the switch should only be about 1/32 inch.

4. The switch plunger should protrude

Fig. 4-22. Magnetic putting green. See next page for additional drawings.

Electricity - Electronics

less than 1/16 inch so the ball will push down on it. If it protrudes too far, the ball will be stopped.

5. The coil is wound with #20 enamelled

copper or cotton-covered wire. Other sizes may be used. The 1 1/4 inch copper spool is filled with windings. Since the coil is connected across 115 volt AC line, it should have sufficient reactance to limit current flow.

Fig. 4-22. Magnetic putting green (continued).

TEST YOUR KNOWLEDGE

1. State the first Law of Magnetism.
2. Why were early natural magnets called Lodestones?
3. Does the compass point toward true north? Explain.
4. Compare a magnetic circuit to an electrical circuit. Use Rowland's Law.
5. State the Third Law of Magnetism.
6. State in your own words the meaning of the following letter symbols.

    B =

    Φ =

    F =

    H =

    μ =

    IN =

7. State the Left Hand Rule for determining the polarity of an electromagnet.
8. What is meant by permeability?
9. What is the relationship between IN and Gilberts?
10. Explain the term residual magnetism.
11. Why are relays used in electrical circuits?
12. Explain the operation of a magnetic circuit breaker.

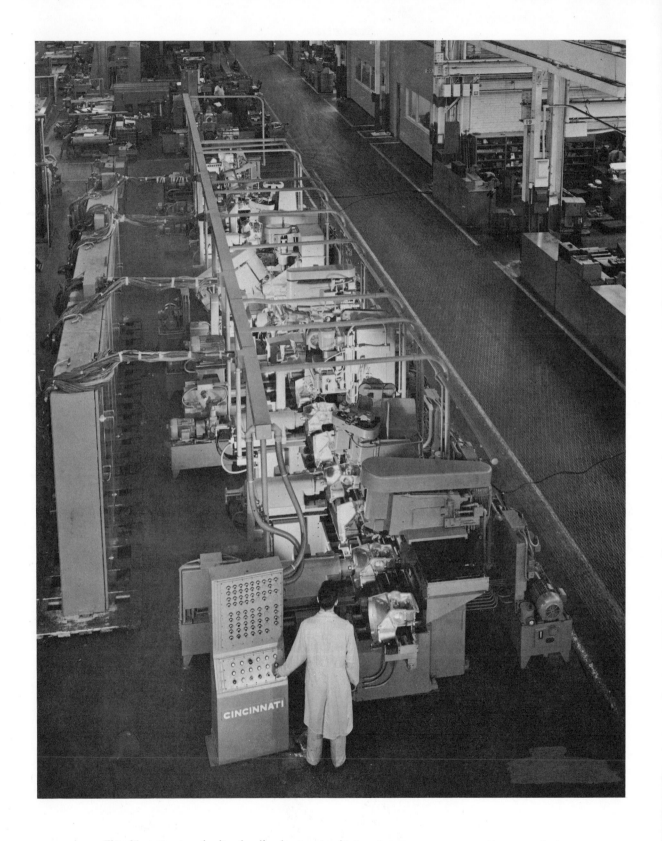

This 26-station transfer line handles fourteen machining operations on an automotive transmission case. The line measures 78 feet from end to end and has more than 10 miles of electrical wiring in its design. (Cincinnati Milling Machine Co.)

Chapter 5

GENERATORS

ELECTRICAL ENERGY FROM MECHANICAL ENERGY

In the studies of magnetism and the construction of the solenoid coil in Chapter 4, the discoveries of Hans Christian Oerstead were cited as proof that an electric current will produce a magnetic field. In 1831 another great scientist, Michael Faraday, pondered this question: If electricity would produce magnetism, can magnetism produce electricity? Based on the research and discoveries of Mr. Faraday, the electric dynamo was developed. He is known as the "father of the dynamo."

A simple experiment may be performed to illustrate the principles of Faraday's discoveries. Referring to Fig. 5-1, the coil is attached to a galvanometer. This sensitive meter indicates the flow and direction of an electric current. Insert a permanent bar magnet into the hollow coil. Notice that as the magnet moves into the coil, the indicating needle of the meter will show a current in one direction. As the magnet is withdrawn from the coil, the needle will indicate a current, but in the opposite direction. Also observe that when the magnet is not moving, no current is produced. Repeat this same demonstration by holding the magnet in a fixed position, and

Fig. 5-1. Using large coil of electro-demonstrator, and a permanent magnet, for Faraday's experiment.

move the coil up and down over the magnet. The conclusions drawn from this experiment are the fundamental principles of the operation of a generator. In order to produce an electric current there must be a magnetic field, a conductor and RELATIVE MOTION BETWEEN THE FIELD AND THE CONDUCTOR. A generator is a device which converts mechanical energy into electrical energy.

The more convenient and practical method of producing relative motion between a magnetic field and a conductor is to suspend a rotating coil within the field. This coil is called the generator ARMATURE. Fig. 5-2 illustrates simple generator action when a single turn coil is rotated in a field. Note the four positions during rotation. In A, both wires of the coil are moving parallel to the field so no voltage is induced. In position B, both sides of the coil are cutting the field at right angles and maximum voltage is induced. Position C is similar to position A and the voltage has dropped to zero. In position D, once again the coil is cutting the field at right angles and maximum voltage is induced but in the opposite direction or polarity. Fig. 5-3 is a graph representing the instantaneous voltages induced in the coil during one revolution. Some explanation of this induced voltage is necessary. Fig. 5-4 shows single conductors passing through a magnetic field, but in opposite directions. Current flow direction is indicated by the arrows. In each case the induced current in the conductor forms a magnetic field around the conductor which opposes or is repelled by the fixed field. This is known as LENZ'S LAW. This opposition to the moving conductor must exist and some form of mechanical force must be applied to overcome this opposition. Water and steam power are used to turn generators in a large power plant.

The strength of the induced voltage in a rotating coil depends upon,

1. the number of magnetic lines of force cut by the coil and

2. the speed at which the conductor moves through the field.

When a single conductor cuts across 100,000,000 (10^8) magnetic lines in one second, one volt of electrical pressure will be produced. The voltage can be increased by winding the armature with many turns of wire and also by increasing its speed of rotation. Reviewing Chapter 4 on Magnetism, this relationship may be expressed by the mathematical equation:

$$E = \frac{\Phi N}{10^8}$$

where, E equals the induced voltage

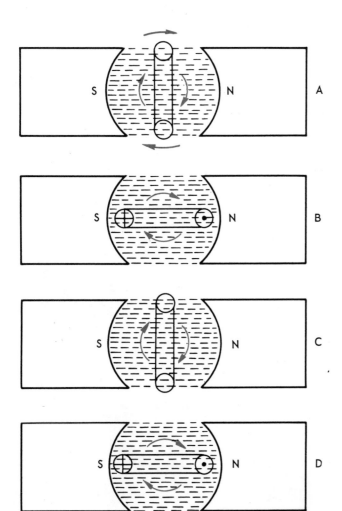

Fig. 5-2. The diagrams show the direction of the induced current as a single turn coil is rotated in a magnetic field.

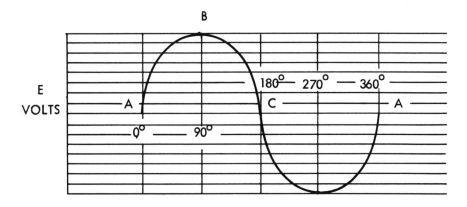

Fig. 5-3. *A graph of voltage induced during one revolution of coil. Notice change in polarity.*

Φ equals the lines of magnetic flux

N equals revolutions per second

For example, if the fixed magnetic field consisted of 10^6 lines of magnetic flux and a single conductor cut across the field 50 times per second, the induced voltage would equal:

$$E = \frac{10^6 \times 50}{10^8} = 50 \times 10^{-2} = .5 \text{ volts}$$

(The use of scientific notation or powers of ten is explained in the appendix.)

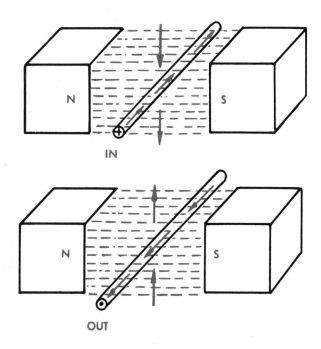

IN

OUT

Fig. 5-4. *The direction of current flow as a conductor conducts across a magnetic field.*

CONSTRUCTION OF A GENERATOR

Improvements must be made on the simple generator described. In order to produce a strong magnetic field, the permanent magnets may be replaced by electromagnets. These are represented by field coils placed over pole pieces or shoes fastened to the steel frame or case of the generator. The revolving armature is suspended in the case with proper bearings. The single coil is replaced by coils of many turns of wire on the armature. External connections to the rotating armature are made through commutator sections and brushes. Commutator is a new word in this discussion.

Referring to the previous explanation, it will be seen that the induced current in the rotating coil flows first to maximum in one direction, then reverses and flows to maximum in the opposite direction. This defines an alternating current, and will be studied later in this chapter. However, it is desired to have a direct current at the output terminals of the DC generator. The alternating current in the rotating armature is converted to a pulsating DC current in the external circuit by means of the commutator. Examination of the diagrams in Fig. 5-5, will explain the action of the commutator and brushes.

Note that the current in the external circuit is always flowing in one direction. The output of this generator would appear as in the graph in Fig. 5-6. It would rise and fall from zero to maximum to zero, but always in the same direction. Following the action in Fig. 5-5, Brush A is in contact with commutator section A, and Brush B is in contact with Section B. The first induced wave of current flows through the armature out of Brush B around the external circuit and into

into section B, completing the circuit. The commutator has acted as a switch and reversed the connections to the rotating coil when the direction of the induced current was reversed. The current in the external circuit is pulsating direct current.

The output of this generator is not a smooth direct current. It is a pulsating or surging current. Further improvements may be made on the generator by increasing the number of

Fig. 5-7. Two coils at right angles are rotated in the magnetic field.

Fig. 5-5. The commutator changes the alternating current in the armature to a pulsating direct current in the external circuit.

rotating coils on the armature, and providing commutator sections for each set of coils. To help you understand the addition of coils to the armature, a simplified generator with two coils at right angles to each other is shown in Fig. 5-7. Each coil has its own induced current and as the current starts to fall off in one, it is replaced by the induced

Brush A, completing the circuit. When the armature revolves one half turn, the induced current will reverse its direction, but the commutator sections have also turned with the armature. The induced current flowing out of section A is now in contact with Brush B and flows through the external circuit to Brush A.

Fig. 5-8. A graph showing the output of the generator in Fig. 5-7.

current in the next coil as it cuts across the magnetic field. The graph of the output would appear as in Fig. 5-8. Notice that it is still a pulsating current, but the pulsations are twice as frequent and not as large. The output of the two coil generator is much smoother. By increasing the number of coils, the output will

Fig. 5-6. A graph representing the generator output in volts.

approach a pure direct current with only a ripple variation.

GENERATOR LOSSES

All of the mechanical power used to turn the generator is not converted into useful electrical power. There are some losses. Reviewing the studies of electrical conductors will emphasize that all wires have some resistance, depending on their size, material and length. Resistance uses power. In the generator coils there are many feet of copper wire. The resistance of this wire must be overcome by the induced voltage. Voltage used in this manner contributes nothing to the external circuit and only produces heat in the generator windings. Power loss in any resistance is equal to:

$$P = I^2R$$

This is a particularly aggravating situation, because the loss increases as the square of the current. To be specific, if the current in the generator doubles, the power loss is four times or 2^2 more. The limiting factor in the generator output is usually the size of the wire and current carrying capacity of the armature windings. Losses resulting from resistance in the windings are classified as COPPER LOSSES or the I²R loss.

The armature windings in the generator are wound on an iron core, which is slotted to hold the coils. If a moving conductor cuts across a magnetic field, a voltage is induced and the armature core may be also considered as a conductor. If the core were a solid block of iron, voltages would be induced in the core causing an alternating current to flow in the core. These alternating currents in the core are known as EDDY CURRENTS. They produce heat which is a loss of energy. To reduce this loss to a negligible value, the core is built up of thin sections or laminations. Each lamination is insulated from the others by lacquer or frequently by only oxide or rust. Laminating the core reduces voltage in the core, and increases the resistance to the eddy currents. The student should also reason that eddy currents will increase in the core, as

the speed of rotation increases or the field density increases. When iron cores are used in rotating machines and transformers, they are laminated to reduce eddy current losses.

A third loss occurring in a generator is more difficult to understand. It is called HYSTERESIS LOSS. It is sometimes called molecular friction. As the armature rotates in the fixed magnetic field, many of the magnetic particles in the armature core remain in a lined-up position with the fixed field. This causes a rotation of these particles in respect to those not in alignment with the field. This rotation causes internal friction between the magnetic particles and creates a heat loss. Generator manufacturers now use a silicon steel which has a low hysteresis loss. Heat treating of the core by annealing further reduces this loss.

TYPES OF GENERATORS

Independently Excited Field

From the previous discussions of the output of a generator, the strength of the magnetic field, and the speed of rotation were factors which determined the output voltage. The strength of the magnetic field is measured in ampere-turns, so an increase in current in the field windings will increase the field strength. Since the output voltage is in direct proportion to the product of the field strength and speed of rotation, most devices used in the regulation of generator output depend upon varying the current in the field. The field windings may be connected to an independent source of DC voltage as illustrated in Fig. 5-9. With the speed constant the output may be varied by controlling the exciting voltage of the DC source. This is accomplished by inserting resistance in series with the source and the field windings. This type of generator is called an independently excited generator.

Shunt Generator

The inconvenience of a separate DC source for field excitation led to the development of the shunt generator, in which a part of the generated current is used to excite the fields. The field windings consist of many turns of relatively small wire and actually use only a small part of the generated current. The total current generated must, of course, be the sum of the field excitation current and the current delivered to the load. Thus, for practical purposes, the output current can be considered as varying according to the applied load. The field flux

does not vary to a great extent, so the terminal voltage remains constant under varying load conditions. This type of generator is considered as a constant voltage machine. A generator of this type is illustrated in Fig. 5-10. It is widely used as the generator in the automobile. If the generator excites its

Fig. 5-11. The diagram of a shunt generator.

Fig. 5-9. The diagram of an independently excited generator.

own field, how does the generator start? The initial generator voltage is produced when the armature windings cut across a small magnetic field caused by the residual magnetism in the pole shoes or field coil cores. The conventional diagram of a shunt generator is shown in Fig. 5-11.

Fig. 5-10. The automotive generator.
(Delco-Remy)

All machines are designed to do a certain amount of work. If overloaded their lives are shortened. A generator is no exception. With an overload the shunt generator terminal voltage will drop rapidly and the excessive current will cause the armature windings to heat and finally break down.

Series Generator

The field windings of a generator may be

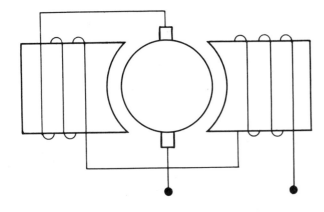

Fig. 5-12. A diagram of a series wound generator.

placed in series with the armature and the load. Such a generator is diagramatically sketched in Fig. 5-12. It is seldom used.

Compound Generators

The compound generator employs both series and shunt windings in the field. The series windings are usually a few turns of relatively large wire and are mounted on the same poles with the shunt windings. Both windings contribute to the field strength of the generator. If both act in the same direction or polarity, an increase in load would cause an increase of current in the series coils, thus increasing the magnetic field and increasing the terminal voltage of the output. The fields would be additive and the resultant field would be the sum of both coils. However, the current through the series winding can produce magnetic saturation of the core and result in a decrease of voltage as the load increases.

The manner by which the terminal voltage behaves is dependent upon the degree of compounding. A compound generator which maintains the same voltage either at no-load or full-load is said to be FLAT COMPOUNDED. An OVER-COMPOUNDED generator will increase the output voltage at full load, and an UNDER-COMPOUNDED generator will have a decreased voltage at full load current. A variable resistance may be inserted in parallel with the series winding to adjust the degree of compounding. Fig. 5-13 shows the schematic diagrams of the compound, the series and the shunt generator for comparison.

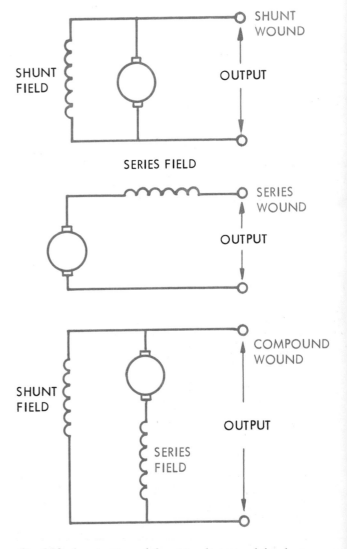

Fig. 5-13. A comparison of the wiring diagrams of the shunt, series and compound generator.

Fig. 5-14. The circuit for a generator voltage regulator.

VOLTAGE AND CURRENT REGULATION

The regulation of a power source, whether it is a generator or a power supply, may be defined as the percentage of voltage drop between no-load and full-load. Mathematically, it may be expressed as:

$$\frac{E \text{ no-load} - E \text{ full-load}}{E \text{ full-load}} \times 100 = \% \text{ Regulation}$$

To explain this formula, assume that the voltage of a generator with no-load applied is 100 volts. Under full load the voltage drops to 97 volts, then,

$$\frac{100v - 97v}{97v} = \frac{3}{97} \times 100 = 3.1\% \text{ approx.}$$

It is desirable in most applications to maintain the output generator voltage at a fixed value under varying load conditions. At this point, you must understand that the output voltage of the generator depends upon the field strength; the field strength depends upon the field current.

Current, according to Ohm's Law, varies inversely with resistance. Therefore, a device which would vary the resistance in the field circuit would also vary the voltage output of the generator. This regulator is drawn in Fig. 5-14, and is a common type used in the automobile. The generator output terminal G is connected to the battery and to the winding of a magnetic relay. The voltage produced by the generator causes a current to flow in the relay coil. If the voltage exceeds a predetermined value, the increased current will cause sufficient magnetism to open the relay contacts. Notice that the generator field is grounded through these contacts. When they open, then the field current must pass through resistance R to ground. This reduces the current which reduces the field strength and reduces the terminal voltage. When the voltage is reduced, the relay contacts close, permitting maximum field current, and the terminal voltage rises. In operation these contact points vibrate, alternately cutting resistance in and out of the field circuit and maintaining a constant voltage output of the generator.

Even though the generator is regulated to a constant voltage, it is possible to overload the generator. As the external load increases, the current in the armature must also increase and may destroy the windings by overheating. Further protection is desired. Referring to Fig. 5-15, a magnetic relay is from generator to battery. However, at times when the battery voltage exceeds the generator voltage, current attempts to flow from battery to generator. This would discharge the battery. The cut-out points will open the circuit, and will remain open until the generator builds up voltage exceeding battery

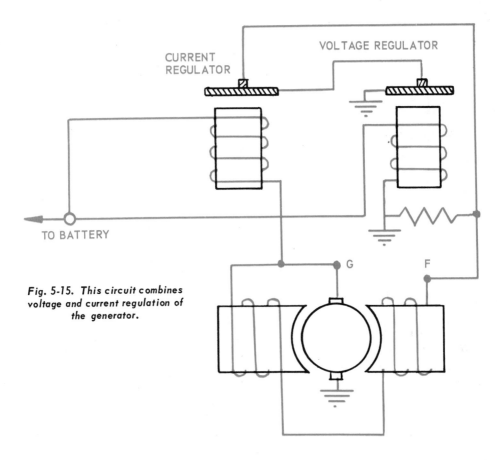

Fig. 5-15. This circuit combines voltage and current regulation of the generator.

connected in series with the output circuit. The relay is calibrated so that when a predetermined current flows in the series coil, sufficient magnetic attraction will open the relay points. As in the voltage regulator, the open points require the generator field current to pass through a resistance to the ground. The reduced field current will reduce the generator current output to a safe value.

An additional device is required in the current-voltage regulator known as a cut-out. A schematic diagram of a cut-out is shown in Fig. 5-16. The cut-out or reverse-current relay permits the charging current to flow

voltage. The cut-out consists of a magnetic relay with a shunt coil and a series coil.

Fig. 5-16. The cut-out or reverse current relay in the generator charging circuit.

Electricity - Electronics

When the automobile is stopped, the cut-out contacts are open. When the engine is started, the generator produces a voltage which is impressed across the shunt coil of the relay, causing a current to flow. As the generator increases speed, sufficient voltage will develop which will cause increased cur-

Fig. 5-17. The complete circuit diagram of current-voltage regulator and cut-out.

rent in the shunt coil. The magnetic force will close the relay at a preset value. The output of the generator then flows through the series winding and the contact points to the battery. The magnetic field produced by the series winding adds to the magnetic field of the shunt winding and holds the relay firmly closed. Decreasing the speed of the generator will cause its voltage to decrease and current from the battery will try to flow toward the generator. This reverse current must flow through the series winding of the cut-out relay and will develop a magnetic field which opposes the field of the shunt coil. This cancellation of fields reduces the magnetic attraction and the contact points open.

These three relays are combined in the modern automobile into a single unit. A current-voltage regulator (CVR) is shown in Fig. 5-17, as a complete schematic diagram. The student should trace the individual circuits, and understand the purpose of each relay. Mechanical-magnetic relays have served this purpose for many years, but electronic devices are now appearing on many models of cars. An electronic regulator using transistors for the switching functions is shown in Fig. 5-18. A study of transistor circuitry will be made in a later chapter of this text.

Fig. 5-18. A transistorized current-voltage regulator now used on many automobiles. (Delco-Remy)

ALTERNATING CURRENT

Up to this point only a brief reference has been made to Alternating Current or AC. Comparing AC to DC, a direct current flows in only one direction in a circuit, but an alternating current periodically reverses its direction of flow in the circuit. In DC the

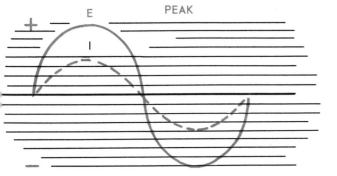

Fig. 5-19. Graph of current and voltage of alternating current.

source voltage does not change its polarity, but in AC the source voltage periodically changes its polarity between positive and negative. The graph in Fig. 5-19, illustrates the magnitude and polarity of an AC voltage. Commencing at zero, the voltage rises to maximum in the positive direction, then falls back to zero, then rises to maximum with the opposite polarity and returns to zero. The current wave is also plotted on the graph showing the flow of current and the direction of flow. Above the zero line, current is flowing in one direction; below the zero line, the current is flowing in the opposite direction. The graph represents instantaneous current and voltage at any point in the cycle. What is a CYCLE? A cycle may be defined as a sequence or chain of events occurring in a period of time. The AC cycle may be described as from zero to maximum positive to zero to maximum negative to zero. The alternating current in your home changes direction sixty times per second, or has a frequency of sixty cycles per second (60 c.p.s.). FREQUENCY, measured in cycles per second, is the number of complete sequences or chains of events occurring per second. If sixty cycles occur in one second, then the time period for one cycle is 1/60 of

a second or .0166 seconds. This is the PERIOD of the cycle. Referring again to Fig. 5-19, the maximum rise of the waveform represents the AMPLITUDE of the wave and the PEAK voltage or current.

In the study of the DC generator, we learned that the current induced in a rotating loop of wire in a magnetic field flowed first in one direction and then in the opposite direction. It was an alternating current. Points to remember: 1. The frequency of this cycle of events increases with an increase in speed of rotation. 2. The amplitude of the induced voltage depends upon the strength of the magnetic field. In the solution of problems involving alternating currents, VECTORS are used to represent the magnitude and direction of a force. A vector is a straight line drawn to a convenient scale representing units of force. An arrowhead on the line shows the direction. The development of an AC wave is shown in Fig. 5-20, as a single coil armature, represented by the rotating vector, revolving one revolution through a magnetic field. Assuming that the peak induced voltage is 10 volts, using a scale of 1 inch equals 5 volts, the vector is two inches or 10 volts long. Vectors of this nature are assumed to rotate in a counterclockwise direction. The time base at the right in Fig. 5-20, is a line using any convenient scale, representing the period of one cycle or revolution of the vector. The time line is divided into intervals representing the time for specified degrees of rotation during the cycle. For example: At 90 deg. rotation, one quarter of the time period is used; at 270 deg. rotation, three quarters of the time period is used. The wave is developed by plotting amplitude of voltage at any instant of revolution against the time interval. The developed wave is called a sine wave because the instantaneous induced voltages are proportioned to the sine of the angle θ (theta) that the vector makes with the horizontal. (Refer to Appendix for explanation of trigonometric functions and tables.) The instantaneous voltage may be found at any point of the cycle by the equation,

$$e = E_{Max} SIN \ \theta$$

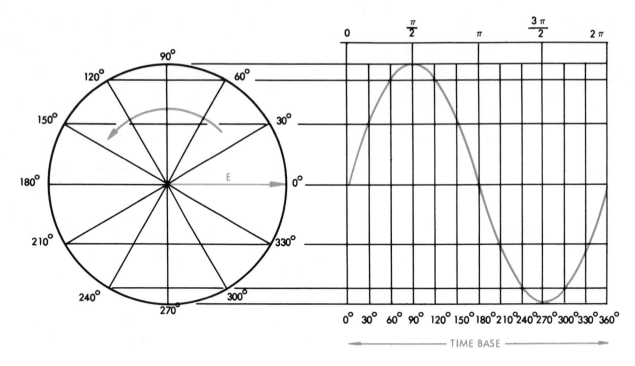

Fig. 5-20. The development of a SINE WAVE.

To apply this equation assume that an AC generator is producing a peak voltage of 100 volts, what is the instantaneous voltage at 45 deg. of rotation,

$$e = 100 \times \sin 45^{\circ}$$
$$= 100 \times .707 = 70.7 \, v.$$

A study of an AC wave by comparison with direct currents raises the important question of the actual value of the AC wave. The voltage and current are constantly varying and are at peak value only twice during a cycle. Frequently it is necessary to find the average value of the wave and this may be found by multiplying the peak voltage by the factor, .637.

$$E_{AVG} = .637 E_{MAX}$$

If E_{AVG} is known, the conversion may be made by,

$$E_{MAX} = 1.57 \, E_{AVG}$$

A more meaningful value of an alternating current is found by comparing it to the heating effect equivalent to a direct current. This has been named the EFFECTIVE VALUE and may be found by the formula,

$$E_{eff} = .707 \, E_{MAX}$$

If E_{eff} is known, the conversion may be made by,

$$E_{MAX} = 1.414 \, E_{eff}$$

The effective value is frequently called the rms (root-mean-square) value because it represents the square root of the average of all currents squared between zero and maximum of the wave. The currents are squared so the power produced may be compared to direct current. Watt's Law states; $P = I^2 R$. By using the .707 factor the value of a direct current may be found which will equal the alternating current. For example; a 5 ampere AC will produce the same heating effect in a resistance as,

$$I_{EFF} = .707 \times 5 = 3.53 \text{ amps. D.C.}$$

Note that average and effective values may be applied to either voltage or current waves.

PHASE DISPLACEMENT

Several wave forms may be drawn on the same time base to show the phase relationship between them. In Fig. 5-21 E and I represent the voltage and current in a given circuit. The current and voltage rise and fall simultaneously and cross the zero line at the same point. The current and voltage are IN PHASE. The "in phase" condition only exists

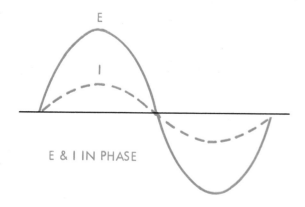

Fig. 5-21. Current and voltage are in phase.

in the purely resistive circuit as will be discovered in later instruction. Many times the current will lead or lag the voltage as in Fig. 5-22, creating a PHASE DISPLACEMENT between the two waves. This displacement is measured in degrees and is equal to the angle θ between the two polar vectors. The waves are out of phase. Several out of phase currents and voltages may be displayed in this manner.

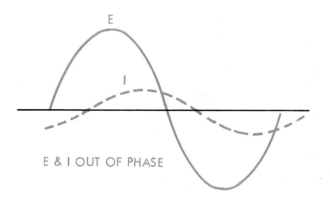

Fig. 5-22. Current and voltage are out of phase.

ALTERNATING CURRENT GENERATOR

The AC generator is similar in many respects to the DC generator with one important exception. The commutator is omitted. The ends of the armature coils are brought out to SLIP RINGS. Brushes sliding on the slip rings provide constant connection to the coils at all times and the current in the externally connected circuit is an alternating current. In large commercial type generators the magnetic field is rotated and the armature windings are placed in slots in the stationary frame or stator of the generator. This method allows the generation of large currents in the armature without the necessity of conducting these currents through moving or sliding rings and brushes.

The rotating field is excited through slip rings and brushes by means of an externally connected DC generator called the EXCITER. DC voltage is necessary for the magnetic field. Commercial power generators are turned by water power and steam.

THE ALTERNATOR

Some of the new models of cars have replaced the DC generator with an AC generator called the alternator. Fig. 5-23, shows the internal construction of this machine. The output is rectified to direct current for charging the battery and other electrical devices in the car. Manufacturers claim certain advantages of the alternator over the DC generator, among which are higher output at lower speeds and trouble-free service.

The principle of the Generator may be demonstrated in the useful and practical rpm meter illustrated in Fig. 5-24. It is simple to construct and provides an opportunity for the individual design of the case. A small DC motor, such as found in toy automobiles, is used as the generator. The shaft of the motor is wrapped with friction tape or rubber. This friction wheel is held against a rotating shaft or wheel. The generated EMF is measured on the 0-10 ma meter. This meter may be calibrated to read directly in RPMs.

GREASE RESERVOIR

BALL BEARING

DRIVE END FRAME

FIELD WINDING

ROTOR POLES

STATOR WINDING ASSEMBLY

BEARING & GREASE RETAINER

SLIP RING END FRAME

BRUSH ASSEMBLY

SLIP RINGS

GREASE RESERVOIR

BALL BEARING

FIELD TERMINALS

BATTERY TERMINAL

POSITIVE SILICON RECTIFIER DIODES

CONNECTOR ASSEMBLY

MOUNTING BUSHING

NEGATIVE SILICON RECTIFIER DIODES

Fig. 5-23. The AC generator used on many automobiles. It is called an "alternator." (Delco-Remy)

The switch permits measurements in either clockwise or counterclockwise rotation. The "adjust screw" is used as a calibrator or range setting control.

Fig. 5-24. A simple and practical rpm meter or tachometer.

TEST YOUR KNOWLEDGE

1. Write a brief description of Faraday's experimentation and discovery.
2. The strength of induced voltage depends upon _____ and _____ .
3. What is the purpose of the commutator?
4. Name and describe three losses associated with the generator.
5. Why are the cores of armatures and transformers constructed of laminated sheets of iron?
6. Name three types of generators and draw a schematic diagram of each.
7. A generator has a no-load voltage of 25 volts. When load is applied, terminal voltage drops to 24 volts. What is the per cent of regulation?
8. How may output of generator be controlled when operating at constant speed?
9. What is the purpose of the cut-out in an automobile generator circuit? Explain operation and draw schematic diagram.
10. Define: cycle, frequency, period, amplitude of an AC wave.
11. A generated voltage has a peak value of 100 volts. Using the vector scale of 1 inch = 50 volts, construct a sine wave. You will need a drawing board and instruments.
12. In problem 11, what is the instantaneous voltage at 69 degrees?
13. What is the effective value of the generated voltage in problem 11?
14. What is the peak value of the alternating current used in your home. (115 volts)
15. Draw waveform diagrams illustrating current and voltage, a) in phase. b) current lagging by 45 deg. c) current leading by 30 deg.

Application of electronics in modern machine shop -- programed tape is being used to control cutting operations of a milling machine.
(Cincinnati Milling Machine Co.)

Chapter 6

INDUCTANCE AND RL CIRCUITS

The study of electricity and electronics revolves around the characteristics of a circuit such as inductance, capacitance, resistance and combinations of these components in series and parallel. An analysis of resistance in a circuit was made in Chapter 3. This chapter will help you to answer these questions:

1. What is an Inductor and Inductance?

2. What is the effect of Inductance in a circuit?

3. What methods are used to measure and compute values of current and voltage in an inductive circuit?

INDUCTANCE

Inductance may be defined as the property in an electric circuit which resists a change in current. This resistance to a change of current is the result of the energy stored within the magnetic field of a coil. A coil of wire will have inductance. Set up again the experiment illustrated in Chapter 5, Fig. 5-1, using the hollow coil A connected to a galvanometer. Move the permanent magnet in and out of the coil, and notice the deflection of the needle in the meter. When the magnet moves in, current will flow in one direction, and the current will reverse direction when the magnet is withdrawn. No current will flow unless the magnet is moved. This is the same principle as demonstrated in Chapter 5, on the theory of generators. By moving the magnet a voltage was induced in the coil which caused current to indicate on the meter.

There was a definite relationship between the movement of the magnet and the direction of current flow. This is an application of Lenz's Law, which states that the field created by the induced current is of such a polarity that it opposes the field of the permanent magnet.

A coil connected to a source of direct current will build up a magnetic field when the circuit is closed. The expanding magnetic field cutting across the coil windings will induce a counter EMF or voltage, which will oppose the source voltage and oppose the rise in current. When the current reaches its maximum value and there is no further change, there is no longer an induced counter EMF. The current is then only limited by the ohmic resistance of the wire. However, if the source voltage is disconnected, the current tends to fall to zero, but the collapsing magnet field again induces a counter EMF which retards the reduction of current.

The inductance of the coil resists any change in current value. The symbol for inductance is the capital letter L and inductance is measured in a unit called a henry (h). A henry represents the inductance of a coil if one volt of induced EMF is produced when the current is changing at the rate of one ampere per second. This may be expressed mathematically as,

$$E = L\frac{\Delta I}{\Delta t}$$

where E equals the induced voltage, L is the inductance in henrys, ΔI is the change of current in amperes and Δt is the change of time in seconds. The symbol Δ means a "change in." Because the strength of an induced voltage is dependent upon the strength of the field, it follows that a stronger magnetic field would produce higher induced voltage. The magnetic field may be strengthened by inserting a core in the coil. The iron core has higher permeability than air and concentrates the lines of force. This was explained in the study of magnetism.

Large inductors are usually wound on laminated iron cores and their inductance is measured in henrys. Smaller inductors, used at higher frequencies, may have powdered iron or air cores. They have inductance measured in millihenrys, (1/1000 of a henry) and microhenrys, (1/1,000,000 of a henry). An inductor used in a power supply called a choke is shown in Fig. 6-1. Radio fre-

Fig. 6-1. Choke, used in filter section of power supply.
(United Transformer Corp.)

quency chokes using air cores are shown in Fig. 6-2.

A changing current through an inductor produces an expanding or collapsing magnetic field which is cutting across the wires of the coil. A counter emf is induced which opposes the change of current. This is called

self induction and the magnitude of the self induction is dependent upon the number of turns of wire in the coil, the relationship between the length of the coil to its diameter

Fig. 6-2. RF or radio frequency chokes.
(J. W. Miller Co.)

and the permeability of the core. This effect may be observed by setting up the experiment in Fig. 6-3. First, connect the light directly to the 6 v. transformer and observe that as the switch is closed the light will burn at full brilliance instantaneously. Connect coil F in series with the light and close the switch. A slight delay in approaching full brilliance should be noted due to the inductance of the coil. Turn the light off and insert the iron core in the coil. Once again close the switch and note that the light comes to brilliance rather slowly and not to full brilliance. Why does the core increase the delay in brilliance? Repeat the above experiment using coil D which has many turns of fine wire. Self inductance is increased by the number of turns of wire in the coil. Move the core in and out of the coil and note the change in brilliance due to the change in self inductance. This principle is used in theaters to dim the house lights.

TRANSIENT RESPONSES

The response of the current and voltage in a circuit after an immediate change in applied voltage is known as a TRANSIENT

Fig. 6-3. The self-induction of a coil may be demonstrated with the electrodemonstrator. Experiment with different sizes and kinds of cores.

RESPONSE. Referring to the diagram in Fig. 6-4, a coil is connected to a DC voltage source. When the switch is closed, the current will build up gradually, due to the self induction of the coil and the internal resistance

Fig. 6-4. The schematic diagram of the L circuit described in the text.

of the battery. When the switch is opened, the current will decay in like manner. The rise and decay of the current in this circuit is shown by the graph in Fig. 6-5. It is important to understand that the opposition to the rise or decay of current occurs only when there is a change in applied voltage. When there is no change, the current remains at its steady-state value, dependent only upon the resistance of the coil.

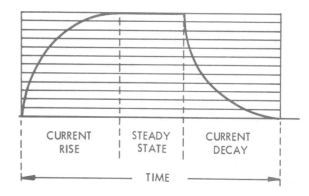

Fig. 6-5. The graph shows the transient response of the L circuit as the switch is closed and opened.

When a resistance is connected in series with an inductor, as in Fig. 6-6, (RL Circuit)

Fig. 6-6. A diagram of the RL circuit.

the behavior of the voltage and current should be carefully studied. When the switch is closed, the counter emf (E_L) of the coil equals the source voltage. As no current has started to flow the IR drop across R equals zero. As the current gradually builds up the voltage E_R increases and the counter emf E_L decreases until a steady state condition exists and all the voltage drop is E_R and there is no drop across L.

Now if the RL circuit is shorted by another switch, S_2, as in Fig. 6-7, the stored energy in the field of L immediately develops a voltage and the circuit is discharged by current flowing through R. The graphs show-

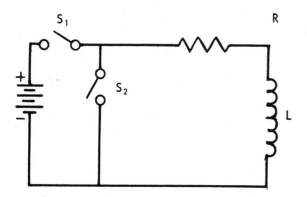

Fig. 6-7. The coil L is shorted through switch S_2 and the magnetic field collapses.

ing the charge and discharge of the circuit appear in Fig. 6-8. The base line or X axis of these graphs represents time and the transient response of an RL circuit does require a definite time, depending upon the values of R and L. This is called the TIME CONSTANT of the circuit and may be found by the formula,

$$t = \frac{L \text{ (in henrys)}}{R \text{ (in ohms)}}$$

when t equals the time in seconds for the current to increase to 63.2 per cent of its maximum value or to decrease to 36.7 per cent. For all practical purposes, the circuit is considered charged or discharged after the duration of five time constant periods. The following table gives the voltage at the

end of each time constant, assuming E source is 100 volts.

Time Constant	Charging	Discharging
1	63.2v	36.8v
2	86.5v	13.5v
3	95v	5v
4	98v	2v
5	99v	1v

These points are plotted in Fig. 6-8 and a clear picture of the rise and decay of the voltage and current may be seen.

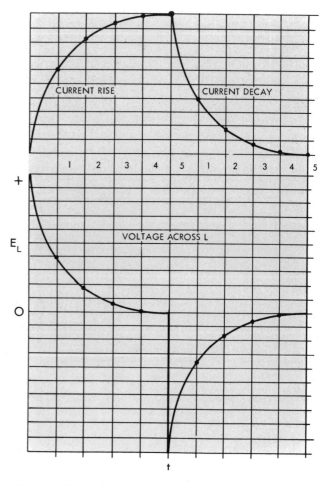

Fig. 6-8. The transient response curves for current and inductive voltage of the RL circuit.

MUTUAL INDUCTANCE

In the study of generator regulation, brief mention was made of the magnetic fields created by the windings of the cut-outs as being additive or cancelling. When two coils are within magnetic reach of each other, so the flux lines of one coil will link with or cut-across the other coil, they would be considered as having <u>mutual inductance</u>. If they are close to each other, many magnetic lines in the flux would link with the second coil. Conversely, if they were some distance apart, there might be very little linkage. The mutual inductance of two coils may be greatly increased if a common iron core is used for both coils. The degree to which the lines of force of one coil link with the windings of the second coil is called COUPLING and if all lines of one cut across all the turns of the other it is UNITY COUPLING. Various percentages of coupling may exist due to the mechanical position of the coils. The amount of mutual inductance may be found by the formula,

$$M = K \sqrt{L_1 L_2}$$

where, M = mutual inductance in henrys

      K = the coefficient or percentage of coupling

      L_1 and L_2 = the inductance of respective coils.

The mutual inductance must be considered when two or more inductors are connected in series or parallel in a circuit.

THE TRANSFORMER

One of the familiar applications of MUTUAL INDUCTANCE is the TRANSFORMER. A transformer may be defined as a device used to transfer energy from one circuit to another by electromagnetic induction. Basically, a transformer consists of two or more coils of wire around a common laminated iron core, so the coupling between the coils approaches UNITY. Transformers have no moving parts and require very little care. They are simple and rugged and efficient devices.

The construction of the simple trans-

former is illustrated in Fig. 6-9 with its schematic symbol. The first winding or input winding is called the PRIMARY and this winding receives the energy from the source. The second winding or output winding is called the SECONDARY and the output load is attached to this winding. The energy in the

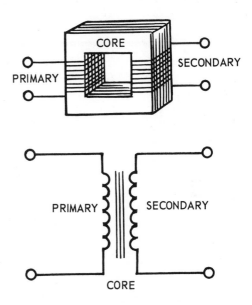

Fig. 6-9. A sketch showing transformer construction and the schematic symbol used in circuit diagrams.

secondary is the result of the mutual induction between the secondary and the primary windings. The varying magnetic field of the primary cuts across the windings of the secondary and induces a voltage in the secondary. Therefore, the transformer is a device which must operate on an alternating current or a pulsating direct current. The primary field must be a moving magnetic field in order for induction to take place.

In Fig. 6-10, two types of construction are shown, namely, the core type and the shell type. In the core type the coils surround the core and in the shell type the core surrounds the coil. Both types are used in general applications. In either type of construction, consideration must be given to assure maximum coupling between the primary and secondary so that very little flux loss or leakage results. In the core type, parts of both windings are wound on each leg of the core. In the shell type the windings are in alternate layers.

CORE TYPE

PRIMARY WINDINGS

CORE

SECONDARY WINDINGS

SHELL TYPE

PRIMARY WINDINGS

SECONDARY WINDINGS

Fig. 6-10. The construction of core and shell type transformers..

TURNS RATIO

One of the major uses of the transformer is the result of its ability to step-up or step-down a voltage. An example is the power transformer in Fig. 6-11, which is found in the power supply of radios and transmitters. In this transformer, several secondary windings are used to provide high and low voltages necessary for proper operation of the equipment. How may this be accomplished? Reference to the diagram in Fig. 6-12, will show that the output voltage in relation to the input voltage is the same as the ratio between the number of turns in secondary and primary. To express this mathematically,

$$\frac{E_{primary}}{E_{secondary}} = \frac{N_{primary}}{N_{secondary}}$$

where E is voltage and N equals the number of turns. This relationship is called the TURNS-RATIO of the transformer. An example will clarify this relationship.

A given transformer has 200 turns in the primary and 1000 turns in the secondary. If the applied voltage is 110 volts AC, what is the secondary voltage?

Fig. 6-11. A power transformer with multiple secondary taps used in the power supply for electronic circuits. (United Transformer Corp.)

$$\frac{110 \text{ volts}}{E_s} = \frac{200}{1000}$$

Fig. 6-12. The turns-ratio determines the output voltage.

transposing this equation,

$$E_s = \frac{1000 \times 110}{200} = 550 \text{ v.}$$

This is an example of a STEP-UP transformer.

If this transformer were constructed with a 10 turn secondary, then,

$$\frac{110 \text{ v}}{E_s} = \frac{200}{10}$$

$$E_s = \frac{110 \times 10}{200} = 5.5 \text{ v.}$$

This exemplifies a STEP-DOWN transformer.

In Fig. 6-13 is shown another example of a power transformer with several taps on the secondary winding to provide a variety of voltages. This is a typical power supply transformer. An experimental transformer developed for educational purposes is illustrated in Fig. 6-14, together with a cut-away

Fig. 6-13. A typical power supply transformer used in radios, TVs, and transmitters. (United Transformer Corp.)

Fig. 6-14. Educational transformer used in teaching transformer fundamentals. (Superior Electric Co.)

secondary circuit must be supplied by the primary. Assuming that the transformer is 100 per cent efficient, then the power $I_s \times E_s$ in the secondary must equal $I_p \times E_p$ in the primary.

Example: A step-up transformer will produce 300 volts in the secondary when 100 volts AC is applied to the primary. If a 100 ohm load is applied to the secondary, as in Fig. 6-16, a current of 3 amperes would flow.

$$I = \frac{300 \text{ volts}}{100 \text{ ohms}} = 3 \text{ amps.}$$

The power used in the secondary would be:

$$P = I_s \times E_s = 3 \text{ amps.} \times 300 \text{ v.} = 900 \text{ watts}$$

Fig. 6-15. *Using the educational transformer as a demonstration of turns-ratio. (Superior Electric Co.)*

view showing its internal construction. This device is essentially the primary winding only, and the secondary may be wound by hand as in Fig. 6-15. The device demonstrates the turns-ratio very effectively. A manual with the Flexiformer describes other laboratory experiments. The development of the transformer explains the reason that alternating current is universally used. The student should realize that the power used in the

Since the primary must supply this power, then

$$I_p = \frac{P_p}{E_p} \text{ or } \frac{900 \text{ watts}}{100 \text{ volts}} \text{ or } 9 \text{ amps.}$$

and

$$I_s \times E_s = I_p \times E_p = 900 \text{ watts.}$$

The important lesson of this transformer action is,

As voltage <u>increases</u> in the secondary, the current in the secondary <u>decreases</u>.

Why is the power company concerned with these facts? Remember, in the study of conductors, that all wires have some resistance. And also remember that the power

Fig. 6-16. *A circuit showing the relationship between voltage, amperage and power in the primary and secondary of a transformer.*

loss in a circuit or conductor is, $P = I^2R$. A long length of wire having a resistance of 2 ohms and carrying a 10 ampere current will have a power loss of,

$$P = I^2R = 10^2 \times 2 = 200 \text{ watts}$$

If the current is doubled to 20 amperes, then the loss would be,

$$P = I^2R = 20^2 \times 2 = 800 \text{ watts}$$

or four times as much. Power loss varies as the square of the current. Therefore, it is more economical to raise the voltage with the associated decrease in current and reduce power loss in the transmission lines. Transformers are used for this purpose, as illustrated in Fig. 6-17.

By turning on an electric appliance in your home, which uses 10 amperes of current, the power consumed would be,

$$P = I \times E = 10 \times 120 = 1200 \text{ watts}$$

In the 12,000 volts city lines a current of .1 amp would flow,

$$1200 \text{ watts} = .1 \text{ amp} \times 12,000 \text{ volts}$$

In the cross country power lines a current of .02 amp would flow,

$$1200 \text{ watts} = .02 \text{ amp} \times 60,000 \text{ volts}$$

By raising the voltage, the power company is able to supply great cities and industries with electricity and use relatively small wires for transmission lines. Although smaller wires do have greater resistance per foot, the loss resulting from this resistance is only in direct proportion to the current used. The power company selects a wire that has the least resistance, yet is large enough to carry the anticipated current. It must also be structurally strong to withstand high winds, ice and snow.

Fig. 6-17. *The use of transformers in the transmission of electric power to reduce line losses.*

TRANSFORMER LOSSES

Three types of losses are associated with transformer construction. All losses result in heat.

1. COPPER LOSSES are the result of the resistance of the wire used in the transformer windings. These are sometimes called the I^2R losses and vary as the square of the current according to Ohm's Law and the Power Law.

2. EDDY-CURRENT losses are caused by small whirlpools of current induced in the core material. These losses are minimized by the laminated core construction.

Each lamination is insulated from its adjacent layer by varnish, thus cutting the path for these currents to flow.

3. HYSTERESIS LOSS is sometimes called molecular friction, and is the result of the magnetic particles changing polarity in step with the induced voltage. Special alloys and heat treating processes are used in the manufacture of core materials, which minimize hysteresis loss.

THE INDUCTION COIL

A transformer requires an alternating current or a pulsating direct current. A simple device to demonstrate transformer action is the "Electric Shocker" or Induction Coil constructed in Fig. 6-18. At first a buzzer is assembled. The armature and point action in the buzzer circuit cause the magnetic field of the coil to expand and collapse. It is a continually moving field. A secondary coil of many turns of fine wire is placed over the primary buzzer coil. A high voltage is induced in the secondary.

LESSON IN SAFETY: People vary in their ability to stand an electric shock. Although

INDUCTION COIL SHOCKER

Fig. 6-18. The electrodemonstrator is used to show transformer action and an induction coil.

Fig. 6-19. The automotive ignition system. (Delco-Remy)

this project does not produce a dangerous shock to a normal healthy person, good judgment should be exercised when operating it.

A capacitor has been added to this circuit to improve its action. Capacitance will be studied in later lessons.

THE IGNITION SYSTEM

To make a practical application of the induction coil, observe the ignition system of the automobile in Fig. 6-19. The primary and secondary coils are clearly identified in the COIL. The breaker points in the distributor are a mechanical switch operated by the camshaft in the engine and provide a means of "making and breaking" the primary circuit of the coil. A voltage of 15,000 volts and more is induced in the secondary of the coil, which is automatically distributed to the spark plugs of the engine. The high voltage causes a spark to jump across the points of the spark plug and ignite the gasoline and air mixture in the cylinder. The spark should occur at just the right instant. This is called "timing" the engine.

PHASE RELATIONSHIP IN TRANSFORMER

The secondary output of a transformer may be in phase or 180 deg. out of phase with the primary voltage, depending upon the direction of the windings and the method of connection. Restating Lenz's Law, the polarity of the induced voltage will be opposite to the voltage producing it. A diagram of a transformer and the waveforms of the primary and secondary voltage appear in Fig. 6-20. The direction of the magnetic flux is indicated by arrows within the core. A trans-

Fig. 6-20. The phase relationship between the primary and secondary of the transformer. The schematic symbol is also shown.

former of this nature actually inverts the alternating voltage wave applied to the primary.

SERIES AND PARALLEL INDUCTANCE

When coils are connected in series so that no mutual inductance exists between them, the total inductance may be found by,

$$L_T = L_1 + L_2 + L_3$$

The individual inductances add like series resistors. However, when there is mutual inductance the formula becomes,

$$L_T = L_1 + L_2 \overset{+}{-} 2M$$

The plus or minus sign before the M indicates that plus (+) should be used when the coils are aiding each other and the minus (-) when the magnetic fields oppose each other.

When inductors are connected in parallel, without mutual inductance,

$$L_T = \cfrac{1}{\cfrac{1}{L_1} + \cfrac{1}{L_2} + \cfrac{1}{L_3}}$$

There are many applications of mutual inductance in electricity and electronics. A skilled technician must have a complete understanding of the characteristics of circuits containing these components.

INDUCTANCE IN AC CIRCUITS

At this point only the transient response of an inductance connected to a DC voltage source has been studied. In an AC circuit the applied voltage is constantly varying and reversing polarity. Consequently the self-inductance is always present in the circuit, developing counter emfs which oppose the source voltage. This phenomenon may be observed by setting up the experiment again in Fig. 6-3. The light is first connected to a 6 v DC source and its brilliance noted. Now connect the light to a 6 v AC transformer and note the brilliance. Is it brighter or dimmer? The inductance indirectly has some effect upon the current flow. This type of resistance to an alternating current is called REACTANCE. Its letter symbol is X and because it is caused by an inductor, its symbol is X_L, called INDUCTIVE REACTANCE. Its unit of measurement is the OHM.

INDUCED CURRENT AND VOLTAGE

A brief review will help in the understanding of Fig. 6-21. Remember that the induced voltage in a coil is the counter emf and opposes the source so therefore is 180 deg. out of phase with the source voltage. Also the greatest counter emf is induced when the current change is at maximum. Studying Fig. 6-21, you will observe that the greatest rate of change of the current is at

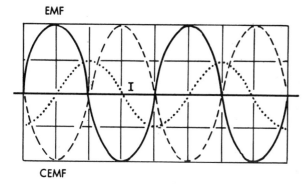

EMF

CEMF

Fig. 6-21. ——— *Electromotive force (voltage),* ------ *Counter Electromotive force,* .... *Current. The greatest CEMF is developed when the current is changing at its most rapid rate.*

the point it is crossing the zero line at 90 deg. and 270 deg. At these points also, the applied voltage must be at maximum and the induced voltage is at maximum. At the points 180 deg. and 360 deg. the current change is minimum. The current is at its maximum value, just ready to start its decrease. It is important to note that the current is 90 deg. out of phase with the applied voltage in a circuit containing pure inductance and the current is lagging behind the voltage. The magnitude of the reactive force opposing the flow of an AC is measured in Ohms and may be mathematically expressed by.

$$X_L = 2\pi fL$$

where,

X_L = Inductive reactance in ohms

f = frequency in cycles per second

L = Inductance in henrys

π = 3.1416

Important: As frequency or inductance is increased, the inductive reactance increases. They are in direct proportion.

The behavior of an inductance in a circuit by applying AC voltages of different frequencies may be observed in the graph in Fig. 6-22. An 8 henry inductor is first connected to a DC (f = 0) and its reactance is zero. Using the formula, $X_L = 2\pi fL$, the reactance is computed for frequencies of 50, 100, 500 and 1000 cps. The graph shows the linear increase of reactance as the frequency is increased.

Fig. 6-22. *As frequency increases; inductive reactance increases.*

In the graph, Fig. 6-23, the frequency is held constant at 100 cps and the reactance is plotted as the inductance is increased from .32 henrys to .8 henrys. Notice the linear increase in reactance as the inductance is increased.

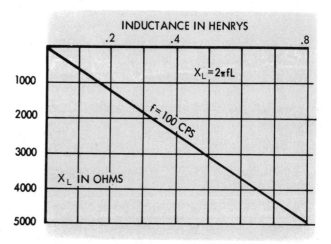

Fig. 6-23. *As inductance is increased; inductive reactance increases.*

In later studies of electronics these principles will be applied to filter and coupling circuits. The student must thoroughly understand the characteristics of reactance and how it changes as a result of inductance and frequency of applied voltage.

REACTIVE POWER

In the study of pure resistive circuits the power consumed by a circuit was found to be the product of the voltage and the current,

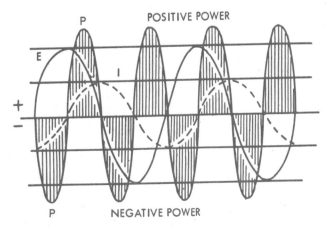

Fig. 6-24. In a theoretical circuit containing inductance only the True Power is zero. The current lags the voltage by 90 deg.

P = I X E. This is not true, however, in an AC circuit containing inductance only. A current will flow, limited by the reactance of the circuit, but the power used to build the magnetic field will be returned to the circuit when the field collapses. This introduces two new terms. TRUE POWER represents the actual power used by a circuit. APPARENT POWER is equal to the product of the effective voltage and the effective current. Reference to Fig. 6-24 will clarify these definitions. An applied AC voltage to the inductive circuit causes a 10 ampere current, so the apparent power will equal,

$$100v \times 10 \text{ amps} = 1000 \text{ volt-amperes}$$

The term "watts" is not used for apparent power. During one cycle equal amounts of positive power and negative power are used which total zero. The relationship between the true power and the apparent power in an AC circuit is called the POWER FACTOR. In the example,

$$\text{Power Factor (p.f.)} = \frac{0}{1000 \text{ volt-amps}} = 0$$

The power factor may also be found trigonometrically by using the cosine of the phase displacement angle θ between the current and the voltage. In this example, the circuit is purely inductive and the current lags the voltage by 90 deg. The power factor is,

$$\text{Cos } \theta \text{ or Cos 90 deg.} = 0$$

RESISTANCE AND INDUCTANCE IN AN AC CIRCUIT

When resistance and inductance are in series in a circuit, power is used. If a circuit contains only resistance as in Fig. 6-25,

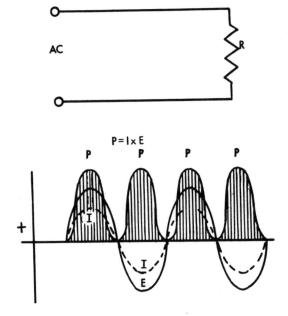

Fig. 6-25. In a pure resistive circuit the True Power and Apparent Power are the same. The current and voltage are in phase.

the current and voltage are in phase and the power consumed is equal to I x E. Even though the polarity of the voltage changes and the current reverses, positive power is consumed. A resistance consumes power, regardless of the direction of the current. The power factor in a circuit of this type is cos 0 deg. = 1 and the apparent power is equal to the true power.

The circuit characteristics change when an inductor is added in series with the resistor. This does not necessarily have to be a resistive component, because the wire from which the coil is wound will have a certain amount of resistance. For the purpose of an example, consider Fig. 6-26. The series

R = 300 Ω

AC

X_L = 400 Ω

Fig. 6-26. The RL circuit described in the text.

resistance equals 300 ohms and the inductive reactance equals 400 ohms. This reactive component will cause the current to lag by an angle of 90 deg. or less. The forces opposing the current can be considered as the resistance and the reactance which are 90 deg. out of phase. To find the resulting opposition, the two forces must be added vectorially as in Fig. 6-27. The vectors may

Fig. 6-27. The vector addition of X_L and R which are 90 deg. out of phase.

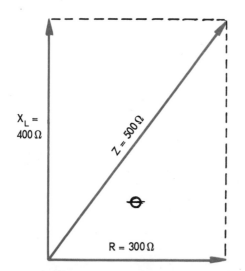

X_L = 400 Ω

Z = 500 Ω

R = 300 Ω

be added graphically by placing the tail of the X_L vector to the arrow head of the R vector. A vector then drawn from origin 0 to the head of the vector X_L represents the magnitude and direction of the combined forces. The total opposition to an alternating current in a circuit containing resistance and reactance is called IMPEDANCE. It is measured in OHMS.

Problems of this nature are usually solved mathematically by applying the PYTHAGOREAN THEOREM for the solution of right triangles. This geometric theorem states that the hypotenuse of a right triangle is equal to the square root of the sum of the squares of the two sides. In the problem,

X_L = 400 Ω and R = 300 Ω, then

$$Z = \sqrt{300^2 + 400^2} = \sqrt{90,000 + 160,000} = 500\Omega$$

or, $Z = \sqrt{R^2 + X_L{}^2}$

The impedance of the circuit is 500 ohms. The angle between vector Z and vector R is the angle θ and represents the phase displacement between the current and voltage resulting from the reactive component. Now Cos θ is equal to the power factor and also equals $\frac{R}{Z}$ (see appendix IV) so:

$$\text{Power Factor} = \text{Cos}\,\theta \text{ and Cos}\,\theta = \frac{R}{Z} \text{ or } \frac{300}{500} \text{ or } .6$$

The angle whose cosine is .6 is 53.10 deg. (approx.)

The current lags the voltage by an angle of 53.1 deg. The true power in this circuit will equal to the apparent power times the power factor or cos. θ :

$$\text{True Power} = \text{Apparent Power} \times \text{Cos } \theta$$

and

$$\text{Cos } \theta = \frac{\text{True Power}}{\text{Apparent Power}}$$

In Fig. 6-28 the wave forms for current, voltage and power are drawn. Assuming an applied AC voltage of 100 v, the current in the circuit will equal:

$$I = \frac{E}{Z} \text{ or } I = \frac{100}{500} = .2 \text{ amps.}$$

and the apparent power can be computed by:

Apparent Power = E x I   or
.2 x 100 = 20 volts-amperes

and the true power equals:

True Power = I x E x cos θ

= .2 x 100 x cos 53.1 deg.

= 20 x .6 = 12 watts

This computation may be proved by:

$$\text{Power Factor} = \frac{\text{True Power}}{\text{Apparent Power}} = \frac{12}{20} = \frac{3}{5} = .6$$

This is not only theory, for in practice the power factor must be considered whenever

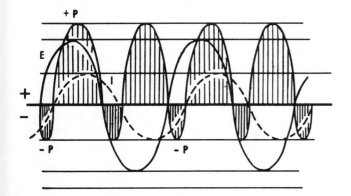

Fig. 6-28. The relationship between voltage, current and power in the example described in the text. θ = 53.1°.

the power company connects its power lines to a manufacturing plant. Industries must keep the power factor of their circuits and machinery within specified limits or pay the power company a premium. Power used by a reactive circuit is sometimes called "wattless power." It is returned to the circuit. In Fig. 6-28 the power in shaded area above the zero line is used, whereas the power below

the line is "wattless power" and is returned to the circuit.

OHM'S LAW FOR AC CIRCUITS

In the computation of circuit values in AC circuits the familiar Ohm's Law is used with the following exception. Z is substituted for R because Z represents the total resistive force opposing the current, then:

$$I = \frac{E}{Z}, \quad E = IZ, \quad Z = \frac{E}{I}$$

The application of Ohm's Law in an AC circuit will be shown in the following problem.

A series circuit containing an 8 henry choke and a 4000 ohm resistor, is connected across a 200 volts, 60 cps AC source. The diagram of this problem appears in Fig. 6-29.

Fig. 6-29. The circuit of the problem analyzed in the text.

Step I.   Find the reactance of L,

$X_L = 2\pi fL$ or
2 x 3.14 x 60 x 8 = 3014 Ω (3000 Ω approx.)

Step II.   Find the impedance of the circuit,

$Z = \sqrt{R^2 + X_L^2}$ or $\sqrt{4,000^2 + 3,000^2}$ or

$\sqrt{16,000,000 + 9,000,000} =$

$\sqrt{25,000,000} = 5,000 \, \Omega$

Step III. Find the current in circuit,

$$I = \frac{E}{Z} \text{ or } \frac{200}{5000} = .04 \text{ amps.}$$

Step IV. Find the voltage drop across R and X_L

$$E_R = I \times R = .04 \times 4000 = 160 \text{ v.}$$
$$E_{X_L} = I \times X_L = .04 \times 3000 = 120 \text{ v.}$$

The sum of the voltage drops does not equal the applied voltage. The reason for this apparent inaccuracy is because the two voltages are 90 deg. out of phase which requires vector addition, so

$$E_s = \sqrt{160^2 + 120^2} = \sqrt{25,600 + 14,400}$$

$$= \sqrt{40,000} \qquad = 200 \text{ volts (approx.)}$$

Step V. Find the phase angle θ between I and E

$$\text{Cos } \theta = \frac{R}{Z} = \frac{4000 \, \Omega}{5000 \, \Omega} = \begin{array}{l} .8 \text{ which is the} \\ \text{cosine of angle } 36^\circ \end{array}$$

Step VI. What is the true power and apparent power?

$$\text{Apparent Power} = I \times E = .04 \times 200 = 8 \text{ volt-amperes}$$

$$\text{True Power} = I \times E \times \text{Cos } \theta = .04 \times 200 \times .8 = 6.4 \text{ watts}$$

Note: Some figures have been approximated in the above problem to avoid uneven figures and to clarify the problem.

TEST YOUR KNOWLEDGE

1. What is inductance in a circuit?
2. Inductance is measured in_____.
3. Convert to henrys:
   200 μ h =
   50 mh =
4. Inductance in a circuit causes the current to_____the voltage.
5. Draw a graph showing the rise and decay of current in a RL circuit.
6. The time constant of a RL circuit may be found by the formula, t = _____.
7. Draw the symbol for a power transformer.
8. The primary of a transformer has 200 turns of wire and the secondary has 800 turns. If 115 volt AC is applied to primary, what will be the secondary voltage?
9. A load attached to the secondary of the transformer in problem 8 draws a 100 ma current. What is the primary current?
10. Name and describe the losses associated with transformers.
11. What is the purpose of the breaker points in the automotive ignition system.
12. The resistance to an alternating current resulting from inductance is called _____. It is measured in_____. Its symbol and formula_____.
13. The only component which uses power in a circuit is_____.
14. In a series RL circuit, L = 2h, R = 500 ohms, E_s = 100 v 60 cycle AC.
    Find:
    X_L = θ =
    Z =   pf =
    I =   True Power =
    E_R =   Apparent Power =
    E_L =
15. On graph paper, draw vectors and sine curves representing current and voltage of Problem 14. With a red pencil, draw the power curve.

DISCUSSION:

1. Why does the power company use high voltages in their cross-country transmission lines?

2. What is the difference between Apparent Power, and True Power?

3. Discuss the differences between a step-up, and a step-down transformer.

4. Power companies request industry to maintain their power factor close to <u>one</u>, or pay additional premiums. Why?

Chapter 7

CAPACITANCE IN
ELECTRICAL CIRCUITS

Early in the history of the science of electricity, the characteristics of the capacitor were investigated. One of the earlier forms was named the Leydon Jar, which consisted of a glass jar covered on the inside and outside by tinfoil. A charge was introduced into the jar by means of a rod and chain. The characteristic of capacitance is a phenomenon of electricity which should be thoroughly understood. Capacitors have thousands of applications in electricity and electronics. In this chapter will be found answers to the following questions:

1. What is a capacitor?

2. How does a capacitor behave in a circuit?

3. How does capacitance affect an AC circuit?

4. What are the results of combining capacitance and resistance in a circuit?

5. What are some of the common applications of capacitors in electronic equipment?

THE CAPACITOR

A capacitor is a simple electronic component, and may be described as two plates of conductive material separated by insulation, which is called the dielectric. The understanding of the capacitor action requires a knowledge of the electron theory. In Fig. 7-1, the capacitor is represented by two metal plates separated by air. These plates are connected to a DC source of voltage. The circuit appears to be an open circuit because the plates are not in physical

Fig. 7-1. The capacitor in its basic form.

contact with each other. The meter in the circuit, however, will show a momentary flow of current when the switch is closed. A study of Fig. 7-2, will show that as the

Fig. 7-2. The capacitor charges to the source voltage.

Electricity - Electronics

switch is closed, electrons from the negative terminal of the source will flow to one plate of the capacitor. These electrons will repel the electrons from the second plate (like charges repel) and these electrons will be attracted to the positive terminal of the source. The capacitor is now charged to the same potential as the source and is opposing the source voltage. The capacitor may be removed from the circuit and it will remain charged. The energy is stored within the electric field of the capacitor.

A LESSON IN SAFETY: Many large capacitors in radios, TVs and other electronic equipment retain their charge after the power has been turned off. These capacitors should be discharged by shorting their terminals to the chassis with an insulated screwdriver. If this is not done, these voltages may destroy test equipment and might give a severe shock to the technician working on the equipment.

Capacitance in a circuit may be defined as that property which opposes any change in voltage. Compare this to inductance, which is the property that opposes a change in current. This capacitive effect will be explained in greater detail later in this chapter. It is important to remember that in the circuit of Fig. 7-2, no electrons flowed through the capacitor. A capacitor will block a direct current. However, one plate became negatively charged, the other positively charged, and a strong electric field exists between them. Insulating or dielectric materials vary in their ability to support an electric field. In electronics this ability is termed the dielectric constant of the material. For comparative purpose the constants of various materials are compared to dry air which is assigned the value of one. Dielectric constants of some familiar materials are listed in Table 7-1.

The capacitance of a capacitor is determined by the number of electrons that may be stored in it for each volt of applied voltage. The unit of measurement of capacitance is the FARAD and represents a charge of one coulomb which raises the

Material	Dielectric Constant
Air	1
Wax paper	3.5
Mica	6
Glass (window)	8
Pure water	81

Table 7-1

potential one volt. This equation states that,

$$C \text{ (in farads)} = \frac{Q \text{ (in coulombs)}}{E \text{ (in volts)}}$$

Capacitors used in electronic work have capacities measured in microfarads $\left(\frac{1}{1,000,000} \text{ of a farad}\right)$ and micromicrofarads $\left(\frac{1}{1,000,000} \text{ of } \frac{1}{1,000,000} \text{ farad.}\right)$

The Greek letter "μ" is used to represent micro and micromicro would appear as "$\mu\mu$." A typical capacitor might be rated as 250 $\mu\mu$fd. meaning 250 micromicrofarads.

Capacitance is determined by;

1. The material used as a dielectric.

2. The area of the plates.

3. The distance between the plates.

These factors are related in the mathematical formula as,

$$C \text{ (in } \mu\mu\text{fds)} = .225 \frac{KA}{d}(n-1)$$

where,

K = dielectric constant

A = area of one side of one plate in square inches

Fig. 7-3. Variable capacitors are made in many types and sizes. (Hammarlund Mfg. Co.)

d = the distance between plates in inches

n = number of plates.

This formula is presented at this time so the student will realize the following facts:

1. Capacity <u>increases</u> when the area of the plates is increased or the dielectric constant is increased.

2. Capacity <u>decreases</u> when the distance between the plates is increased.

This information will be useful in later studies of capacitance in electronic circuits.

TYPES OF CAPACITORS

There are hundreds of sizes and types of capacitors manufactured today. Some of the more common ones will be illustrated and discussed.

1. VARIABLE CAPACITORS, Fig. 7-3. This group of capacitors consists of metal plates which intermesh as the shaft is turned. The stationary plates are called the <u>stator</u> and the rotating plates are the <u>rotor</u>. Many of these are used in radio transmitters and receivers. It is a component like one of these that you turn when tuning a

radio. Referring to the past discussion, this capacitor is at maximum capacity when the plates are fully meshed. Notice the schematic symbol for a variable capacitor.

2. FIXED PAPER CAPACITOR, Fig. 7-4. This common variety of capacitor is made up of layers of tin-

Fig. 7-4. A fixed value paper capacitor encapsulated in plastic. (Sprague Products Co.)

foil separated by waxed paper as the dielectric. The wires extending from the ends connect to the foil plates. The assembly is tightly rolled into a cylinder and sealed with special compounds. To provide rigidity, some manufacturers encapsulate these capacitors in plastic. These molded capacitors will withstand severe heat, moisture and shock.

Fig. 7-5. The oil filled capacitor.

3. RECTANGULAR OIL FILLED CAPACITORS, Fig. 7-5. These capacitors are hermetically sealed in metal cans. They are oil filled and have extremely high insulation resistance. This type is found in the power supply of radio transmitters and other electronic equipment.

4. ELECTROLYTICS, CAN TYPE, Fig. 7-6. This kind of capacitor employs a different method of plate

Fig. 7-6. Can type electrolytic capacitor.

construction. Some manufacturers use aluminum plates and a wet or dry electrolyte of borax or carbonate. A DC voltage is applied during manufacture and by electrolytic action a thin layer of aluminum oxide is deposited on the positive plate, effectively insulating it from the electrolyte. The negative plate is a connection to the electrolyte; the electrolyte and positive plates form the capacitor. These capacitors are very convenient when a large amount of capacity is needed in a small space. The polarity of these capacitors must be observed. A reverse connection will destroy them. The cans may contain from one to four different capacitors. The terminals are marked by ▲, ●, ■ and ▬ symbols. The metal can is usually the common negative terminal for all the capacitors. A

Capacitance

special metal and a fibre mounting plate is supplied for easy installation on a chassis.

5. ELECTROLYTICS, TUBULAR, Fig. 7-7. The construction of these capacitors is similar to the can type. The main advantage is the

Fig. 7-7. The tubular electrolytic capacitor. (Sprague Products Co.)

smaller size. They have a metal case which is enclosed in an insulating tube. These also are made in dual, triple and quadruple units in one cylinder.

6. CERAMIC DISC, Fig. 7-8. A very popular small capacitor which is

Fig. 7-8. A group of ceramic disc capacitors. (Centralab)

used extensively in radio and TV work. It is made of a special ceramic dielectric on which is fixed the silver plates of the capacitor. The whole component is treated with special insulation to withstand heat and moisture.

7. MICA CAPACITOR, Fig. 7-9. These small capacitors are made by stacking tin foil plates together

Fig. 7-9. Mica Capacitors. (See Appendix 2 on How to read the capacitor color code.)

with thin sheets of mica as the dielectric. The assembly is then molded into a plastic case.

8. TRIMMER CAPACITOR, Fig. 7-10. This is a form of a variable capacitor. The adjustable screw compresses the plates and increases the capacitance. Mica is used as a dielectric. These, as the name

Fig. 7-10. Several types of trimmer capacitors. (Centralab)

suggests, are used where a fine adjustment of capacitance is necessary. They are used in conjunction with larger capacitors and are connected in parallel with them.

LESSON IN SAFETY: When making adjustments on trimmer and padder capacitors, the screw should be turned with a special fibre or plastic screwdriver called an alignment tool. The capacitive effect of a steel screwdriver, if used, would result in inaccurate adjustment.

TRANSIENT RESPONSE OF THE CAPACITOR

The response of the current and voltage in a circuit after an immediate change in applied voltage, is known as a TRANSIENT RESPONSE. Referring to the diagram, Fig. 7-11, a capacitor and a resistor are connected in series across a voltage source. When the

Fig. 7-11. A series RC circuit used to demonstrate transient response.

switch is closed, maximum current will flow, gradually decreasing until the capacitor has reached its full charge, which is the same as the applied voltage. However, the voltage initially is zero across the capacitor, and when the switch is closed this voltage will gradually build up to the value of the source voltage. This is graphically illustrated in Fig. 7-12. When the switch is opened, the capacitor remains charged. Theoretically it

Fig. 7-12. A graph showing current and voltage in the series RC circuit.

would remain charged but there is always some leakage through the dielectric and during a period of time the capacitor will discharge itself.

In Fig. 7-13, the series combination of charged capacitor and resistor are short-circuited by providing a discharge path. Because there is no opposing voltage, the discharge current will instantaneously rise to maximum and gradually fall off to zero.

Fig. 7-13. The RC circuit is short-circuited by closing switch S_2.

The combined graph showing the charge and discharge of C is shown in Fig. 7-14. Consideration must also be given to the voltages appearing across R and C in this circuit. As the voltage across R is a result of current flow, E = IR, then the maximum voltage appears across R when maximum current is flowing. This is immediately after the switch is closed in Fig. 7-11, and after the discharge switch is closed in Fig. 7-13. In either case the voltage across R drops off or decays as

Fig. 7-14. The rise and decay of current and voltage in the RC circuit.

the capacitor approaches charge or discharge. The graph of the voltage across R is drawn in Fig. 7-15.

RC TIME CONSTANT

During the charge and discharge of the series RC network previously described, a period of time did elapse. This time is indicated along the base of x-axis of the graphs in Fig. 7-14 and 7-15. The time duration for the capacitor to charge or discharge

Fig. 7-15. The graph shows the voltage drop across R as the capacitor is charged and discharged.

63.2 per cent is known as the TIME CONSTANT of the circuit. It may be computed by the formula:

$$t \text{ (in seconds)} = R \text{ (in ohms)} \times C \text{ (in farads)}$$

For complete charge or discharge five time constant periods are required. Assuming a source voltage equal to 100 volts, table 7-2 shows the time constant, percentage and voltage.

Time Constant	Percent of Voltage	E Charging	E Discharging
1	63.2%	63.2v	36.8v
2	86.5%	86.5v	13.5v
3	95.0%	95.0v	5 v
4	98.0%	98.0v	2 v
5	99+%	99+ v	1 v

Table 7-2

A problem will clarify this charging action. A .1 microfarad capacitor is connected in series with a megohm (1,000,000 ohm) resistor across a 100 volts source. How much time will elapse during the charging of C. (Using powers of ten is explained in the appendix.)

$$t = .1 \times 10^{-6} \times 1 \times 10^{6} = .1 \text{ sec.}$$

One tenth of a second is the time constant and C would charge to 63.2 volts during this time. At the end of five time constants or 5 x .1 = .5 sec., the capacitor is considered fully charged.

An interesting experiment may be performed by setting up the circuit in Fig. 7-16. A neon lamp will remain out until a certain voltage is reached. At this voltage called the "ignition or firing voltage" the lamp glows and offers negligible resistance in a circuit. In this circuit capacitor C charges through resistance R. When the voltage across C develops to the ignition voltage, the lamp glows and C is rapidly discharged. This cycle repeats over and over, causing the neon light to flash. The frequency of the flashes may be changed by varying either the value of C or R. Time constants have many uses in elec-

Fig. 7-16. The flashing circuit called a relaxation oscillator.

tronic circuits and frequent reference will be made to them in the following chapters. Timing circuits are used in industry to control the sequence and duration of machine operations. The photo-enlarger uses a time-delay circuit to control the exposure time. These circuits provide many interesting effects for the experimenter in electronics.

WISE OWL PROJECT

The wise old owl in Fig. 7-17 is named "Hooty-Hoot." His eyes flash at night. He is an amusing toy and a conversation piece, that demonstrates the principles of RC time con-

Fig. 7-17. Hooty-Hoot employs RC circuits so that his eyes will alternately flash. The blinking feature is covered by U. S. Patent No. 2,647,222, owned by Gold Seal Co., Bismarck, N. Dak. Used by permission of patent holder.

stants. Follow the circuit diagram and make your own "bird" or "animal." The body is made of paper mache over a chicken wire frame.

Parts List for HOOTY-HOOT

2 NE2 Neon Lamps

2 2.2 megohm resistors

1 .1 μfd Paper Capacitors, 200 volts

1 90 volt B Battery, Portable size.

PARALLEL AND SERIES CIRCUITS

Many times the technician is required to work with capacitors connected in series and parallel, and the effect of such connections should be explored. When capacitors are connected in parallel as in Fig. 7-18, the total

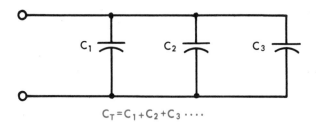

$$C_T = C_1 + C_2 + C_3 \cdots$$

Fig. 7-18. Capacitors in parallel.

capacitance is equal to the sum of the individual capacitances.

$$C_T = C_1 + C_2 + C_3 \ldots \ldots \ldots \ldots$$

When two capacitors are connected in series, then,

$$C_T = \frac{C_1 \times C_2}{C_1 + C_2}$$

and if two or more are connected in series as in Fig. 7-19:

$$C_T = \frac{1}{\frac{1}{C_1} + \frac{1}{C_2} + \frac{1}{C_3}} \ldots \ldots \ldots$$

Up to this point the WORKING VOLTAGE of a capacitor has only been briefly mentioned.

The dielectrics used for capacitors can only withstand certain voltages. If this voltage is exceeded, the dielectric will breakdown and arcing will result. This may possibly cause a short circuit and ruin other parts of the circuit in which it is connected. Increased voltage ratings require special materials and thicker dielectrics. When a

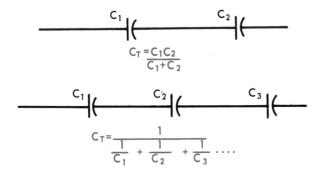

$$C_T = \frac{C_1 C_2}{C_1 + C_2}$$

$$C_T = \frac{1}{\dfrac{1}{C_1} + \dfrac{1}{C_2} + \dfrac{1}{C_3} \dots}$$

Fig. 7-19. Capacitors in series.

capacitor is replaced, special attention should be paid to its capacitance value and also to its DC working voltage.

When a capacitor is used in an AC circuit, the working voltage should safely exceed the peak AC voltage. A 120 volt effective AC voltage will have a peak voltage of 120v x 1.414 = 169.7 volts.

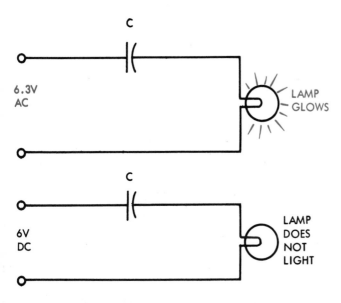

Fig. 7-20. The light will glow when connected to an AC source. The capacitor will block direct current.

CAPACITANCE IN AC CIRCUITS

The previous lesson has explained that a capacitor will block a direct current. Current only flows in the circuit during the charging or discharging time. If an AC voltage is applied to a capacitor, the plates charge to one polarity during the first half cycle. During the next half cycle they charge to the opposite polarity. An AC meter in the circuit would indicate a current flow at all times. In Fig. 7-20 this is proved experimentally by connecting the light and capacitor in series to a 6 volt DC source. Does the light glow? Now connect the same circuit to a 6 volt AC source and notice that the light burns dimly, showing that alternating current is flowing as a result of the alternate charging of the capacitor.

For purposes of emphasis, the current and voltage in a capacitive circuit will be reviewed. Referring to Fig. 7-21, as the AC voltage starts to rise, the current flow is maximum because C is in a discharged state. As C becomes charged to the peak AC voltage, the charging current drops to zero,

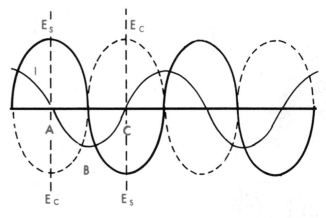

Fig. 7-21. A graph showing applied voltage, current and the voltage across C, when the circuit is connected to AC.

Point A. As the voltage begins to drop, the discharging current begins to rise in a negative direction and reaches maximum at the point of zero voltage, Point B. This phase difference continues on throughout each cycle. In a purely capacitive circuit the current leads the voltage by an angle of 90 deg. The magnitude of the current in the circuit depends upon the size of the capacitor. Larger capacitors (more capacitance) require a larger current to charge them. Also affecting the current flow is the frequency of the AC voltage. The current flow depends upon the rate of charge and discharge of the capacitor. As the frequency of the AC is increased, then current will increase. These relationships are stated mathematically by,

$$X_C = \frac{1}{2\pi fC}$$

where,

X_C = Capacitive reactance in Ohms
f = Frequency in cycles per second
C = Capacitance in farads

Similar to inductive reactance, the resistance to the flow of an alternating current as a result of capacitance is called CAPACITIVE

Fig. 7-22. The graph shows that as frequency increases, the capacitive reactance decreases.

REACTANCE. It is measured in ohms, like DC resistance and X_L. The formula indicates that:

1. As the frequency increases, X_C decreases.

2. As capacitance is increased, X_C decreases.

Problem: What is the reactance of a 10 μfd

capacitor operating in a circuit at a frequency of 120 cycles per second (cps)?

$$X_C = \frac{1}{2\pi \times 120 \times 10 \times 10^{-6}} = \frac{1}{6.28 \times 120 \times 10}$$

$$= \frac{1 \times 10^5}{753.6} = .0013 \times 10^5 \text{ or } 130 \ \Omega$$

The reactance of a .1 mfd capacitor as frequency is varied may be observed in the graph of Fig. 7-22. As frequency is changed to 50, 100, 1,000 and 10,000 cps, the reactances are computed respectively by the formula, $X_C = \frac{1}{2\pi fC}$.

In Fig. 7-23 the frequency is held constant at 1,000 cps and the reactance is plotted for capacitors of .5 mfd, .1 mfd, .05 mfd, .01 mfd and .001 mfd. These are some common sizes of capacitors used in electronic work. They are used in filtering, coupling and by-passing networks. More detailed explanations will be included in later studies.

REACTIVE POWER

When a capacitor is discharged, the energy stored in the dielectric is returned to the circuit. This may be compared to inductance which returns the energy stored in the magnetic field to the circuit. In either case

Fig. 7-23. This graph shows that as capacitance increases, the reactance decreases.

electrical energy is used temporarily by the reactive circuit. This power in a capacitive circuit is also called <u>wattless power.</u> In Fig. 7-24 the voltage and current waveforms are drawn for a circuit containing pure capacitance. The power wave form is a result of plotting the products of the instantaneous voltage and current at selected points. The power waveform shows that equal amounts of positive power and negative power are

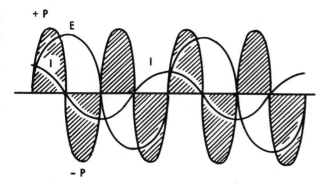

Fig. 7-24. The wave forms showing current, voltage and power in a pure capacitive circuit.

used by the circuit, resulting in zero power consumption. The TRUE-POWER therefore is zero. (Refer to Chapter 6 to study of Reactive Power in an Inductive Circuit and compare these circuits.) The <u>apparent power</u> is equal to the product of the effective voltage and the effective current. Referring to the circuit in Fig. 7-25 an applied AC voltage to the capacitive circuit causes a 10 ampere current. The apparent power will equal,

100v x 10 amps = 1000 volt-amperes

The relationship between the true power and

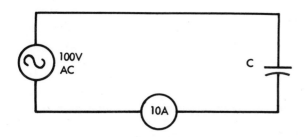

Fig. 7-25. The schematic of the theoretical capacitive circuit.

the apparent power in an AC circuit is called the <u>power factor</u>. In this example,

Power Factor (p.f.) =

$$\frac{0 \text{ (true power)}}{1000 \text{ volt-amps (apparent power)}} = 0$$

The power factor may also be found trigonometrically. It is equal to the cosine of the phase displacement angle θ between the current and the voltage. In the pure capacitive circuit, the current leads the voltage by an angle of 90 deg. and θ therefore is 90 deg.

Cos θ or Cos 90° = 0

The true power may be found by,

True Power = I x E x Cos θ

$$= 10 \text{ x } 100 \text{ x Cos } 90^{\circ} \text{ (Cos } 90^{\circ} = 0)$$

$$= 0$$

RESISTANCE AND CAPACITANCE IN AN AC CIRCUIT

When resistance is present in a circuit, power is consumed. If the circuit contains only resistance, then the voltage and current are in phase. There is no phase angle θ and the power factor is one,

Cos 0° = 1

and the apparent power equals the true power.

The circuit characteristics change when capacitance is added in series with the resistor. The capacitive reactance is also a force which resists the flow of an alternating current. Because the capacitive reactance causes a 90° phase displacement, the total resistance to an AC current must be the vector sum of the X_C and R. These vectors are drawn in Fig. 7-26. Assuming the circuit has 300 ohms resistance and 400 ohms capacitive reactance, then the resultant force is 500 ohms which is called the impedance Z of the circuit.

$$Z = \sqrt{300^2 + 400^2} = \sqrt{90,000 + 160,000} = 500\Omega$$

$$Z = \sqrt{R^2 + X_C^2}$$

The angle between vector Z and vector R represents the phase displacement between

Fig. 7-26. Above. The vector relationship between R and X_C and the resultant vector Z for impedance. Below. The circuit for the problem in the text.

the current and the voltage as a result of the reactive component. This is angle θ (theta). Now cosine θ is equal to the power factor and also equals $\frac{R}{Z}$ so,

Power Factor = Cos θ and Cos θ =

$$\frac{R}{Z} \text{ or } \frac{300}{500} = .6$$

The angle which has a cosine of .6 is 53.1° (approx.). The current then leads the voltage by an angle of 53.1°. The true power in this circuit will equal to:

Apparent Power x Cos θ = True Power
or
Apparent Power x power factor = True Power

Also the power factor is the relationship between the true power and the apparent power, and this equality may be expressed as,

$$\text{Cos } \theta = \text{power factor} = \frac{\text{true power}}{\text{apparent power}}$$

Using Ohm's Law for AC circuits, the current flowing in circuit, Fig. 7-26 is equal to, (100 volts AC is applied)

$$I = \frac{E}{Z} \text{ or } I = \frac{100}{500} = .2 \text{ amps.}$$

The apparent power is therefore,

I x E or .2 x 100 = 20 volt-amps

and,

True Power = I x E x Cos θ
= .2 x 100 x Cos. 53.1°
= 20 x .6 = 12 watts

Proof of this equation may be realized by,

$$\text{Power Factor} = \frac{\text{True Power}}{\text{Apparent Power}} = \frac{12}{20} = .6$$

There are three electrical properties of any circuit, R, L, and C. These will be found in many combinations including R, RL, and RC networks which have been studied in the last two chapters. In Chapter 8, RCL circuits will be considered. Always review previous lessons, if the theory discussed is not clearly understood. The nature of the study of electricity and electronics requires the student to have a firm grasp of all previous knowledge before progression into more difficult applications.

AUTOMATIC CONTROL FOR GARAGE LIGHTS

This project makes a very fine present and may prevent some accidents. It uses two principles you have already studied: 1. The photocell. 2. RC time constants. It works like this. When the headlights from the car strike the photocell, it automatically turns on the garage lights. The lights remain on for several minutes depending on the setting of R_3.

This project is illustrated in Fig. 7-27A, B and C. The tube on the metal box acts as a shade so the circuit will be triggered only by direct approaching light. It may be soldered or screwed onto the box. The sun battery B_2 is mounted behind the tube. The switch activates the circuit. The AC plug permits connection by extension cord to the toggle switch which operates the garage lights. It should be connected across the switch. This is in parallel with the switch.

Here's how it works: When the sun cell is activated by light, transistor Q_1 conducts and charges C_1, and also Q_2 conducts through the relay coil, which closes the switch points. Garage lights go on. When the light source is removed (headlights off) the charge on C_1 keeps Q_2 conducting. The charge on C_1 gradually bleeds off through R_3 and R_2. At a predetermined point, set by R_3, the relay points open. (Garage lights turn off.) Sufficient time has passed so that you can turn on the garage lights in the usual manner.

R_1 is a sensitivity control, and should be adjusted so that the headlights will trigger the circuit.

No attempt is made to show you the exact physical wiring of this circuit. The photo only suggests one way of many to build the project. It should be compact. Care must be taken always when working with transistors. See Chapter 17.

Fig. 7-27C. Courtesy, Sylvania Electric Products, Inc.

Fig. 7-27-A. Automatic control for garage light.

Fig. 7-27-B. Parts hookup for garage light control.

PARTS LIST

B1 - 15-volt battery
B2 - Sun battery, International Rectifier Corp., Type B2M or equivalent
C1 - 1000 mfd electrolytic, 15-volt
CR1 - Sylvania 1N34 diode
I1 - 115-volt light bulb, wattage not greater than 100
K1 - 1 kohm sensitive relay, Sigma 11F-1000G or equivalent
Q1 - Sylvania 2N1265 transistor
Q2 - Sylvania 2N229 transistor
R1 - 10 k potentiometer
R2 - 22 k, 1/2 w
R3 - 1 meg potentiometer
R4 - 1 k, 1/2 w
S1 - Single-pole, single-throw switch; slide, toggle, or push button

Fig. 7-27-C. Wiring diagram for garage light control, shown in 7-27A and 7-27B.

DISCUSSION

1. Why should adjustments on trimmer capacitors be made with a plastic or fibre screwdriver?

2. Why does a capacitor block DC, yet will pass an AC signal?

3. What is meant by the term TRANSIENT RESPONSE?

4. Why does a theoretical circuit containing only capacitance consume no power?

5. Should a capacitor with a working voltage of 150 volts be used in circuit with 117 volts AC supplied from your house circuit? Why?

TEST YOUR KNOWLEDGE

1. Draw a circuit of a battery, switch and capacitor in series. Explain the charging of C. Show direction of electron flow.

2. What SAFETY precaution should be followed when working on capacitors in a radio or TV?

3. Capacitance in a circuit may be defined as that property which opposes a change in _____.

4. What is meant by the term DIELECTRIC CONSTANT?

5. Capacitance is measured in _____.

6. What three physical characteristics de-

Capacitance

termine the capacity of a capacitor?

7. Ask your instructor to show you a sample of each of the different types of capacitors illustrated in the text.

8. The time constant of an RC circuit is equal to _____ x _____ and, _____ time constant periods are required for fully charging the capacitor.

9. Capacitors in parallel add together like _____ in series.

10. State formula for C_T when two unequal capacitors are in series.

11. The opposing force to an alternating current as a result of capacitance is called _____ _____. Its symbol is _____. It is measured in _____ and may be found by the formula _____.

12. As capacitance is increased, X_C _____. As frequency is increased, X_C _____.

13. In a theoretical circuit containing only capacitance, the current _____ the voltage by an angle of _____ or less. The power consumed is _____.

14. A series circuit of R = 3000 ohms and C = .1 μfd is connected to a 50 volt 400 cps source.
Find:

X_C

Z

E_{X_C}

E_R

I

θ

15. A capacitor has a value of .1 μfd.
What is its reactance at, 50 cps - X_C =
100 cps - X_C =
1000 cps - X_C =
10 kc - X_C =

16. The frequency of the current in a circuit is 1000 cps.
What is reactance of a .5 μfC =
.1 μfC =
.05 μfC =
.01 μfC =
.001 μfC =

Chapter 8

TUNED CIRCUITS : RCL NETWORKS

RCL NETWORKS

The effects of resistance, capacitance and inductance have been studied in previous chapters. These principles should be reviewed before progressing into combination circuits.

1. In an AC circuit containing resistance only, the applied voltage and current are in phase. There is no reactive power and the power consumed by the circuit is equal to the product of volts times amperes.

2. In an AC circuit containing inductance only, the current lags the voltage by an angle of 90°. They are not in phase. The power consumed by the circuit is zero.

3. In an AC circuit containing resistance and inductance, the current will lag the voltage by a phase angle of less than 90°. The total resistive force is the vector sum of the ohmic resistance and the inductive reactance. This is the impedance of the circuit.

4. In an AC circuit containing capacitance only, the current leads the voltage by an angle of 90°. The power consumed is zero.

5. In an AC circuit containing resistance and capacitance, the current will lead the voltage by an angle of less than 90°. The impedance is equal to the vector sum of the resistance and the capacitive reactance.

6. In an AC circuit containing resistance, inductance and capacitance in series, the resulting impedance is equal to the vector addition of R in ohms, X_L in ohms and X_C in ohms.

RESONANCE

A special condition exists in a RCL circuit, when it is energized at a frequency at which the inductive reactance is equal to the capacitive reactance, $X_L = X_C$. As inductive reactance, X_L, increases as frequency increases and capacitive reactance, X_C, decreases as frequency increases, there is one frequency at which they are both equal. This is the RESONANT FREQUENCY of the circuit, (f_o). In the vector diagram of Fig. 8-1, $X_L =$

Fig. 8-1. The condition of resonance exists when $X_L = X_C$ and the circuit appears as a resistive circuit.

Tuned Circuits

100, X_C = 100, and R = 50. X_L and X_C are opposing each other because they are 180° out of phase, and the algebraic sum of these vectors is <u>zero</u>, and only resistance R of 50 ohms remains. The current and voltage are in phase. This particular frequency of the circuit may be computed by the resonant frequency formula:

$$f_o = \frac{1}{2\pi\sqrt{LC}}$$

where,

    f_o = resonant frequency in cycles per second

    L = inductance in henrys

    C = capacitance in farads

The derivation of this formula may be understood by the following steps,

    At resonance $X_L = X_C$

    or

$$2\pi fL = \frac{1}{2\pi fC}$$

Transpose: $2\pi L$ to right side of the equation by dividing both sides by $2\pi L$

$$f = \frac{1}{(2\pi)^2 fLC}$$

Move f to left side by multiplying both sides by f,

$$f^2 = \frac{1}{(2\pi)^2 LC}$$

Take square root of both sides of the equation,

$$f = \frac{1}{2\pi\sqrt{LC}}$$

To simplify the equation further, $\frac{1}{2\pi}$ or $\frac{1}{6.28}$ = .159, so

$$f_o = \frac{.159}{\sqrt{LC}} \text{ (approximately)}$$

Example: What is the resonant frequency of a circuit which has 200 μh inductance and 200 $\mu\mu$fd capacitance?

Solution:

$$f_o = \frac{.159}{\sqrt{200 \times 10^{-6} \times 200 \times 10^{-12}}} = \frac{.159}{\sqrt{40,000 \times 10^{-18}}}$$

$$= \frac{.159}{\sqrt{4 \times 10^4 \times 10^{-18}}} = \frac{.159}{\sqrt{4 \times 10^{-14}}} = \frac{.159}{2 \times 10^{-7}}$$

$$= .08 \times 10^7 = 800,000 \text{ c.p.s. or } 800 \text{ kc. or } .8 \text{ mc.}$$

(Review both Conversions and Scientific Notation in Appendix.)

THE ACCEPTOR CIRCUIT

First, consider the performance of a series LCR circuit at its resonant frequency. The diagram is drawn in Fig. 8-2. At resonance $X_L = X_C$ so the impedance of the circuit equals,

$$Z = \sqrt{R^2 + (X_L - X_C)^2} \text{ or } \sqrt{R^2} = R$$

and only the ohmic resistance impedes the current flow in the circuit. <u>In a series resonant circuit the impedance is minimum.</u> At frequencies above or below the resonant

AT RESONANCE $X_L = X_C$

Fig. 8-2. *The series resonant circuit is an Acceptor circuit.*

frequency X_L is not equal to X_C and the reactive component <u>increases</u> the impedance of the circuit. The response of the series tuned circuit appears as a bell-shaped curve in Fig. 8-3A. Notice that the impedance of the circuit is minimum at resonance, and that maximum current flows at resonance and rapidly falls off on either side of resonance

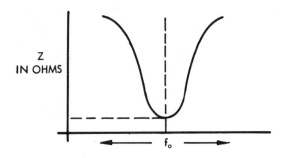

Fig. 8-3-A. *The curve shows the increase in impedance as the frequency is varied above or below resonance.*

due to the increased impedance, Fig. 8-3B. This describes an ACCEPTOR CIRCUIT because it provides maximum response to currents at its resonant frequency.

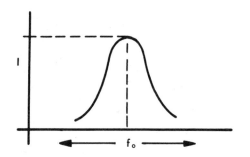

Fig. 8-3-B. *The response curve showing the current flow in the circuit above or below resonance.*

Example: R = 10 ohms, L = 200 μh, C = 200 $\mu\mu$fd. These components are connected across a 500 μ volt RF generator at 800 kilocycles. This circuit is diagrammed in Fig. 8-4. From the previous problem, the resonant frequency of this RCL circuit was 800 kilocycles, so $X_L = X_C$ at f_o.

Fig. 8-4. *The series-tuned acceptor circuit described in the text.*

Then Z = 10 ohms and I = $\frac{E}{Z}$ or $\frac{500 \times 10^{-6}}{10}$ = 50 μ amps

Also,

$$X_L = 2\pi \times 800 \times 10^3 \times 200 \times 10^{-6} = 1000\,\Omega \text{ approx.}$$

and

$$X_C = \frac{1}{2\pi \times 800 \times 10^3 \times 200 \times 10^{-12}} = 1000\,\Omega \text{ approx.}$$

The voltage drops around the circuit equal,

$$\begin{aligned}
E_R &= 50\mu a \times 10 &&= 500\,\mu v \\
E_{X_L} &= 50\mu a \times 1000 &&= 50{,}000\,\mu v \\
E_{X_C} &= 50\mu a \times 1000 &&= 50{,}000\,\mu v
\end{aligned}$$

It would appear that the sum of these voltages would be 100,500 μ v, but E_{X_L} and E_{X_C} are 180° out of phase. Therefore a vector addition must be made,

$$E_{source} = \sqrt{(E_R)^2 + (E_{X_L} - E_{X_C})^2} = 500\,\mu$$

It should be noted that, at resonance, the voltage drops across X_L and X_C are equal and also the voltage drop across R equals the source voltage. In a resonant circuit of this nature the interchange of energy between the inductance and the capacitance builds up a voltage which exceeds the supply voltage. In the first half cycle the magnetic field of the inductance stores the energy of the discharging capacitor. In the next half cycle the stored energy in the magnetic field of the inductance charges the capacitor. This action occurs back and forth, limited only by the series resistance between the two components. At resonance, the charging times for the inductance and capacitance must be the same, or they would have a cancelling effect.

Summarizing the series tuned circuit:

1. At resonance, the impedance is minimum and the line current is maximum.

2. At resonance, the voltage drop, E_{X_L}, is equal to E_{X_C}, but is 180° out of phase.

3. The vector sum of all voltage drops equals the applied voltage. Chart 8-1 shows the changing values as the circuit frequency is changed.

ceptor circuit. The parallel tuned circuit is one of the more important circuits in the study of electronics and the student should become thoroughly acquainted with it.

f	X_L ohms	X_C ohms	Z ohms	I μa	E_{X_L} μv	E_{X_C} μv
200 kc	250	4000	3750	.13	33	520
400 kc	500	2000	1500	.33	165	660
600 kc	750	1500	750	.66	495	990
800 kc	1000	1000	10	5.0	50,000	50,000
1000 kc	1250	800	450	1.1	1375	880
1200 kc	1500	666	833	.6	900	400
1600 kc	2000	500	1500	.33	660	165

Chart 8-1

Note: Above figures taken to nearest whole number for ease in understanding. Resistance of 10 ohms is insignificant, and is not included in computations except at resonance.

THE TANK CIRCUIT

The behavior of the circuit containing resistance, capacitance and inductance in parallel, differs from the series tuned ac-

A study of Fig. 8-5 will reveal the behavior of this circuit. In the first place, switch S_1 is closed, and capacitor C is charged to the supply voltage. Now S_1 is opened and C remains charged. When S_2 is

Fig. 8-5. The charge and discharge of C through inductance L is similar to flywheel action. It is called a tank circuit.

C DISCHARGES THROUGH L

123

closed, the capacitor discharges through L in the direction of the arrows. As the current flows through L, a magnetic field is built up around L, and this field remains as long as the current flows. However, when the charges on the plates of C become equalized, current ceases to flow and the magnetic field around L collapses, and the energy stored in this field is returned to the circuit. In the study of inductance in Chapter 6, we discovered that the induced EMF opposes the current change. This is also true in the parallel circuit. When the current drops to zero as a result of the discharged capacitor, a current is induced by the collapsing magnetic field which drives a charge onto the capacitor, but opposite to the original polarity. Now the capacitor discharges in the opposite direc-

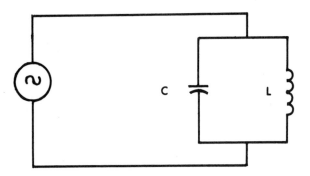

Fig. 8-6. A parallel LC circuit connected to a variable frequency generator.

tion. Once again the cycle of events occurs, and the capacitor again becomes charged as in its original state. This discharge-charge cycle repeats over and over and the current periodically changes direction in the circuit. The circuit is said to be OSCILLATING. The periodic reversals of current in the circuit may be described as FLY-WHEEL ACTION and the circuit is called a TANK CIRCUIT. If no energy were used during the cycles of oscillation, the circuit might oscillate indefinitely, but there is always some resistance due to the windings of the coil and the circuit connections. This resistance uses up the energy stored in the circuit and DAMPENS out the oscillation. The AMPLITUDE of each successive oscillation decreases due to the resistance. The oscillations of a tank circuit may be likened to a

child on a playground swing. The child may be swinging back and forth or oscillating, and if no one adds a little push to the swing, it will successively decrease in the amplitude of the swing until it finally comes to rest. If it were not for the friction or resistance, the swing might continue forever. This would be perpetual motion. A way to accomplish this feat has yet to be discovered. Now if another boy stood behind the swing and gave it a little push each time it reached its maximum backward position, the added energy would replace the energy lost by the friction, and the swinging would continue as long as the boy pushed. The tank circuit is similar to the playground swing. If pulses of energy are added to the oscillating tank circuit at the <u>correct frequency, it will continue to oscillate</u>.

Let's examine the meaning of correct frequency. During the discharge and charge of the capacitor C in the circuit, Fig. 8-5, a definite period of time must pass. In other words, during one cycle of oscillation a definite interval of time must pass. The number of cycles that occur in one second would be called the <u>frequency</u> of oscillation and is measured in <u>cycles per second</u> (cps.).

A thoughtful consideration of this circuit would disclose that if C or L were made larger so that it required a longer time to charge, the frequency of the circuit would decrease. This relationship may again be expressed mathematically by the resonance formula:

$$f_o = \frac{1}{2\pi\sqrt{LC}}$$

where,

f_o = resonant frequency in cycles per second

L = inductance in henrys

C = capacitance in farads

In electronic work, L usually has values in microhenrys (μh) and C in micromicrofarads ($\mu\mu$f). If this is the case, the equation may be simplified to read,

$$f_o = \frac{159}{\sqrt{LC}}$$

where,

f_o = resonant frequency in <u>megacycles</u>

L = Inductance in <u>microhenrys</u>

C = Capacitance in <u>micromicrofarads</u>

THE REJECT CIRCUIT

If a parallel tuned circuit were connected across a generator of variable frequency, as in Fig. 8-6, you would discover that at the resonant frequency of the tuned circuit a minimim line current would flow. This is very useful information, because the resonant frequency may be determined by the minimum value or "dip" in the line current as measured by a current meter in the line. The radio transmitter operator always "dips the final" which means that he tunes the final tank circuit to resonance which is indicated by a dip in current flow in the final circuit.

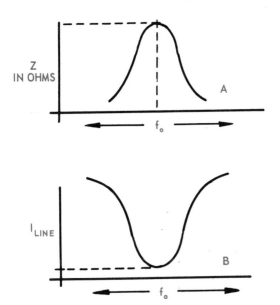

Fig. 8-7. A. The curve shows maximum impedance at resonant frequency. B. The circuit response shows minimum line current at resonance.

If minimum current flows in the circuit at resonance, then one may assume that at resonance a parallel-tuned circuit presents maximum impedance (Z). At frequencies other than resonance, the impedance is less. So, at resonance the circuit <u>rejects</u> currents at resonant frequency, and allows currents of frequencies other than resonance to pass. The characteristics are illustrated in the response curves in Fig. 8-7. There will be many applications of this principle in later studies of electronics.

It is difficult for the beginning student to understand why a parallel tuned tank presents maximum impedance at resonance. At resonance, $X_L = X_C$, and both have reactive values in parallel across the generator source. It would appear that these two reactive branches

Fig. 8-8. The parallel resonant circuit used as an example in the text.

would combine to form a low reactive path for the line current. However, the current flowing in the X_L branch is lagging the applied voltage and the current in the X_C branch is leading the applied voltage. The currents, therefore, are 180° out of phase and cancel each other. The total line current is the sum of the branch currents and therefore is zero, except for a small amount of current which will flow due to the resistance of the wire in the coil.

A typical problem will further clarify these circuit characteristics. Referring to Fig. 8-8, a 200 μh inductor and a 200 $\mu\mu$fd capacitor are connected in parallel across a generator source of 500 μv. The resistance R = 10 ohms represents the lumped resistance of the wire of the inductor. These same components were used in the study of the series resonant circuit and comparisons should be made.

The resonant frequency of this tuned circuit is:

$$f_o = \frac{159}{\sqrt{LC}} \text{ or } \frac{159}{\sqrt{200 \times 200}} = \frac{159}{200} = .8 \text{ mc}$$
$$\text{(approx.)}$$

(Note use of convenient formula when L is in μh and C is in $\mu\mu$f and f_o is in megacycles.)

At resonance:

$$X_L = 2\pi fL \quad \text{or} \quad 1000\,\Omega$$

$$X_C = \frac{1}{2\pi fC} \quad \text{or} \quad 1000\,\Omega$$

The voltage across both branches of the parallel circuit is the same as the applied voltage or 500 μ volts. The current, therefore, in the X_L branch is:

$$I_{X_L} = \frac{500 \mu \text{ v.}}{1000\,\Omega} \text{ or } \frac{500 \times 10^{-6}}{10^3} \text{ or}$$

500 x 10^{-9} amps or .5 μ amps.

The current in the X_C branch is,

$$I_{X_C} = \frac{500 \mu \text{ v.}}{1000\,\Omega} = .5 \mu \text{ amps.}$$

Since these two currents are 180° out of phase then,

$$I_{X_L} - I_{X_C} = .5 \mu a - .5 \mu a = 0$$

In this computation R has been neglected, because of its small value. Actually some current will flow as a result of R. For frequency above and below resistance, the performance of the circuit may be observed in Chart 8-2.

Note that the line current is the difference between the branch currents. This chart could be carried a step further to show the decreasing impedance due to frequencies

other than resonance, for

$$Z = \frac{E}{I}$$

and as I increases, Z must decrease.

Q OF TUNED CIRCUITS

The Q of the circuit is described as the relationship between the inductive reactance and the resistance in the circuit, or

$$Q \quad \frac{X_L}{R}$$

In a series tuned circuit, for example, if the inductive reactance is 1000 ohms at resonance, and the resistance of the wire of the coil is 10 ohms, the FIGURE OF MERIT Q would be:

$$Q = \frac{1000}{10} = 100$$

The Q of a circuit is an indication of the sharpness of the reject or accept characteristics of the circuit. It is a quality factor. In the series acceptor circuit, an increase in resistance reduces the maximum current at resonance. See Fig. 8-9. The Q may also

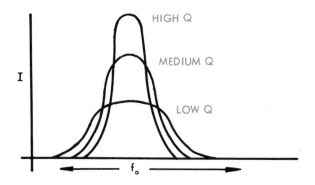

Fig. 8-9. As the Q of a circuit is lowered, the curve flattens out. Its selectivity decreases and its band pass increases.

be used to determine the rise in voltage across L or C at resonance, for:

$$E_{X_L} = E_{X_C} = Q \times E_S$$

In the example on page 122, the supply voltage was 500 μ v and the Q is 100. Therefore

Tuned Circuits

f kc	X_L ohms	X_C ohms	I_{X_L} μa	I_{X_C} μa	I_{Line} μa
200	250	4000	2.0	.125	1.875
400	500	2000	1.0	.25	1.75
600	750	1500	.66	.33	.33
800	1000	1000	.5	.5	0
1000	1250	800	.4	.625	.225
1200	1500	666	.33	.75	.42
1600	2000	500	.25	1.00	.75

Chart 8-2

the voltage rise across X_L or X_C at resonance is equal to,

$$E_{X_L} = E_{X_C} = 100 \times 500\mu v = 50,000\mu v$$

If the circuit had a lower Q, the magnified voltage would be considerably less. For example, if R were increased to 20 ohms, then the Q would equal 50 and the voltage rise would equal:

$$E_{X_L} = E_{X_C} = 50 \times 500 \mu v = 25,000 \mu v$$

High Q circuits are very useful in selective electronic circuits and typical Qs range from 50 to 250. The higher value of Q produces a greater response of the circuit at resonance. Also a high Q circuit will have increased selectivity. Selectivity is determined by bandwidth which is the band of frequencies above and below resonance, during which the circuit response does not fall below 70.7% (half power point) of the response at resonance.

The bandwidth of the tuned circuit may be found by the formula,

$$Bw = \frac{fo}{Q}$$

Continuing the previous problem, the

bandwidth equals:

$$Bw = \frac{800,000 \text{ c.p.s.}}{100} = 8000 \text{ c.p.s.}$$

Since 800 kc (the resonant frequency) is at the maximum response point, the bandwidth will extend 4000 cps below resonance to 4000 cps above resonance. The circuit may be considered, then, as passing all frequencies between 796 kc and 804 kc. Beyond either of these limits, the response will fall below the 70.7% value.

In the case of the parallel tuned circuit, the Q may be computed in like manner by using X_L at resonance and R which is the resistance of the coil L. The Q of a tank circuit may be used to determine the maximum impedance of the circuit at resonance for:

$$Z = Q \times X_L$$

where:

Z = impedance at resonance

$Q = \frac{X_L}{R}$ at resonance

X_L = reactance at resonance

In the example on page 125 the impedance at resonance would be:

$$Z = 100 \times 1,000 \text{ ohms} = 100,000 \text{ ohms}$$

Another case which should be mentioned, is when a resistance is shunt across or in parallel with a tank circuit. In Fig. 8-10 this circuit is shown. R_S is called a damping resistor, and effectively broadens the frequency response of the circuit, because this resistor will carry a part of the line current which cannot be cancelled at resonance. Shunt damping lowers the Q of the circuit and makes it less selective.

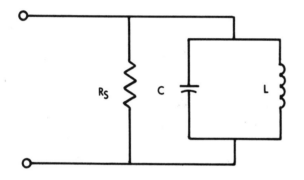

Fig. 8-10. The resistor R is a damping resistor and broadens the circuit response.

LOADING THE TANK CIRCUIT

The parallel tuned circuit is used to couple energy from one circuit to another. Coupling transformers, used in radio and television sets, employ the tuned circuit to transfer signals from one stage to another. The radio transmitter uses a coupling device to a tank circuit to feed energy to the antenna system.

If another coil is inductively coupled to the coil in the tank circuit, the varying magnetic field of the oscillating tank inductance will induce a current to flow in the coil. Fig. 8-11 shows the circuit of an intermediate frequency transformer used in a radio receiver.

Since both the primary and secondary of this transformer are tuned circuits, maximum transfer of radio frequency energy may be achieved, by carefully tuning the circuits to resonance. The intermediate frequency used in most radios is 455 kc. The IF transformer is tuned for maximum response at this frequency. A band pass of 5 kc above and below the center frequency is maintained so that signals between 450 kc and 460 kc may pass without attenuation. The adjustment of IF transformers is a part of radio servicing called ALIGNMENT.

FILTERING CIRCUITS

Inductance and capacitance have many useful applications in electronic circuitry. A circuit which is purposed to separate specified frequencies is known as a FILTER.

Filters may perform intended filtering action by separating the AC variations from a direct current. They may be designed to pass low frequencies and reject high frequency current, or reject low frequency and pass high frequency currents or either pass or reject specified bands of frequencies. A filter derives its name from its function and is named:

1. Low Pass Filter

12-C1

Fig. 8-11. An intermediate frequency transformer used to couple energy from one tube to another in a radio receiver. (J. W. Miller Co.)

2. High Pass Filter
3. Band Pass Filter
4. Band Reject Filter

The output of a rectifier circuit is a pulsating direct current. For most purposes

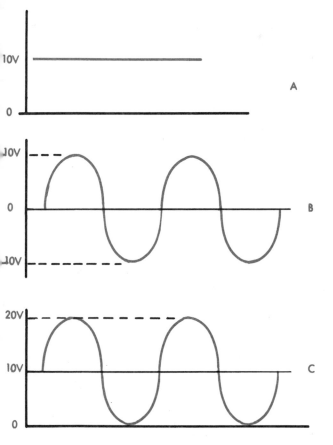

Fig. 8-12. A. A steady direct current. B. A 10 v peak alternating current. C. The combined DC and AC.

in electronics a pure direct current is needed with a low percentage of ripple. These filter circuits will be described in the section on power supplies.

In the study of filtering action these points should be reviewed:

1. A capacitor will block a direct current, but will pass an alternating current.

2. A conductor may carry a current which has both a DC component and an AC component.

Reference to Fig. 8-12A shows a graph representing a steady DC voltage of 10 volts and Fig. 8-12B represents an AC voltage with a peak value of 10 volts. The combination of these two voltages is shown in Fig. 8-12C. This wave represents the algebraic sum of the two waves. Particular notice should be given to the new axis of the AC voltage, which is now varying above and below the 10 volt DC level. Because the axis has been raised by the DC voltage, the AC voltage no longer reverses polarity and the current is a varying direct current. It varies in amplitude between 0 and 20 volts. When this varying direct current is connected to a circuit, such as shown in Fig. 8-13, the capacitor C immediately charges up to the average DC level of voltage, which in this case would equal 10 volts. When the incoming voltage rises to 20 volts, current flows through R to charge

Fig. 8-13. The AC generator and DC source are connected in series to the RC circuit.

capacitor C. In the next half cycle the incoming voltage drops to zero, and capacitor C discharges to zero through R.

IMPORTANT: A voltage appears across R due to the charge and discharge of C, so the output of this circuit, taken from across R, represents only the AC component of the incoming signal voltage. See Fig. 8-14. The DC component is blocked by capacitor C. There is very little phase shift between the input and output waves, because the value of R is selected as ten times or more the value of the reactance of C at the frequency of the input voltage. When this ratio of resistance

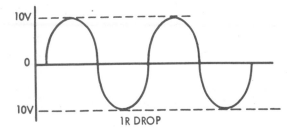

Fig. 8-14. *The voltage across R is the result of the charge-discharge current and represents the AC component of the signal.*

to reactance is maintained, the phase shift is negligible.

EXPERIMENT: Select a 1 mfd. capacitor from your stock of parts and connect circuit as in Fig. 8-15. As 60 cps AC will be used

EXPERIMENT

Fig. 8-15. *This experiment shows the blocking of the DC signal component and the passing of the AC component.*

in this experiment, the reactance of C should be computed:

$$X_C = \frac{.16}{fC} \text{ or } \frac{.16}{60 \times 1 \times 10^{-6}} = .0026 \times 10^6$$

or 2600 ohms

Now R should equal 10 times X_C or 10 x 2600 ohms or 26,000 ohms. A 25,000 ohm resistor will be close enough for this experiment. Connect the 6.3 volts (rms) terminals of a power supply in series with the 10 volt DC supply and connect to the circuit. Measurements with DC voltmeter across C should read 10 volts. An AC meter across the same points should read zero. An AC meter across R should read 6.3 volts and a DC meter would read zero across R.

CONCLUSIONS: The DC component of the incoming signal appears across C. The AC component appears across R. This is a very important principle, and will be discussed in more detail in later chapters when it is necessary to couple a signal voltage (AC voltage) from one radio tube or stage to another. It will be called RC Coupling.

BYPASSING

In certain applications it is desirable to by-pass an AC signal or voltage around a resistance, so that the voltage drop across the resistor will be the result of only the DC component of the signal voltage. These circuits are shown in Fig. 8-16A and 16B. To aid in understanding of the by-pass capacitor, Fig. 16A consists of two resistors of 1500 ohms connected to a source voltage of 10 volts DC. The total resistance is equal to $R_1 + R_2$ or 1500 ohms + 1500 ohms = 3000 ohms, and the current in the circuit;

$$I = \frac{E}{R} \text{ or } \frac{10 \text{ v}}{3000 \, \Omega} = .0033 \text{ amps or 3.3 ma.}$$

The voltage drop across R_1 = I x R or .0033 x 1500 = 5 v and the voltage drop across R_2 = I x R or .0033 x 1500 = 5 v.

When a 10 volt AC source is now connected, an AC voltage would appear across both resistors, but it is desired to bypass this AC component around R_2. To accomplish this, a capacitor of such a value as to have a low reactance to the AC voltage is connected in parallel with R_2. If the reactance of C is one-tenth of resistance R, the greater part of the varying current will flow through C and not through R. For further clarification, assume values as indicated in Fig. 8-16B. C is chosen to have a reactance of 150 ohms to the frequency of the alternating current. This is one-tenth the value of R_2. For all practical purposes the impedance of CR_2 in parallel

Fig. 8-16. A. A DC voltage produces equal drops across R_1 and R_2. B. The voltage drop across R_2 is held constant by bypassing the AC component.

can be considered as 150 ohms, and the voltage distribution around the circuit may be measured or computed.

Total resistance equals $R_1 + R_2X_C = 1650$ ohms. And R_2C represents one eleventh of the total resistance to alternating current. As voltage drop is a function of resistance, then ten-elevenths of the voltage appears across R_1 and only one-eleventh across R_2C in parallel. The applied AC voltage is 10 volts so;

$$E_{R_1} = 9.1 \text{ v. and } E_{R_2} = .9 \text{ v.}$$

If a 10 v DC voltage is connected in series with the 10 v AC voltage for the combined input voltage, the DC voltage divides equally between R_1 and R_2 with 5 volts each. C is an

open circuit for a direct current. The AC voltage divides according to the above mentioned ratio, and most of this voltage appears across R_1. The voltage across R_2 remains relatively constant due to the by-pass capacitor action. In both audio and radio frequency circuits many applications are made of bypass capacitors. Summarizing, a capacitor may be selected which will form a low reactance path around a resistor or to ground for currents of selected frequencies.

LOW-PASS FILTERS

It is sometimes desirable to construct a filter which will pass low frequencies, yet attenuate high frequency currents. This filter is called a LOW-PASS FILTER. The circuit configuration always places a resistance or an inductor in series with the incoming signal voltage, and a capacitor in shunt or across the line, as in Fig. 8-17. As the frequency is increased, the reactance of L increases so that a larger amount of the voltage appears across L. Also as the frequency increases, the reactance of C will decrease, thus providing a bypass for the higher frequency currents around the load resistance R. In

Fig. 8-17. A low-pass filter circuit.

both respects the higher frequencies appear in small amounts across the load, and low frequencies develop higher voltages across the load. To summarize: Low frequencies pass; high frequencies are rejected.

HIGH-PASS FILTER

The opposite to the low-pass filter is the HIGH-PASS FILTER, which passes selected high frequency currents, and rejects the low frequency currents. The circuit configuration always places a capacitor in series with the incoming signal voltage, and an inductance shunt across the line as in Fig. 8-18. As the frequency increases, X_L increases, and a higher voltage is developed across L and R in parallel. As frequency increases X_C decreases providing a low reactance path for high frequency signals. Low frequencies are

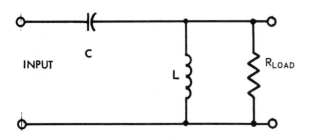

Fig. 8-18. The high-pass filter circuit.

shunted or bypassed around the load R by the low reactance of L at low frequencies.

To improve the filtering action of both low and high pass filters, frequently two or more sections are connected together. They are named as suggested by the circuit configuration. In Fig. 8-19, the schematic draw-

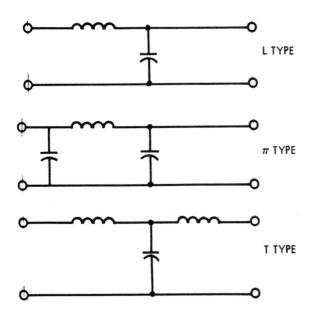

Fig. 8-19. Filter circuits may be named by the circuit configuration.

ings and the names of several types of filters are given.

TUNED CIRCUIT FILTERS

Earlier in this chapter the series and parallel resonant circuits were described as accept or reject circuits respectively. These tuned circuits may be used conveniently and effectively as filters, because of their abilities to give maximum response at their tuned resonant frequency. In Fig. 8-20, the series resonant circuit is used as a band pass filter

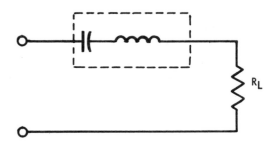

Fig. 8-20. The series tuned circuit used as a BAND PASS filter.

and accepts only currents near its resonant frequency. In Fig. 8-21 the series resonant circuit is shunted across or parallel to the load. This provides a low impedance path, around or bypassing the load, for currents

Fig. 8-21. The series tuned circuit arranged as a BAND REJECT filter.

at resonant frequencies. In this case the filter would respond as a band reject filter.

The circuits using the parallel tuned circuit appear in Fig. 8-22. Its effect is the opposite to the series tuned circuit. When the tank circuit is in series with the incoming

BAND REJECT

A

BAND PASS

B

Fig. 8-22. A. The parallel tuned circuit as a Band Reject filter. B. The parallel tuned circuit as a BAND PASS filter.

currents, it provides maximum impedance or rejects the frequencies at its resonant frequency. When the tank circuit is shunt across the load, it causes the maximum response across the load at resonance. Frequencies other than resonance are bypassed because of the decreased impedance of the shunt tuned-tank circuit. Combinations of both series and parallel tuned circuits may be used to provide sharper cut-off and greater attenuation. A typical high-pass filter to remove

Fig. 8-23. A High Pass Filter used to remove interference to the television by other radio services.

interference from your TV is illustrated in Fig. 8-23. This filter attenuates all signals below Channel 2, yet all TV channels are passed through to the receiver.

THE NOMOGRAPH

The nomograph or alignment chart illustrated in Fig. 8-24 provides a rapid and convenient method of solving problems involving X_L, X_C and resonance. These examples will permit you to use and understand this chart.

1. What is the reactance of a .01 μf capacitor at 10 kc? Using upper chart, place a ruler or straight edge on 10 kc on the frequency scale and .01 on the capacitance scale. The rule crosses the reactance scale at 1590 ohms.

2. What is the reactance of an 8 henry choke coil at 60 cps? Use lower chart. Place rule on 60 cps and 8 h and read 3014 ohms.

3. What is the resonant frequency of a tuned circuit when C = 250 $\mu\mu$f and L = 200 mh? Use upper chart. Place rule on 200 mh and 250 $\mu\mu$f and read 22.5 kc on frequency scale.

REACTANCE—FREQUENCY CHART

A straight edge across known values in any two columns will locate the corresponding values in the other two columns. For example, take an inductance of 1 Henry at 50 cycles. A straight edge across these points will intersect the reactance line at 310 ohms, and the capacity line at 10 mfd. indicating the capacity required for resonance.

Fig. 8-24. Nomograph or alignment chart.

DISCUSSION

1. How can a series resonant circuit develop voltages higher than the applied voltage?
2. Explain fly-wheel action and relate it to frequency.
3. A simplified formula for resonant frequency is $f_o = \dfrac{159}{\sqrt{LC}}$, when f is in megacycles, L is in μh and C is in $\mu\mu$f. Explain mathematically the derivation of this formula from $f_o = \dfrac{1}{2\pi\sqrt{LC}}$
4. Why does the "dip" in the line current of a parallel LC circuit indicate resonance?
5. What is the relationship between the Q and the selectivity of a tuned circuit?

TEST YOUR KNOWLEDGE

1. A series resonant circuit is sometimes called an _____ circuit.
2. The formula for resonance is f_o = _____ .
3. At resonance the impedance of the series LC circuit is _____ · _____ .
4. Compute the resonant frequency of the following circuits.

   L = 100 μh   C = 250 $\mu\mu$f f_o =

   L = 200 μh   C = 130 $\mu\mu$f f_o =

   L =   8 h   C =   1 μf f_o =

5. In a series resonant circuit E_R = _____ and the vector sum of E_L, E_C, and E_R = _____ .
6. Refer to Chart 8-1. At frequencies above resonance the circuit appears _____ . (inductive or capacitive)
   What is the Q of this circuit? _____ .
   Why does circuit current decrease above or below resonance?
7. Frequency is measured in _____ .
8. A parallel resonant circuit is sometimes called a _____ circuit.
9. In reference to a parallel LC circuit, at resonance,
   Line current is _____ . (minimum or maximum)
   Z is _____ .
10. Refer to Chart 8-2.
    At frequencies above resonance the circuit appears _____ . (inductive or capacitive)
    Why does current increase above and below resonance?
11. What is the effect of a damping resistor across a parallel tuned circuit.
12. Name four general types of filters.
13. What is the purpose of a by-pass capacitor?
14. Distinguish between a high-pass and a low-pass filter.

Chapter 9

ELECTRIC MOTORS

A philosopher once characterized electricity as the "invisible wonder of the world." He was correct in many respects, for scientists have yet to see electricity. However, the many useful effects of electricity have been discovered and harnessed, to make our lives richer and more pleasant. The conversion of electrical power into mechanical power represents one of the most useful and labor saving discoveries in electrical technology. Such a device is the now familiar electric motor. Motors are used to turn the wheels of industry. Motors are used in the home for refrigeration, air conditioning, mixing foods, cleaning rugs and on a myriad of other labor saving appliances. Motors are used on the farm for turning grinders, mixers, pumps and machinery. In the school shop the motor powers the bench saw, the lathe and numerous wood and metal machines. The motor is man's willing and able servant.

PRINCIPLES OF MOTOR OPERATION

The operation of a motor depends upon the interaction of magnetic fields. A review of the Laws of Magnetism will reveal that:

LIKE POLES REPEL EACH OTHER
UNLIKE POLES ATTRACT EACH OTHER

or

A NORTH POLE REPELS A NORTH POLE
A SOUTH POLE REPELS A SOUTH POLE

but

A NORTH POLE ATTRACTS A SOUTH POLE

To understand the theory of the simple DC motor refer to the series of drawings, Figures 1 to 9 inclusive, and their descriptive captions.

Fig. 9-1. A magnetic field exists between the North and South poles of a permanent magnet.

Fig. 9-2. An electromagnet is wound on an iron core and the core is placed on a shaft so it can rotate. This assembly is called the ARMATURE.

Fig. 9-3. The armature is placed in the permanent magnetic field.

In order to make the motor more powerful, the permanent field magnets may be replaced by electromagnets called FIELD

Fig. 9-4. The ends of the armature coil are connected to semi-circular sections of metal called the COMMUTATOR.

Brushes contact the rotating commutator sections and provide a means of energizing the armature coils from an external power source. NOTE: The polarity of the armature electromagnets depends upon the direction of current flow through the coil. Review Chapter 4.

A battery is connected to the brushes and current flows into Brush A to Commutator section A, through the coil to section B and back to the battery through brush B, completing the circuit. The armature coil is magnetized as indicated on drawing.

Fig. 9-5. The north pole of the armature is repelled by the north pole of the field magnet and the south pole of the armature is repelled by the south pole of the field magnet. The armature turns one quarter revolution or 90 deg.

Fig. 9-6. The north pole of the armature is attracted by the south pole of the field magnet and the south pole of the armature is attracted by the north pole of the field. The armature turns another quarter turn. It has now turned one-half revolution.

Fig. 9-7. As the commutator sections have turned with the armature, section B now contacts brush A and section A now contacts brush B. The current now flows into section B and out section A. The current has been reversed in the armature due to the commutator switching action. This reversal of current changes the polarity of the armature, so that unlike poles are next to each other.

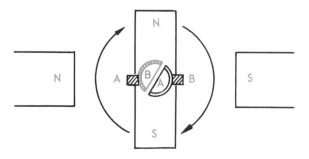

Fig. 9-8. Like poles repel each other and the armature turns another quarter turn.

Fig. 9-10. Sketches and schematic diagrams of: (A) Shunt wound motor. (B) Series wound motor. (C) Independently excited field motor.

Fig. 9-9. Unlike poles attract each other and the armature turns the last quarter turn, completing one revolution. The commutator and brushes are now lined up in their original positions, which causes the current to reverse in the armature again. The armature continues to rotate by repulsion and attraction. The current is reversed at each one-half revolution by the commutator.

A demonstration motor may now be constructed using the laboratory equipment, as illustrated in Fig. 9-11. Connect the motor as a series motor, then as a shunt motor, and compare the speed and power.

Commercially, motors are manufactured in a slightly different manner and obtain their rotational force by the interaction of the magnetic field around a current carrying conductor and the fixed magnetic field. A conductor carrying a current will have a magnetic field around it and the direction of the field depends upon the direction of the current. When this conductor is placed in a

WINDINGS. These field windings may have an independent source of voltage connected to them, or they may be connected in series or parallel with the armature windings, to a single voltage source. All three types are diagrammed in Fig. 9-10.

Fig. 9-11. The electrodemonstrator may be set up to operate as a series or shunt motor.

fixed magnetic field, the interaction between the two fields will cause motion.

See Figures 9-12 to 9-16 inclusive.

Fig. 9-12. A magnetic field exists between the poles of a permanent magnet. The arrows indicate the direction of field.

Fig. 9-13. A current carrying conductor has a magnetic field, its direction depends upon direction of current. USE LEFT HAND RULE, page 59, Chapter 4.

Fig. 9-14. In this illustration the field around the conductor reinforces the permanent field above the conductor, but opposes the permanent field below the conductor. The conductor will move toward the weakened field as indicated by the arrows.

Fig. 9-15. The current has been reversed in the conductor causing the conductor field to reverse. Now the field is reinforced below the conductor and weakened above the conductor. The conductor will move upward as indicated by arrow.

Fig. 9-16. The single conductor is replaced by a coil of conductors wound in the slots of an armature core. Notice how the interaction of the two fields will produce rotation. Coil side A moves up and coil side B moves down. The rotation is clockwise.

The armature coils are connected to commutator sections as in the experimental motor and the theory of operation is similar. A practical motor would have several armature coils wound in separate slots around the core. Each coil would have its respective commutator sections. Also, the number of field poles may be increased to give the motor greater power. A four pole motor is sketched in Fig. 9-17. The current divides into four parts and the current flowing in windings under each field pole produces rotation and increases the turning power or TORQUE of the motor.

COUNTER EMF

In the study of generator action in Chapter 5, it was explained that if a conductor cut through a magnetic field, voltage would be induced in the moving conductor. Although a motor is intended to convert electrical energy into mechanical energy, it also becomes a

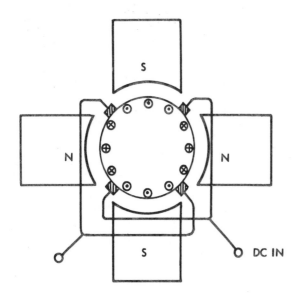

Fig. 9-17. The torque of the motor is increased by adding armature coils and field coils.

generator when the armature begins to rotate. The induced electromotive force opposes the applied EMF, and is called COUNTER EMF as a result of the GENERATOR ACTION of the motor. The magnitude of the counter EMF is directly proportional to the speed of rotation and the field strength. This may be represented mathematically by:

Counter EMF = Speed x Field Strength x K

K equals other constants in any motor such as the number of windings. The actual effective voltage then applied to the windings

in the armature must equal, $E_{source} - E_{counter} = E_{armature}$. The current flowing in the armature windings at any given instant may be found by Ohm's Law, when the ohmic resistance of the windings is known:

$$I_{armature} = \frac{E_{armature}}{R_{armature}}$$

COMMUTATION AND INTERPOLES

As the motor armature rotates, the current in the armature windings is periodically reversed due to commutator action. Due to the self inductance of the windings, the current does not immediately reverse. This results in sparking at the commutator brushes. Such arcing may be prevented by moving the brushes slightly against the direction of rotation and taking advantage of the counter EMF induced by the previous pole. This counter EMF would oppose the self-induction caused by the decreasing current in the coil, thus eliminating the sparking. This is not a satisfactory method, because, as the load is varied on the motor, it would be necessary to manually change the position of the brushes.

Larger motors depend upon INTERPOLES or COMMUTATING POLES to reduce the sparking as a result of commutation. An interpole is another smaller field pole with the same polarity, following the main field pole in the direction of rotation. The counter EMF developed as the armature passes the interpole overcomes the EMF caused by self-induction in the armature windings. The windings of the interpole are connected in series with the armature and carry the armature current. As a result, the interpole field strength varies as the load varies, and provides automatic control of commutator sparking. For a sketch of a motor with interpoles see Fig. 9-18.

SPEED REGULATION

Various motors are designed for special purposes. Some develop full power under load, whereas others must be brought up to speed before the load is applied. When the speed is determined for a motor on the job, it is desirable to have the motor maintain that speed under varying load conditions. A comparison of the speed under no-load, to the speed at full-load expressed as a per-

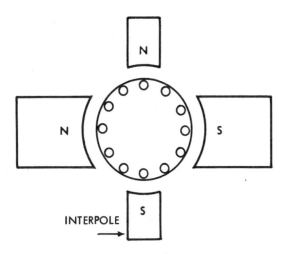

Fig. 9-18. Interpoles prevent "sparking" at the commutator.

centage of the full-load speed, is called the Percent of SPEED REGULATION. Thus:

Percent Speed Regulation =

$$\frac{\text{Speed no-load - Speed full-load}}{\text{Speed full-load}} \times 100$$

A low percent speed regulation would indicate that the motor would operate at a rather constant speed regardless of load applied.

THE SHUNT DC MOTOR

The shunt motor may be identified as having the field windings shunt across or in parallel to the armature. The schematic drawing of this motor may be seen in Fig. 9-19. The shunt motor is generally referred to as a constant speed motor. It finds applications in driving machine tools, or other machines requiring a relatively constant speed under varying loads.

In the shunt motor, both the field and the armature are connected across the power line. Under no-load conditions the counter EMF is almost equal to the line voltage, so very little armature current flows and very little torque is developed. When a load is

applied and the armature decreases its speed, the counter EMF also decreases, which increases the armature current and the torque. When the torque matches the load, the motor remains at constant speed. This action may be summarized as,

AT NO-LOAD

High counter EMF
Low armature current
Low torque

AT FULL-LOAD

Decreased counter EMF
Increased armature current
Increased torque

You should realize that the total current, used by this motor, is the sum of the field

Fig. 9-19. Schematic of a shunt motor.

and armature currents and the input power may be computed by Watt's Law as:

Power = Applied E x Total Current

This, however, is not the output power, because the motor is not one hundred percent efficient.

THE SERIES DC MOTOR

In the series wound motor the field windings are connected in series with the armature windings. A diagram of this motor is given in Fig. 9-20. It is apparent that all the line current must flow through both the field and armature windings. Under loaded conditions the counter EMF opposes the line voltage and limits the current to a safe value. If the load were suddenly removed, the armature would speed up and develop a higher CEMF (counter EMF). This reduces the current flowing through the field and reduces the field strength which causes the motor to increase its speed, because:

$$\text{Speed} = \frac{\text{c.e.m.f.}}{\text{Field Strength x K}}$$

This action is cumulative, and the series motor would develop a speed which would cause the motor to literally fly-apart, due to centrifugal force. A series motor is never operated without a load. It is usually directly connected to a machine or through gears. It is not safe to use a belt from motor to machine. If the belt should break or slip off, the motor would "run wild" and destroy itself.

Fig. 9-20. Schematic of a series motor.

One of the main advantages of the series motor is its ability to develop a high torque under load. Under load conditions, the armature speed is low and the CEMF is low which results in a high armature current and increased torque. Series motors have heavy armature windings to carry these high currents. As the motor increases in speed and the CEMF builds up, the line current decreases and the torque decreases. Series motors are used on electric trains, cranes and hoists, and other traction equipment.

COMPOUND DC MOTORS

The compound motor has both the series and the shunt field. The intention of the inventor, in this case, was to combine the desirable characteristics of each type of motor. The schematic drawings of this motor are shown in Fig. 9-21. As one might expect, the series winding which must also carry the armature current consists of several turns of heavy wire; the shunt field winding consists of many turns of finer wire. Both windings are wound on the same field poles.

Fig. 9-21. Schematic of a compound motor.

Two methods may be used to connect these windings. If the magnetic field on the series winding aids or reinforces the magnetic field of the shunt winding, the motor is said to be a CUMULATIVE COMPOUND motor. If the two windings are so connected as to oppose each other magnetically, the motor is a DIFFERENTIAL COMPOUND MOTOR. A detailed study of compound motors is beyond the scope of this text; however, the characteristics of different types as described here should be noted.

The differential compound motor behaves in most respects like the shunt motor. The starting torque is low, and it has good speed regulation if loads do not vary too severely. However, it is not widely accepted.

The cumulative compound motor develops high starting torque. It is used where heavy loads are applied and some variance in speeds can be tolerated. The load may be safely removed from this motor.

MOTOR STARTING CIRCUITS

The armature resistance in most motors is quite low, and when the motor is stopped or at low speed, very little CEMF is developed to oppose the line voltage. Consequently dangerously high currents will flow. In order to protect the motor, until it builds up its speed and CEMF, a current limiting resistor may be placed in series with the armature to hold the current at a safe value. A simplified motor starting circuit is drawn in Fig. 9-22. The resistance is variable. Starting from a dead stop, maximum resistance is inserted in the armature circuit. As the speed builds up the resistance may

VARIABLE
STARTING RESISTANCE

Fig. 9-22. Simplified motor starting circuit.

gradually be decreased until the motor reaches full speed. The resistance may then be removed. An application of Ohm's Law will give meaning to this explanation. Assuming the armature resistance is .1 ohm and the applied voltage 100 volts, then the initial armature current would be:

$$I_{armature} = \frac{100 \text{ v.}}{.1} \text{ or } 1000 \text{ amps.}$$

This current would burn the insulation off from the wires and the motor would be destroyed. When the motor is up to speed and CEMF has developed, then the voltage across the armature is equal to:

$$E_{Line} - CEMF = E_{Armature}$$

If the motor develops a CEMF of 95 volts as it approaches full speed, the armature current would be:

$$I_{armature} = \frac{100 \text{ v.} - 95 \text{ v.}}{.1} \text{ or } 50 \text{ amps.}$$

This is a safe current for this motor armature to carry. Therefore, it is necessary to

start the motor with the full series resistance in the armature circuit and gradually decrease the resistance until the motor can limit the current by its own CEMF.

The adjustment of starting resistance may be done manually by a lever which decreases the resistance step-by-step until the motor reaches full speed. This circuit is diagramed in Fig. 9-23. In step one the maximum resistance is in series and with each successive step the resistance is decreased. At step 4, the lever arm is held magnetically by the holding coil which is also in series with the circuit. If the line voltage should fail, the lever arm would snap back to "off" position and the motor would need to be restarted. This is a protective device. The operator must use his judgment when starting the motor. He should not move the lever

HAND STARTER FOR SERIES MOTOR

Fig. 9-23. Circuit of a typical step motor starter.

to the next lower resistance position until the motor has gained sufficient speed.

Automatic starters remove the human element of error and also permit remote starting of the motor. Several devices are used.

Fig. 9-24 shows one type of starting switch. When line switch S is closed, voltage is applied to the field which is across the line, and to the armature through R_1, R_2 and R_3 in series with the armature. CONTACTORS C_1, C_2 and C_3 are a special type which will not close until the current has <u>decreased</u> to a predetermined value. The initial surge of current in the armature circuit flows through series coil of C_1 which holds it open. As the motor increases speed and the armature current decreases, C_1 contactor closes and cuts R_1 out of the circuit.

your shop may be equipped with starting boxes containing RED and BLACK push buttons marked STOP and START. A push button starter is illustrated in Fig. 9-25. The circuit diagram is in Fig. 9-26. This

Fig. 9-24. Circuit for an automatic motor starter.

Similar action occurs in C_2 and C_3. When the motor reaches full speed, all contactors will be closed. The protective resistance is no longer needed.

Before leaving motor starters, mention should be made of the PUSH BUTTON START-ER. This is a familiar device. The motors in

starter is a relay switch which operates on only a momentary pulse of current. Follow the action. When the black button is pushed, the contacts close and energize the relay coil which closes contacts S. The push button does not have to be held down, be-

Fig. 9-26. Circuit of push-button control showing how relay is "locked out."

Fig. 9-25. Push Button motor control.

cause once the relay switch is closed, it remains closed or "locked out." The closed switch S completes the circuit to the motor or device. The contacts of button "STOP" or RED are normally closed. To stop the motor, a momentary push on the RED button opens the circuit to the relay, and allows contacts S to open. For larger motors, the push button starter may be used to activate other starting devices.

SPEED CONTROL

The speed of a DC motor may be controlled by varying the field strength by

Fig. 9-27. Schematic showing speed control of a DC motor.

means of a variable resistor in series with the field windings. This type of circuit is diagrammed in Fig. 9-27. Reviewing our earlier discussion on motor principles, the equation:

$$CEMF = Speed \times FS \times K$$

where:

CEMF = Counter-electromotive force

Speed = RPM

FS = Field strength or magnetic flux Φ

K = constants

then:

$$CEMF = RPM \times \Phi \times K$$

or

$$RPM = \frac{CEMF}{\Phi \times K}$$

This equation tells us that the speed of a motor varies directly with the counter EMF and inversely with the field strength.

Using the simple two pole motor assembled as an earlier experiment, connect a 100 ohm variable resistor in series with the field coils. Follow the photograph in Fig. 9-28. Start the motor by closing the switch. Vary its speed by increasing and decreasing the field resistance.

THE UNIVERSAL MOTOR

In the discussion of motor principles, the Laws of Magnetism were used to explain the operation of the DC motor. Will a DC motor operate on alternating current? Yes, to a limited extent. With an alternating current the poles of both the field and armature windings would be periodically reversing. However, two north poles repel each other as well as two south poles, so the motor

Fig. 9-28. The electrodemonstrator kit set up as a variable speed DC shunt motor.

action continues in the DC motor when AC is applied. For best results the series motor should be used. When the shunt motor is connected to AC, the inductance of the field windings will cause a phase displacement, and the motor action will be impaired. Experimentally, connect the laboratory con-

Fig. 9-29. A fractional horsepower induction motor. Notice the stator coils and rotor. (Delco Products, General Motors Corp.)

structed DC motor as a series motor, and apply about 6 to 8 volts AC to its terminals.

When this universal type motor is used commercially, the series wound type is preferred. These motors are not used for heavy duty purposes because of excessive sparking at the brushes. Commercial types are used for small fans, drills, and grinders.

INDUCTION MOTORS

One special class of motor, especially designed to operate on alternating current, is the INDUCTION MOTOR. The induction motor is constructed with the usual field poles and windings. Because the field poles and windings remain stationary, they are called the STATOR. Refer to Fig. 9-29. Since an alternating current is connected to these field coils, the polarity of the coils will change periodically according to the frequency of the current. Consider these windings as the primary of a transformer. If another coil of wire is closely coupled to this primary, a current will be induced to flow in it. (Review Chapter 6.) According to Lenz's Law, the induced current will produce a field polarity which is opposite to the field which causes it, namely, the primary or stator windings. Therefore, there is an attractive force between the two coils. In the induction motor these secondary coils are mounted in slots in a laminated armature. The armature is called the ROTOR. See Fig. 9-30. Now this motor will not start rotation, it will only hum. If it is manually started, then it will continue rotation at a speed of 3600 rpm if used on 60 cps AC. The 3600 is derived from 60 x 60 = 3600 or the number of cycles per minute. A little thought on this motor action will disclose that the alternations of the

Motors

AC are performing a function similar to the commutator in a DC motor. It is periodically reversing the current and polarity.

Experimentally, replace the armature on the laboratory constructed motor with the AC rotor. See Fig. 9-31. Connect the field windings to a 6 volt source of AC. The motor will

Fig. 9-30. The rotor and centrifugal switch assembly in an induction motor. (Delco Products, General Motors Corp.)

not start by itself. Twirl the rotor with your fingers and notice that the motor continues to rotate. It appears that some method is needed to start the induction motor.

THREE PHASE INDUCTION MOTOR

A three phase alternating current repre-

sents three separate currents, 120 deg. out of phase with each other. This type of AC is useful in producing a rotating magnetic field in the stator. If the field rotates, then it will cause the rotor to follow the field around. A partial diagram of a stator with three poles is drawn in Fig. 9-32. Phase 1 current is connected to Pole A. Phase 2 is connected to Pole B. Phase 3 is connected to Pole C. Notice

Fig. 9-32. One phase of the three-phase current is connected to each of the respective stator coils.

Fig. 9-31. The electrodemonstrator set up as an AC motor.

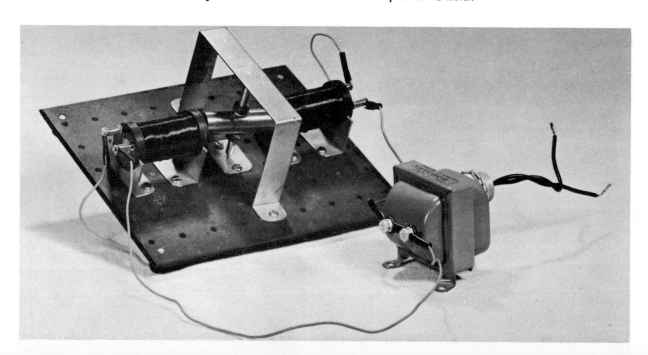

the sine waves showing the phase relationship on each line. When phase 1 rises to maximum, the rotor is attracted to Pole A. As phase 1 starts to decrease, phase 2 rises to maximum and attracts the rotor to Pole B. As phase 2 starts to decrease, phase 3 rises to maximum and attracts the rotor to Pole C. Starting with Pole A and phase 1 again, the field rotates around the stator and attracts the rotor with it. The phase relationship between currents is shown in Fig. 9-33. The rotor consists of a laminated iron cylinder with heavy closed

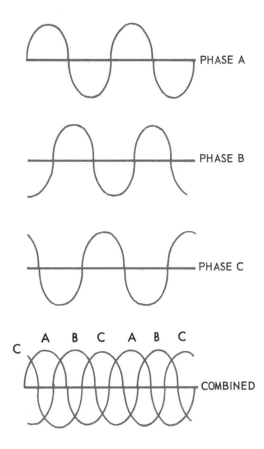

Fig. 9-33. The phase relationship between currents in a three-phase power source.

loops of copper wire imbedded in slots around the surface. Because the rotor appears like a cage, it is called a SQUIRREL CAGE rotor.

A polyphase motor is illustrated in Fig. 9-34. The rotor cannot follow the rotating field exactly. If both were in step, the rotor would not cut-across any magnetic lines of force. No current would be induced in the rotor coils. A certain amount of SLIP exists between the rotating field and the rotor. Generally this is about 4 to 5 per cent causing the rotor to turn at 1720 rpm when the field rotates at 1800 rpm. As the motor is loaded, the slippage increases and heavier currents are induced in the rotor.

SINGLE PHASE INDUCTION MOTORS

In shops and industry, three phase electricity is available for starting the large induction motors. At home, such currents are not readily available, so other means must be provided for starting the induction motor. If a means could be provided to divide a single phase current into a polyphase current, the starting problem would be solved. This is called SPLITTING PHASES. Two methods are commonly used to produce the SPLIT PHASE. In Chapter 6, it was learned that an inductance causes the current to lag in the circuit. If the single phase current is caused to flow through two parallel paths that contain unequal amounts of inductance, then one current will lag behind the other and a phase displacement will exist between them. In effect, a two phase

Fig. 9-34. A polyphase motor, (cut-away view). (Delco Products, General Motors Corp.)

current has been made of a single phase current. The many turns of wire which make up the field windings of the induction motor are excellent inductances and may be used for the purpose of phase splitting. A schematic diagram of a split phase motor is shown in Fig. 9-35. The STARTING windings consist of many turns of relatively fine wire and the RUNNING windings have many turns of heavier wire. The windings are placed in slots around the inside of the stator. When electricity is applied to the motor terminals, cur-

Fig. 9-35. Schematic diagram of a split-phase motor, showing starting windings.

rent flows in both windings because they are in parallel. The main winding has many turns of wire and high inductance which causes the current to lag almost 90 deg. The starter windings of fine wire have considerably less inductance, and the current does not lag by as great an angle. The phase displacement creates a rotating field similar to the three phase motor and the rotor starts to run. When the motor reaches speed, a centrifugal switch opens the starter winding circuit and the motor runs as a single phase induction motor. The fine wire in the starting winding will not stand continuous operation and is cut out of the circuit after it has performed its function of starting.

Fig. 9-36. Diagram of a capacitor-start split-phase motor.

The second method of phase splitting involves the use of a capacitor. Review Chapter 7. Capacitance causes the current to lead the applied voltage. If a capacitor is connected in series with the starting winding, a much larger phase displacement can be created. The capacitor is switched out of the circuit when the motor approaches full speed. Refer to Diagram, Fig. 9-36. This motor is known as a CAPACITOR-START induction motor. These motors are useful for many jobs around the shop and home. They maintain a reasonably constant speed under varying loads. They do not develop a strong starting torque when compared to the three phase squirrel cage motor. A capacitor-start motor is shown in Fig. 9-29. Note starting capacitor mounted on top.

REPULSION INDUCTION MOTOR

Another type of motor, strongly resembling the DC motor with commutator and brushes, is the replusion-start motor. The major difference is that the brushes are connected together, rather than to the source of power. The brushes are so arranged that only selected coils of the armature are closed or complete circuits at a given time. The currents induced by transformer action in the rotor windings are displaced by the shorting brushes and poles are created which oppose the stator poles. Rotation is started by repulsion. When the motor reaches about 75% of its speed, a centrifugal shorting ring "shorts out" all the commutator sections, and the motor runs as an induction motor. The repulsion induction motor has high starting torque, but does not readily come up to speed under load. It is being replaced by the cheaper capacitor - start motor.

THE SHADED POLE MOTOR

A simple two pole motor involving an unusual method of starting rotation is sketched in Fig. 9-37. The rotor is the typical squirrel cage type and the stator resembles the usual DC motor, except that a slot is cut in the face of each pole and a single turn of heavy wire is wound in the slot. This is called SHADING THE POLE. The single

SHADED TWO POLE MOTOR

Fig. 9-37. Sketch of a shaded-pole motor.

turn of wire is the SHADING COIL. The action of the shading coil may be followed with reference to Fig. 9-38. As the current rises in the first quarter cycle of the AC wave, a magnetic field is produced in the field winding. However, the expanding magnetic field cuts across the shading coil which induces a current and polarity which opposes that of the field coil. This tends to subtract from

SHADED POLE ACTION

LINES SHOW DENSITY OF MOVING FIELD

Fig. 9-38. The magnetic field moves from left to right as the result of shading.

and weaken the total field on the side of the shading coil. At the top of the AC wave very little change in current is taking place so the total magnetic field becomes equalized across the face of the pole. When the current starts to decrease in the next quarter cycle, the induced current in the shading coil is of such a polarity as to resist the decreasing current. So the pole has a strong magnetic field on the right side. Notice that during this half cycle, the magnetic field has moved from left to right. This movement of the field causes the rotor to start rotation. The starting torque of a motor of this type is relatively small, but the motor has many applications on such items as small fans and electric clocks.

The studies of this chapter have been intended to give an exploratory experience in types of motors and their operation. Advanced design and theory of motors is detailed and complex and is beyond the scope of this text. The student is encouraged to continue his studies from one of the selected advanced texts suggested in the Bibliography.

FOR DISCUSSION

1. Why does a motor increase in speed when its field strength is decreased?
2. Why does a motor get hot when overloaded?
3. If the load is removed from a series motor, it will destroy itself by centrifugal force. Explain.
4. Why are motor starters necessary on heavy duty motors?
5. Will your experimental DC motor run on 6 volts AC? Explain.
6. Compare an induction motor to a transformer.

TEST YOUR KNOWLEDGE

1. What is the purpose of the commutator in the DC motor?
2. A motor is a device which changes _____ energy into _____ energy.
3. Draw diagrams of the series motor and the shunt motor.
4. Draw a diagram and explain the motion of a current carrying conductor in a fixed magnetic field.
5. What is generator action in a motor?
6. What determines the current used by the motor?
7. Why are interpoles used on large DC motors?
8. Diagram a Push Button motor starting switch and explain its action.
9. If the starting windings were burned out in a split-phase motor, how would it behave when the power is turned on?
10. Name two common methods of splitting a single phase current to start a motor.

Fig. 10-1. A phantom view of the D'Arsonval meter movement.
(Daystrom, Weston Instruments Div.)

Chapter 10

INSTRUMENTS AND MEASUREMENTS

One of our American scientists recently remarked that "greater progress in scientific development depends upon accuracy of measurements."

The student in electricity and electronics must rely upon the accuracy of his instruments to determine the performance and characteristics of a circuit. Skill in the use of instrumentation marks the level of technical competency. The technician must know what he is trying to measure and how to measure it. Experience and correct measurements are valued assets in the design of

electronic equipment as well as in the diagnosis and correction of circuit failures.

BASIC METER MOVEMENT

One of the more popular types of meter movements used to measure current and voltage is the D'Arsonval or stationary-magnet moving-coil meter. See Fig. 10-1. The movement consists of a permanent type magnet and a rotating coil in the magnetic field. To the rotating coil is attached an indicating needle. See Fig. 10-1A. When a current passes through the moving coil, a magnetic field is produced which reacts with the stationary field, and causes rotation or deflection of the needle. This deflection force is proportional to the intensity of the current flowing in the moving coil. The moving coil is returned to its "at rest" position by hair springs which also act as connections to the coil. The deflecting force rotates the coil against the restraining force of these springs.

IMPORTANT: To change the direction of current in the moving coil would cause deflection of the needle in the opposite direction.

Fig. 10-1A. *Indicating needle is attached to rotating coil of meter.*

Be sure that correct polarity of voltages and current are observed when connecting a meter to a live circuit.

An improvement on this simple meter movement includes a dampening device. A dampener prevents the indicating needle from overshooting and oscillating when making a measurement. To accomplish this, the moving coil is wound on an aluminum bobbin. As the bobbin tends to oscillate in the magnetic field, an EMF is induced in it which opposes the change in motion. (Lenz's Law.) As a result, any tendency for the coil to oscillate is quickly dampened out.

Meters are expensive instruments and should be used with skill and judgment. Precision types have jewel bearings like fine watches. The quality of the meter can be judged by its sensitivity and accuracy.

AMMETER

The instrument to be studied first is the AMMETER. This meter measures current flow in a circuit in amperes, milliamperes or microamperes, depending upon the scale selected. The moving coil of the meter is wound with many turns of very fine wire. If a large current were allowed to flow in the coil, it would quickly burn out. In order to measure larger currents with the basic movement, a SHUNT or alternate path is provided, through which the major amount of current will flow leaving only sufficient current to safely operate the moving coil. This shunt is in the form of a precision resistor connected in parallel with the meter coil.

In order to understand the use of shunts refer to Fig. 10-2 and follow this problem. The specification of a certain meter movement states that it requires .001 amps or one milliampere for full scale deflection of the needle and the ohmic resistance of the moving coil is 100 ohms. Compute the shunt resistor values so that the meter will measure currents from 0-1 ma, 0-10 ma, 0-50 ma, and 0-100 ma. Each range involves using a different shunt.

COIL RESISTANCE 100 Ω

METER READS 0-1MA

Fig. 10-2. Above. *A sketch of the basic ammeter. Below. Step 1. The voltage which causes the full scale deflection current is computed.*

Step 1. Calculate the voltage which, if applied to the coil, will cause one milliampere of current to flow and full scale deflection of needle.

$$E = I \times R \qquad E = .001 \times 100 \text{ or } .1 \text{ volt}$$

where:

I = .001 amps for full scale deflection

R = resistance of meter coil.

The meter will read from 0-1 ma without a shunt.

METER READS 0-10MA

Fig. 10-2. Step 2. The shunt carries 9/10 of the current.

Step 2. To convert this same meter to read from 0-10 ma, a shunt must be connected which will carry nine tenths of the current or 9 ma, leaving the one milliampere to operate the meter. Since .1 volt must be applied across the meter, and also across the shunt, the shunt resistance must be:

$$R_S = \frac{.1 \text{ v.}}{.009 \text{ amps.}} = 11.1 \text{ ohms}$$

The meter, with 11.1 ohms shunt will measure from 0-10 ma.

METER READS 0-50MA

Fig. 10-2. Step 3. The shunt carries 49/50 of the current.

Step 3. To convert this meter to read from 0-50 ma, a shunt must be used which will carry 49/50 of the current or 49 ma. The computation is the same as in step 2:

$$R_S = \frac{.1 \text{ v.}}{.049 \text{ amps.}} = 2.04 \text{ ohms}$$

METER READS 0-100MA

Fig. 10-2. Step 4. The shunt carries 99/100 of the current.

Step 4. To convert the meter for the 0-100 ma scale, a shunt must be used which will carry 99/100 of the current or 99 ma.

$$R_S = \frac{.1 \text{ v.}}{.099 \text{ amps.}} = 1.01 \text{ ohms}$$

The meter with the 1.01 ohms shunt will measure currents from 0-100 ma. Look again at the circuit in Fig. 10-2, and notice the switching device used to change the ranges of the meter. The correct scale on the dial must be used to correspond to the selected range.

IMPORTANT: An <u>Ammeter</u> must always be connected in series with a circuit. <u>Never across or parallel with it</u>. <u>To make a series connection requires breaking the circuit to connect the meter</u>. A parallel connection may instantaneously destroy the meter. See Fig. 10-3.

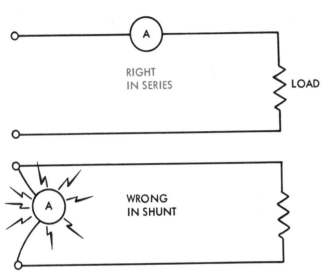

Fig. 10-3. *The RIGHT and WRONG way to connect an ammeter.*

VOLTMETER

The same basic movement used for the ammeter may also be used to measure voltage, providing the impressed voltage across the coil never exceeds .1 volt as computed for full scale deflection. To arrange the meter to measure higher voltages, MULTIPLIER RESISTORS are switched in series with the meter movement. Using the same meter as used for the ammeter, refer to Fig. 10-4 and follow the steps as the multipliers are computed so that the meter will measure voltages from 0-1 v., 0-10v., 0-100v., and 0-500v.

Step 1. As no more than .1 volt is permitted across the meter coil at any time, a resistor must be placed in series with the meter which will cause a voltage drop of .9v., if the meter is used to measure one volt. Also the meter only allows .001 amperes

Fig. 10-4. Step 1. *The multiplier causes an IR drop of .9 v.*

for full scale deflection, which is the maximum allowable current in the circuit. The multiplier resistor must produce a .9 volts drop when .001 amperes flows through it.

$$R_M = \frac{.9 \text{ v.}}{.001 \text{ amps.}} = 900 \text{ ohms}$$

Fig. 10-4. Step 2. *The multiplier causes an IR drop of 9.9 v.*

Step 2. To convert to the 0-10 volt range, a resistor must be selected to produce a 9.9 volt drop.

$$R_M = \frac{9.9 \text{ v.}}{.001 \text{ amps.}} = 9,900 \text{ ohms}$$

Fig. 10-4. Step 3. *The multiplier causes an IR drop of 99.9 v.*

Step 3. To convert to the 0-100 volt range, a resistor must be selected to produce a 99.9 volts drop.

$$R_M = \frac{99.9 \text{ v.}}{.001 \text{ amps.}} = 99,900 \text{ ohms}$$

Fig. 10-4. Step 4. The multiplier causes an IR drop of 499.9 v.

Step 4. Finally, to use the 0-500 volt range, the resistor must cause a 499.9 volts drop.

$$R_M = \frac{499.9 \text{ v.}}{.001 \text{ amps.}} = 499,900 \text{ ohms}$$

A switching device is again used to select the correct multiplier resistor for the range in use. Read the scale on the dial which corresponds to the range selected.

Fig. 10-4. Step 5. A switch selects the range.

IMPORTANT: <u>A voltmeter is always connected in parallel or across</u> the circuit. <u>Never in series.</u> <u>To measure voltage the circuit does not have to be broken.</u> See Fig. 10-5. Added precautions: When measuring an unknown voltage, always start with the meter on its highest range. Be sure that the leads are

connected with the correct polarity. <u>BLACK</u> is negative. <u>RED</u> is positive.

VOLTMETER SENSITIVITY

The sensitivity of a meter is an indication of its quality. <u>Ohms-per-volt</u> for full scale deflection is the usual descriptive terminology. In step 4 of the previous example, the total resistance of the meter and its multiplier resistance is:

$$\begin{array}{r}
499,900 \text{ ohms in } R_M \\
\underline{100 \text{ ohms for meter resistance}} \\
500,000 \text{ ohms total resistance}
\end{array}$$

This amount of resistance is used in the 500

Fig. 10-5. The RIGHT and WRONG way to connect a voltmeter.

volt range which is equivalent to:

$$\frac{500,000 \text{ ohms}}{500 \text{ v.}} \text{ or } 1,000 \text{ ohms per volt.}$$

By Ohm's Law, $I = \frac{E}{R}$ and the reciprocal of I equals $\frac{R}{E}$ which is the same as sensitivity. Therefore, sensitivity is equal to the reciprocal of the current required for full scale deflection. For the meter used in the above example:

$$\text{Sensitivity} = \frac{1}{I} \text{ or } \frac{1}{.001} \text{ or } 1000 \text{ ohms/volt}$$

This is an easy method of determining the sensitivity.

A good quality meter will have a sensitivity of 20,000 ohms/volt and precision laboratory meters are as high as 200,000 ohms/volt. Accuracy of the meter is usually expressed as a percentage such as 1 percent. The true value will be within one percent of the indicated scale reading.

OHMMETERS

A meter used to measure the value of an unknown resistance is called an OHMMETER. The same meter movement as used for the voltmeter and ammeter may be used for this purpose. A voltage source and a variable resistor are added to the circuit. The series type ohmmeter is diagrammed in Fig. 10-6.

Fig. 10-6. The schematic diagram of the series ohmmeter.

A three volt battery is used as source, and is built into the meter case. As the meter movement permits only .1 volt for a current of .001 amps for full scale deflection, a multiplier resistor is placed in series with the meter to drop the voltage:

$$R_M = \frac{2.9 \text{ v.}}{.001 \text{ amps.}} = 2900 \text{ ohms}$$

This resistance plus the meter resistance is equal to 3000 ohms. Part of this resistance is made variable to compensate for changes in battery voltage due to aging. To use the meter, the test terminals are shorted. This is equal to zero resistance and the meter deflects from left to right. The needle is adjusted to zero, by the variable resistor marked, "OHMS ADJUST." An unknown resistor, R_X, is now placed between the test terminals. The needle will deflect less than

full scale depending upon the resistance value. The scale reads directly in ohms, or other ranges may specify that the scale value should be multiplied by 10, or by 1,000 or by 100,000. It is interesting to note that with this circuit the meter scale reads <u>right to left</u> which is opposite to the voltmeter or ammeter scale.

A shunt ohmmeter may be connected as in Fig. 10-7. In this circuit the unknown re-

Fig. 10-7. The shunt ohmmeter.

sistance R_X is shunted across the meter. Low values of R_X cause lower currents through the meter. High values of R_X cause higher meter currents. With this arrangement, the indicating needle deflects from right to left in the customary manner. Zero resistance is on the left, and the scale increases from left to right.

MULTIMETER

Modern meters used by technicians, called Multimeters, usually include the voltmeter, ammeter and ohmmeter in one case. See Fig. 10-8. Adequate switching is provided to

Fig. 10-8. The multimeter combines the voltmeter, ammeter, and ohmmeter. (Simpson Electric Co.)

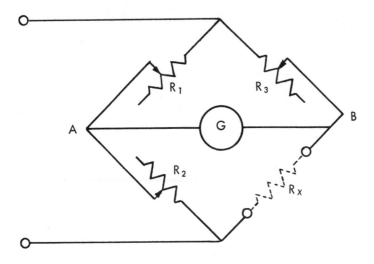

Fig. 10-9. The Wheatstone Bridge Circuit.

change function and range of the meter. Precaution: Before using the ohmmeter to test a circuit, be sure that the power is turned-off the equipment under test. Better pull the plug to be sure. Also discharge all electrolytic capacitors by shorting terminals to ground with an insulated screwdriver. Multimeters are expensive and carelessness will ruin one.

WHEATSTONE BRIDGE

Many bridge circuits of various types are used in electrical measurements. To familiarize the student with this circuit the WHEATSTONE BRIDGE will be described to measure unknown resistance. Fig. 10-9 is the schematic diagram. R_1, R_2 and R_3 are precision variable resistors. R_X is the unknown. When voltage is applied to the circuit, current will flow through the branch $R_1 R_2$ and parallel branch $R_3 R_X$. Each resistor will cause a voltage drop. The bridge is balanced by connecting a meter between points A and B, and then adjusting the variable resistors until the meter reads zero. The balanced condition indicates that:

$$E_{R_1} = E_{R_3}$$

and,

$$E_{R_2} = E_{R_X}$$

Since voltage is proportional to resistance,

$$\frac{R_1}{R_2} = \frac{R_3}{R_X} \quad \text{and} \quad R_X = \frac{R_2 \times R_3}{R_1}$$

The values of the precision variable resistors are indicated on an accurately calibrated dial.

IRON VANE METER MOVEMENT

The principle of operation of the iron vane meter movement may be understood by reference to Fig. 10-10. If two pieces of iron

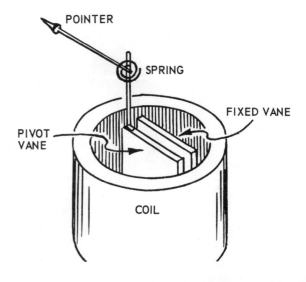

Fig. 10-10. A sketch which shows the operating principle of the iron vane meter movement.

are placed in the hollow core of a solenoid, they will <u>both become magnetized with the same polarity</u>, when a current passes through the solenoid. But, like poles repel each other. So the two pieces of metal are repelled. One

wire, because the coil must be connected in series with the circuit and carry the circuit current.

Regardless of the polarity of the applied

Fig. 10-11. The phantom view of a concentric type iron vane meter movement. (Daystrom, Weston Instrument Co.)

piece of metal is fixed and the other pivoted so that it may turn away from the fixed metal. An indicating needle is attached to the moving vane, which also has hair springs so that the vane must move against the spring tension. An applied voltage causes a current to flow in the solenoid and produces the magnetic field. The moving vane is repelled against the spring in proportion to the strength of the magnetic field. The needle may indicate either voltage or current and is calibrated for the magnitude of the applied voltage or current.

When the iron vane movement is used for a voltmeter, the solenoid is usually wound with many turns of fine wire. Proper multiplier resistances may be used to increase the range of the meter.

When used as an ammeter, however, the solenoid has relatively few turns of heavy

voltage or current, the iron vane meter movement always deflects in the same direction. (Two north poles repel as well as two south poles.) Either AC or DC may be measured by this instrument. Generally this type of meter is better suited for measurements in high power circuits. A phantom view of the interior construction of the concentric type iron vane meter is shown in Fig. 10-11.

THE WATTMETER

Power in an electric circuit is equal to the product of the voltage and the current. To devise a meter which may be read directly in watts, a movement similar to the D'Arsonval movement may be used, except the permanent magnetic field is replaced by the coils of an electromagnet. This type of meter is usually referred to as an electro-dynamometer movement. The circuit diagram of a simple wattmeter is shown in Fig. 10-12.

The moving coil, with the proper multiplier resistance, is connected across the voltage in the circuit. The coils of the electromagnet are connected in series with the circuit under measurement. The interaction between the two fields is proportional to the product of

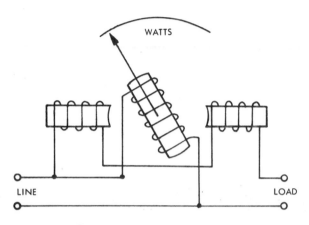

Fig. 10-12. Diagram of a wattmeter.

the voltage and the current and deflection of the indicating needle is read on a calibrated scale in <u>watts</u>. A commercial type meter movement is illustrated in Fig. 10-13.

The wattmeter will measure the instantaneous power used in the circuit. To determine the amount of power used for a given time, an entirely different device is used, called a watt-hour meter. This meter sums up

Fig. 10-13. Phantom view of the electrodynamometer movement used in a wattmeter (Daystrom, Weston Instrument Co.)

all the powers used for an interval of time. Such a meter is installed by the power company on the outside of your home. As the watt-hour is a relatively small unit, the customary meter reads in kilowatt-hours or 1000 watt-hours, (KWH). Electric power consumed is paid for at the prevailing rates per KWH.

The watt-hour meter is a rather complicated type of induction motor using field coils in series with the line current and also field coils connected across the line voltage. An aluminum disc rotates within these fields, at a rate proportional to the power consumed. The disc is geared to an indicating dial, from which may be read the power used. This rotating disc may be observed in the meter on your home. To read the meter, observe the four dials in Fig. 10-14. Dial A, on the extreme right, reads from 0-10 units of kilo-

Fig. 10-14. The dials of the watt-hour meter.

watt hours. For each revolution of dial A, the next dial B reads one. For each revolution of dial B, dial C reads one. For each revolution of dial C, dial D reads one. Mathematically:

Dial A reads in units of one.
Dial B reads in units of ten.
Dial C reads in units of one hundred.
Dial D reads in units of one thousand.

To read the meter illustrated in Fig. 10-14:

Dial A points to 5.
Dial B points between 5 and 6.
Dial C points between 2 and 3.
Dial D points between 4 and 5.

The correct reading would be, 4255 KWH. Notice that when the indicating arrow is between numbers, the lowest number or the number just passed should be taken. To practice reading the meter, why not read the meter at your home each day for several days and compute the power used? The power consumed may be found by subtracting the previous reading from the present reading to obtain the difference.

AC METERS

The typical DC meter movement, such as the D'Arsonval movement, may also be used to measure alternating currents and voltages with certain changes in the circuit. Remember that the DC meter must always be connected with the correct polarity. Incorrect polarity, causing a reversal of current through the moving coil, would cause deflection to the left below zero and possible damage to the meter. If an AC voltage were connected to the meter, the periodic changes in direction of the current would cause the needle to vibrate at zero. In order to measure this AC voltage a rectifier must be used. Detailed discussion of rectifiers will be included in the chapter on Power Supplies. For the present, however, a rectifier may be described as a device which permits current to flow in only one direction. When used in a meter, the rectifier allows one half cycle of the AC current to pass, but effectively cuts off the current when it reverses itself in the second half cycle. A simple circuit with a copper-oxide rectifier is shown in Fig. 10-15.

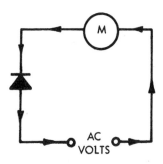

Fig. 10-15. The basic circuit for the AC meter using a single rectifier.

Notice the symbol used for the rectifier. Its output is a pulsating direct current which will cause the meter to deflect in one direction only. An improved circuit, which serves the

same purpose, is the full wave bridge rectifier shown in Fig. 10-16. By using four rectifiers, both half cycles of an AC current may be applied to the meter. When AC voltage is applied to terminals AB, and A is positive, electron flow is from B to 1 to 2 to 3 to 4 to A. When B is positive, electron flow is from A to 4 to 2 to 3 to 1 to B. Notice that, regardless of the polarity of the AC voltage, the current flow from point 2 to 3 through the meter is always in the same

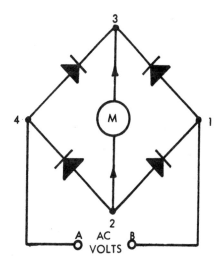

Fig. 10-16. A bridge rectifier circuit for an AC meter.

direction. The deflection of the meter needle usually is calibrated to indicate effective or rms voltage. Effective value of an AC voltage is equal to .707 x peak value. This is the most useful value of an AC voltage for the technician to measure.

LOADING A CIRCUIT

When a voltmeter is connected across a circuit to measure a potential difference, it is in parallel with the load in the circuit, and may introduce errors in voltage measurement. This is especially true when a meter with a low sensitivity is used. In the circuit of Fig. 10-17A, two 10,000 ohm resistors form a voltage divider across a ten volt source. The voltage drops across R_1 = 5 volts and R_2 = 5 volts. If a meter with a sensitivity of 1,000 ohms/volt on the ten volt range is used to measure the voltage across

R_1, the meter resistance will be in parallel with R_1 and the combined resistance will equal to:

$$\frac{10,000 \, \Omega}{2} = 5,000 \, \Omega$$

Fig. 10-17A. *The meter loads the circuit and introduces an error in the voltage reading.*

With the meter connected, the total circuit resistance becomes,

$$10,000 \, \Omega + 5,000 \, \Omega = 15,000 \, \Omega$$

and the current is .00066 amps.

By Ohm's Law, E_{R_1} = 3.4 v and E_{R_2} = 6.6 v. The meter has caused an error of more than one volt due to its shunting effect. To avoid excessive errors resulting from this shunting effect, a more sensitive meter should be used.

In circuit of Fig. 10-17B, a 5,000 ohms/

Fig. 10-17B. *A more sensitive meter gives more accurate readings.*

volt meter is used, and the combined resistance of meter and R_1 equals 8,333 ohms and the total circuit resistance equals 18,300 ohms. By Ohm's Law then, I = .00054 amps and E_{R_1} = 4.6 volts and E_{R_2} = 5.4 volts. An error of .4 volts still exists, but the increased sensitivity of the meter has reduced this error. More expensive meters with a sensitivity of 20,000 ohms/volt would reduce the error to a negligible amount.

HOW TO USE A METER

1. A meter is a delicate instrument. It should be handled with care and respect. Jarring, pounding, dropping and otherwise rough treatment may destroy a valuable meter.

2. When measuring voltage, the meter must be connected across the circuit (in parallel or shunt). Start on the highest range when measuring an unknown voltage and then to lower range for increased accuracy. Observe correct polarity! Red or positive lead to the positive side of the circuit. Black or negative lead to the negative or grounded side of the circuit.

3. A meter has its greatest accuracy at about two thirds deflection on the scale. Use the range which will give as close to this deflection as possible.

4. When measuring current, the meter must be connected in SERIES with the circuit. A wire must be disconnected or unsoldered to insert the meter. It is wise to make a rough current calculation by Ohm's Law to determine proper current range on the meter. Observe correct polarity. Red or positive to positive side of circuit and black to the negative side.

5. When measuring resistance, be certain that no power is applied to the circuit and that capacitors are discharged. It is not necessary to observe polarity. Always zero and adjust meter on proper range before measurements are made. A closed circuit has zero resistance; an open circuit has infinite resistance.

ON ALL METER MEASUREMENTS, THE WISE TECHNICIAN WILL MAKE A "FLASH CHECK" BEFORE PERMANENTLY CONNECTING THE METER IN THE CIRCUIT. WHAT DOES THIS MEAN? MAKE YOUR DECISION ON HOW THE METER SHOULD BE CONNECTED IN THE CIRCUIT, BUT LEAVE ONE METER LEAD DISCONNECTED. NOW VERY QUICKLY TOUCH AND REMOVE THIS UNCONNECTED METER LEAD, WHILE OBSERVING THE METER. DOES THE NEEDLE MOVE IN THE WRONG DIRECTION? CHANGE POLARITY. DOES THE NEEDLE MOVE TOO VIOLENTLY? CHANGE TO A HIGHER RANGE. THE "FLASH CHECK" WILL SAVE YOU MANY DOLLARS IN METER REPAIRS AND WASTED TIME.

6. High voltages are frequently measured in electronic circuits. Make sure your meter connections do not short or touch other parts of the circuit. Use a well insulated test prod to reach difficult and obstructed test points in the circuit.

APPLAUSE METER

No school should be without an applause meter. Why not build one and use it at school assembly programs and popularity contests? This is a real worthwhile experience in constructing electronic circuitry. Noise is converted to electricity by the speaker. It is amplified by the transistors, rectified by the diodes and measured on the meter. The louder the applause, the greater deflection of the meter.

Follow the circuit diagram, but design your own case, Fig. 10-18.

You have become acquainted with the loudspeaker as a device which produces music from your radio or HiFi system. In this application the speaker is used in reverse to pick up the sound from the ap-

Fig. 10-18. An Applause Meter.

plauding audience. In later studies you will discover how this is possible. Potentiometer R_1 is a sensitivity control, and should be set for the correct level and not changed. The output of the three stage grounded emitter transistor amplifier is rectified by the bridge circuit consisting of CR_1, CR_2, CR_3 and CR_4. The DC value is measured on the milliammeter.

In Fig. 10-18 the speaker has been omitted. It will plug into the jack on the front panel at the right. When in use the speaker should face the audience to pick up the sound.

Applause Meter
Parts List

B1-6-volt battery
C1, C2, C3, C4-10 mfd electrolytic, 25-volt
CR1, CR2, CR3, CR4-Sylvania 1N64 diode
LS1-3-6 ohm loudspeaker
M1-1 milliampere full-scale meter
Q1, Q2, Q3-Sylvania 2N1265 transistor
R1-5k, 1/2w potentiometer
R2, R5, R8-150k, 1/2w
R3, R6, R9-100Ω, 1/2w
R4, R7, R10-2.2k, 1/2w
T1-Stancor TA-33 or equivalent

This is another way by which electronics serves you. Devices of this nature are used in industry and medical science. One interesting study has been made to determine the effect of noise upon human fatigue. Noise levels are measured by electronic sensing devices.

FOR DISCUSSION

1. Discuss the safety rules and precautions pertaining to meters.
2. Why is a rectifier necessary in measuring an AC current or voltage?
3. What is meant by "loading a circuit" with a meter?
4. Name some applications of the applause or noise meter which you may have heard about.
5. How could electronic circuitry be used to test human hearing?
6. Who was Alexander Graham Bell?

TEST YOUR KNOWLEDGE

1. Name three types of meter movements.
2. A meter movement has a moving coil resistance of 50 ohms and requires .001 amperes for full scale deflection. Compute the shunt values for meter to read in the following ranges:
    0-1 ma
    0-10 ma
    0-50 ma
3. Compute multipliers for the meter in questions 2 to use on the following ranges:
    0-1 volt
    0-10 volts
    0-100 volts
4. Draw the circuit of a series ohmmeter and explain its operation.
5. Ask your instructor for six different resistors. Measure and record their value and compare measured value to color code value.

	Measured	Coded Value
1		
2		
3		
4		
5		
6		

6. A voltmeter must always be connected in _____ with the circuit or component. The ammeter must always be connected in _____ with the circuit.
7. Draw a circuit to measure AC using a full wave bridge rectifier.
8. A Wheatstone bridge is used to measure an unknown resistance. The following values will balance the bridge.
    R_1 = 500 ohms, R_2 = 100 ohms,
    R_3 = 300 ohms, R_X = ?
9. What is the major difference between an iron vane current meter and an iron vane voltmeter?
10. Read and record the electric meter on the outside of your home. The reading represents _____. Read and record again in one week. How much power has been consumed? At five cents per kilowatt hour, how much will this power cost?

Chapter 11

THE ELECTRON TUBE

Thomas Alva Edison is best remembered for his invention of the incandescent lamp. The dramatic exhibition of the worlds first electric lamp at Menlo Park in 1879 eclipses many of the other scientific discoveries made by Mr. Edison. An obscure experiment with the incandescent lamp led to the invention of the vacuum tube by which the "wonders of electronics" contribute daily to our pleasure and standard of living. Mr. Edison placed a metal plate in the vacuum bulb containing his light. By connecting a battery and a meter in series between the light filament and the plate, he discovered that an electric current would flow through the light, if the POSITIVE terminal of the battery were connected to the plate. If the negative battery terminal were connected to the plate, NO CURRENT WOULD FLOW. This experiment is diagramed in Fig. 11-1. The electron theory was yet to be discovered and the scientific explanation of the current flow through the light was quite mysterious.

Today the electron theory provides a satisfactory explanation. Certain metals and oxides of metals give up free electrons when heated. The heat supplies sufficient energy to the electrons so that they break away from the forces holding them in orbit and become "free electrons." This is described as a THERMIONIC EMISSION. In Mr. Edison's experiment, a cloud of these free electrons was emitted from the filament of his light bulb. When a positive plate was placed in the bulb, the free electrons were attracted to the plate. (Unlike charges attract.) A flow of electrons constitutes a current, so the meter in the plate circuit indicated that electrons were passing from filament to plate. The modern vacuum tube, although improved by more recent inventions, still uses the principles discovered in the laboratory of Thomas Edison.

THERMIONIC EMITTERS

Better emitting materials have been developed in the years since Edison's carbon filament. Many materials, when heated to the point of emission, will melt. Tungsten seemed to be the most satisfactory material for many years, but it required considerable heat for satisfactory emission. Yet, it was strong and durable. Tungsten is still used in large high-power vacuum tubes.

To lower the operating temperatures and power consumption the thoriated-tungsten emitter was developed. An extremely thin layer of thorium is deposited on the tungsten emitter. THORIUM is one of the heavier metallic elements. (Symbol TH, atomic weight 232.2.) It is mined in India. This type of

Fig. 11-1. Circuit diagram of the Edison discovery.

emitter produces satisfactory emission at much lower temperatures than pure tungsten.

The most efficient of emitters is the oxide-coated type. Usually the emitter is metal such as nickel on which is formed a thin layer of barium or strontium oxide. Because of its low power consumption and high emission, this type is widely used in vacuum tubes for radios, television and other electronic devices.

CATHODE

The emitter in the vacuum tube is called the CATHODE. Heat may be supplied either directly or indirectly. Both methods have certain advantages. Schematic diagrams of both types are shown in Fig. 11-2. For portable equipment that employs batteries as a source of power, the directly heated type is more advantageous. There are less heat losses and the filament can be so designed that only a small amount of power is consumed during use.

Fig. 11-2. Schematic symbols showing directly and indirectly heated cathodes.

DIRECTLY HEATED   INDIRECTLY HEATED

When a source of alternating current is available, the indirectly heated cathode is more practical. The power loss is insignificant. The indirect method provides isolation between the heater voltage source and the cathode, so that HUM may not be introduced into the circuit.

Research and development in electron tube technology has led to the use of many specialized materials in the construction of the modern tube. An appreciation of engineering materials may be gained by studying the illus-

tration in Fig. 11-3. Note the several special alloys and combinations of materials used in the manufacturing of the tube.

THE DIODE

A tube which contains a cathode and a plate is called a DIODE. The prefix "Di" signifies two elements in the tube. The cathode may be

1. ENVELOPE- Lime glass
2. SPACER- Mica sprayed with magnesium oxide
3. PLATE- Carbonized nickel or nickel-plated steel
4. GRID WIRES- Manganese-nickel or molybdenum
5. GRID SIDE-RODS- Chrome copper, nickel, or nickel-plated iron
6. CATHODE- Nickel coated with barium-calcium-strontium carbonates
7. HEATER- Tungsten or tungsten-molybdenum alloy with insulating coating of alundum
8. CATHODE TAB- Nickel
9. MOUNT SUPPORT- Nickel or nickel-plated iron
10. GETTER SUPPORT AND LOOP- Nickel or nickel-plated iron
11. GETTER- Barium-magnesium alloys
12. HEATER CONNECTOR- Nickel or nickel-plated iron
13. STEM LEAD-IN WIRES- Nickel, dumet, copper
14. PRESSED STEM- Lead glass
15. BASE- Bakelite
16. BASE PINS- Nickel-plated brass

Fig. 10-3. Typical Electron Tube. (RCA)

either directly or indirectly heated. In either case the heater is not considered when counting the tube elements. The plate is usually a cylindrical piece of metal surrounding all the elements in the tube. The plate acts as the collector of electrons, emitted from the cathode. A circuit employing a diode is drawn in Fig. 11-4. This is very similar to the original circuit used by Thomas Edison. The

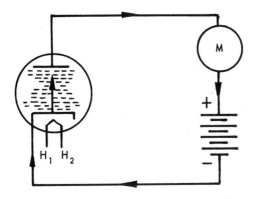

Fig. 11-4. Diode circuit showing direction of electron flow.

heater connections are shown as H_1 and H_2 and may be connected to an alternating current source. The first number in a tube designation expresses the approximate voltage which should be applied to the heaters. For example, a 6H6 tube requires 6.3 volts, a 12AX7 requires 12.6 volts and a 25Z6 needs 25 volts. This is important to remember.

When the tube in Fig. 11-4 is turned on, the heaters indirectly heat the cathode and cause thermionic emission of many electrons. If the plate of the diode is connected to the positive terminal of the battery in the circuit, ELECTRONS WILL FLOW IN THE CIRCUIT, from cathode to plate. If the connections are reversed and the negative battery terminal is connected to the plate, NO ELECTRONS WILL FLOW. This electron tube acts as a one way valve permitting electron flow in one direction only. In fact, the term "valve" is still used in England to describe the tube.

At a given operating temperature of the diode the cathode emits the greatest possible number of electrons. These form a space

charge around the cathode. Some of these electrons are attracted back to the cathode which has been made slightly positive as a result of emitting electrons. When the plate is made positive, many of the electrons are attracted to it which constitutes electron flow. If the plate is made MORE POSITIVE BY APPLYING A HIGHER VOLTAGE, a greater number of electrons is attracted and consequently there is an increase in current. The chart in Fig. 11-5 graphically illustrates the increase in current as a result of an increase in plate voltage. A point may be reached by increasing the voltage, at which all the emitted electrons are attracted to the plate and any further increase in voltage will not increase the current. This is called the SATURATION POINT of the electron tube.

Diodes find wide application as rectifiers, voltage regulators and detectors. Each of these uses will be discussed in later chapters in this text.

THE TRIODE

One of the greater contributions to the scientific age was made by Dr. Lee DeForest and his experimentation with a third element, called a GRID, added to the electron tube. This

Fig. 11-5. This graph indicates that as plate voltage is increased, plate current increases.

three element tube is called the TRIODE. By placing a mesh of fine wire between the cathode and the plate of the tube, the scientist was able to control the flow of electrons through the electron tube. The grid usually is cylindrical in shape and surrounds the cathode. Sufficient space is allowed between the grid wires to permit electrons to pass through to the plate. Because this grid controls the electron flow, it is commonly referred to as the CONTROL GRID. Probably no other single discovery has stimulated the development of radio, television and electronic equipment to its present state than the GRID in the triode. Upon this discovery is based the ability of an electron tube to AMPLIFY.

In the previous study of the diode it was learned that the electron flow was controlled by variations in plate voltage. In the triode, the grid also has a pronounced effect upon this electron flow. If the grid is made negative in respect to the cathode, many of the electrons

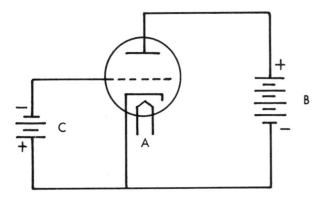

Fig. 11-6. This triode circuit shows the connections for plate voltage and grid bias voltage.

emitted from the cathode are repelled by the negative grid back to the cathode, thus limiting the number of electrons passing on to the plate. As the grid is made more and more negative a point may be reached at which no electrons will flow to the plate. This is described as the CUT-OFF point of the tube. It represents the negative voltage applied to the control grid which cuts-off the electron flow through the tube. The voltage applied to the control grid is the BIAS VOLTAGE and at cut-off it would be called the CUT-OFF-BIAS.

The circuit in Fig. 11-6 shows a triode with both plate and grid voltages. Notice that the grid bias battery has its negative terminal connected to the grid. In electronic work,

one should remember, these voltages are referred to as:

A voltage - for the heaters in the tube
B voltage - for the plate of the tube
C voltage - for the grid of the tube

Portable radios and equipment use dry batteries called A and B batteries for these voltage sources. In the familiar radio operating on AC power these voltages are obtained from the power supply. Earlier portable radios used the C battery also, but now improvements have permitted the C battery to be discarded. The C bias voltage may be obtained by other methods which will be studied later.

The graph in Fig. 11-7 shows the current flow through an electron tube as the grid bias is changed. The plate voltage is held at a constant value. The curve in this graph is plotted by measuring the value of current at each change of grid voltage. At a grid bias of

Fig. 11-7. The graph shows the change in plate current I_p as a result of a change in grid voltage E_g. The plate voltage is held at a constant value.

negative 2 volts the current is 8 ma. At negative 6 volts the current drops to 3 ma.

ELECTRON TUBE CHARACTERISTICS

The performance of any electron tube with different applied voltages to the grid, plate and cathode may be plotted on a series of graph curves which represent the STATIC characteristics of the tube. These characteristic curves differ somewhat from curves produced under actual operation conditions. Curves of characteristics under operating conditions would be termed DYNAMIC CHARACTERISTICS. The ability of a tube to amplify was previously mentioned. What does amplification mean? If you were unfortunate to have a flat tire on your car and wished to change to the spare, it would be necessary to jack up the car to make the change. A jack is a mechanical device to amplify your power to lift. In fact, only a few pounds of pressure on the jack handle will lift hundreds of pounds of automobile. In the case of the electron tube, a small change of voltage on the grid of the tube may produce a relatively large change of voltage at the plate. The ability of a tube to amplify a voltage or signal is known as its AMPLIFICATION FACTOR or MU. It represents the ratio between the change in plate voltage to the change in grid voltage, which will produce an equal change in plate current. It is expressed as:

$$\mu\,(MU) \;=\; \frac{\Delta E_p}{\Delta E_g} \text{ (with } I_p \text{ held constant)}.$$

where:

μ or MU equals the amplification factor

ΔE_p means a change in plate voltage

ΔE_g means a change in grid voltage

I_p means plate current or electron flow through tube.

To further clarify the MU of a tube, refer to the typical circuit in Fig. 11-8 used for the determination of tube characteristics. Notice the voltmeter for measuring the plate voltage (E_p), the voltmeter to measure grid voltage (E_g) and the ammeter to measure plate current (I_p). The plate voltage and grid voltage supplies are variable. Assuming the plate voltage is set at 120 volts and the grid voltage at negative 2 volts, the current through the tube (I_p) is 8 ma. If the grid voltage is changed to negative 4 volts (a change of 2 volts) the current will drop to 3 ma. Now increase the plate voltage until the current rises to the original 8 ma. If the plate voltage is increased to 160 volts (a change from 120 volts to 160

volts equals 40 volts) the current rises to 8 ma. From this explanation then, a 40 volt change in plate voltage was required to overcome a 2 volt change in grid voltage, while the current was held at 8 ma. The MU then equals,

$$\mu\,(MU) \;=\; \frac{\Delta E_p}{\Delta E_g} \;=\; \frac{40\ volts}{2\ volts} = 20 \text{ (amplification factor)}$$

Plate current, I_p, is held at 8 ma.

The above example applies to a 6J5 tube and values are taken from the average plate characteristics chart in the Tube Manual.

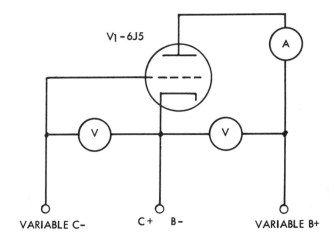

Fig. 11-8. *The typical circuit used to determine the static characteristics of a triode.*

A second characteristic of an electron tube is the PLATE RESISTANCE, designated as r_p. It may be determined by holding the grid at a constant voltage and measuring the change in plate current resulting from a change in plate voltage. It is expressed in ohms and the mathematical relationship appears as:

$$r_p \;=\; \frac{\Delta E_p}{\Delta I_p}$$

Grid voltage, E_g, is held constant.

Continuing the previous experiment with reference to the 6J5 tube and the circuit in Fig. 11-8, set the grid voltage at negative 4 volts. At a plate voltage of 120 volts the plate current reads approximately 3 ma. When the plate voltage is increased to 160 volts (a change of 40 volts) the plate current increases to 8 ma (a change of 5 ma). Substituting these results in the equation, then;

$$r_p = \frac{\Delta E_p}{\Delta I_p} = \frac{40 \text{ volts}}{5 \text{ ma}} = \frac{40 \text{ volts}}{.005 \text{ amps}} = 8000 \text{ ohms}$$

A curve resulting from this experiment is shown in Fig. 11-9. The characteristics of AC PLATE RESISTANCE of the tube may be determined from this curve.

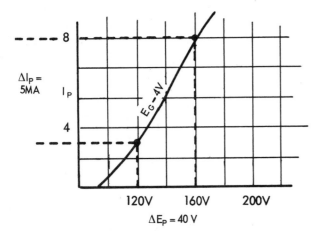

Fig. 11-9. *This curve shows graphically the determination of the plate resistance of a tube.*

The third characteristic of the electron tube is its TRANSCONDUCTANCE, (g_m) sometimes called the control grid-plate transconductance or MUTUAL CONDUCT-ANCE. This characteristic may be expressed as a ratio between the change in plate current resulting from a change in grid voltage, while the plate voltage is held at a constant value. This ratio is expressed in "mhos" (ohms spelled backwards). Because a mho is a relatively large unit, the transconductance is converted to "micromhos" or μ mhos. The mathematical expression of this ratio becomes,

$$g_m = \frac{\Delta I_p}{\Delta E_g} \text{ (with } E_p \text{ constant).}$$

To further clarify the meaning of transconductance the previous experiment is continued. Refer to Fig. 11-10. At a fixed plate voltage of 120 volts and a grid voltage of

negative two volts, the plate current reads approximately 8 ma.

When the grid voltage is changed to negative four volts (a change of two volts), plate current decreases to 3 ma, (a change of 5 ma). Then,

$$g_m = \frac{I_p}{E_g} = \frac{5ma}{2 \text{ volts}} = \frac{.005 \text{ amps}}{2 \text{ volts}} = .0025 \text{ mhos}$$

Converting, .0025 mhos = 2500 micromhos

The three electron tube characteristics now are summarized in these three formulas.

Amplification Factor, $\mu = \dfrac{E_p}{E_g} \Big|_{I_p \text{ constant}}$

AC Plate Resistance, $r_p = \dfrac{E_p}{I_p} \Big|_{E_g \text{ constant}}$

Transconductance, $g_m = \dfrac{I_p}{E_g} \Big|_{E_p \text{ constant}}$

An interrelationship between these three

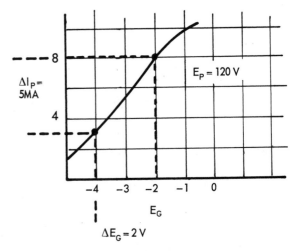

Fig. 11-10. *The determination of the transconductance of an electron tube by using its characteristic curves.*

characteristics exists and may be expressed as,

$$\mu = g_m r_p \text{ or } g_m = \frac{\mu}{r_p} \text{ or } r_p = \frac{\mu}{g_m}$$

when g_m is in mhos and r_p is in ohms.

A set of characteristic curves for the 6J5 tube is illustrated in Fig. 11-11. A family of

Fig. 11-11. Average plate characteristics of the 6J5 tube.
(RCA)

average plate characteristic curves for a tube may be found in a Tube Manual. Practice in applying the curves leads to a better understanding of the electron tube. The engineer uses the curves when designing electronic circuitry.

INTERELECTRODE CAPACITANCE

In our studies of capacitance in Chapter 7, we discovered that by definition a capacitor was two plates of metal separated by a dielectric or insulating material. Also the action of the capacitor was described as blocking a direct current, yet effectively passing an alternating current. An examination of the triode electron tube discloses that the cathode, grid and plate are metallic parts separated from each other by a vacuum, and by definition are capacitors. The capacitance resulting from these electrodes is termed INTERELECTRODE CAPACITANCE. Actually three capacitances are involved. These are shown schematically in Fig. 11-12.

C_{gp} = capacitance between grid and plate

C_{gk} = capacitance betweeen grid and cathode

C_{pk} = capacitance between cathode and plate

Interelectrode capacitance can be undesirable or desirable depending upon the application of the electron tube. If the tube is used at low frequencies, the high capacitive

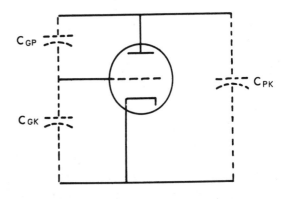

Fig. 11-12. Dotted symbols show capacitance between the elements in a tube.

171

reactance prevents little interaction between the tube elements. However, as the frequency is increased the reactance decreases, and causes a shunting effect between the elements. This shunting effect may be counteracted by feeding a small part of the plate voltage back to the grid of the tube by means of a capacitor. This feedback voltage will be 180° out of phase with the internal feedback caused by the interelectrode capacitance and therefore cancels it. This is called NEUTRALIZATION and is used extensively in rf amplifier circuits. Feedback and neutralization will be discussed in later chapters.

In some electronic circuits, such as oscillators, interelectrode capacitance is purposely used to transfer energy from the plate circuit to the grid circuit in order to sustain oscillation. This application will be described in Chapter 14.

THE TETRODE

Because of the shunting effect of the electrode capacitance at high frequencies, the triode is limited as an amplifier, without neutralization circuits. An improvement upon the triode is made by inserting another grid, called the SCREEN GRID, between the control grid and the plate. This electron tube now becomes a four element tube (cathode, control grid, screen grid and plate) called a TETRODE. It is represented schematically in Fig. 11-13. The screen grid is bypassed to

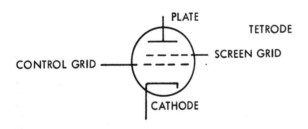

Fig. 11-13. Symbol for a TETRODE.

ground, externally, through a capacitor making the grid an effective screen between the control grid and plate and eliminating the (C_{gp}) grid-plate capacitance. A DC voltage of slightly less value than the

plate voltage is usually applied to the screen grid and the screen grid acts as an accelerator for the electrons passing between cathode and plate. Some electrons are attracted to the screen grid and will cause a current to flow in the screen circuit. However, most electrons pass through the screen to the plate. High amplification is possible in the tetrode because the control grid is placed quite close to the cathode. A decrease or increase in plate voltage has comparatively little effect on the plate current due to the isolation effect of the

Fig. 11-14. Symbol for a PENTODE.

screen grid. The transconductance of the tetrode is relatively high.

THE PENTODE

In the tetrode, the accelerated electrons strike the plate with considerable velocity. When this occurs, loosely held electrons on the plate are knocked-off into free space and form a space charge around the plate. This is called SECONDARY EMISSION. Some of these electrons are attracted to the screen and subtract from the useful plate current through the tube. This effect is more pronounced at times when the plate voltage is below the screen voltage. To overcome the undesirable effects of the secondary emission, a third grid is placed in the tube between the screen grid and plate. The tube now has five elements (cathode, control grid, screen grid, suppressor grid and plate) and is called a PENTODE. This third grid is named the SUPPRESSOR GRID. It is usually internally connected to the cathode and is at cathode potential. This grid repels the free electrons resulting from secondary emission and drives them back to the plate. The pentode is diagramed in Fig. 11-14. These tubes have high amplification factors, high plate resistance and transconductance. Interelectrode capacitance is at a minimum. Pentodes have wide application as rf amplifiers and also as audio power amplifiers. An exploded view of a miniature pentode is shown in Fig. 11-15.

BEAM POWER TUBES

A special development in electron tubes is the BEAM POWER TUBE which was designed for use in high powered amplifiers. It

Fig. 11-15. Parts of a Miniature Pentode. (RCA)

Fig. 11-16. Construction of RCA-813 Beam Power Tube.

differs from the usual tetrode or pentode by the introduction of special plates which form the electron stream into a concentrated beam. The grid wires also are lined-up so that they will cause only a minimum interference to the electron stream. Since the screen grid is in the shadow, so to speak, of the control grid very few electrons actually hit the screen grid and the screen current is low in the beam power tube. In comparison to the conventional tetrode or pentode the beam power tube provides a greater power output for the similar plate and screen voltages. The construction of a Beam Power Pentode is illustrated in Fig. 11-16.

1. MEDIUM METAL CAP - nickel-plated brass
2. SHORT RIBBON PLATE CONNECTOR - molybdenum
3. FILAMENT SUPPORT SPRINGS - tungsten
4. MOUNT SPACER - nickel-chromium strip
5. MOUNT SUPPORT - ceramic
6. TOP SHIELD - nickel
7. HEAVY-DUTY FILAMENT - thoriated tungsten
8. PLATE - zirconium-coated graphite
9. ALIGNED-TURN CONTROL GRID (GRID No. 1) AND SCREEN GRID (GRID No. 2) - molybdenum
10. BULB OR ENVELOPE - hard glass
11. BEAM-FORMING ELECTRODE - nickel
12. PLATE-SUPPORT SPACER - ceramic
13. BOTTOM SHIELD DISK - nickel
14. FILAMENT CONNECTOR - nickel-plated steel
15. DIRECTIVE-TYPE GETTER
16. MOLDED-FLARE STEM - hard glass
17. GIANT BASE - nickel-plated brass with ceramic insert
18. TUNGSTEN-TO-GLASS SEAL

174

MULTI-ELEMENT TUBES

In addition to the electron tubes previously discussed, many special purpose tubes with more elements have been developed. One such tube is the PENTAGRID converter used in the superheterodyne radio. Extra grids allow the addition of signals of other frequencies. The schematic diagrams in Fig. 11-17 show a few of the many dual purpose and special purpose

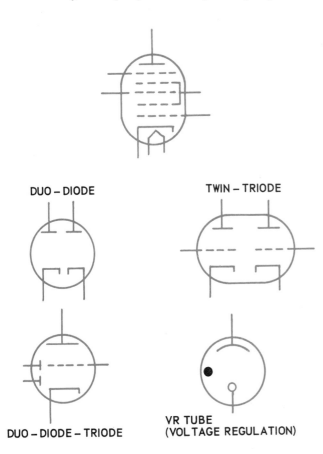

DUO – DIODE

TWIN – TRIODE

DUO – DIODE – TRIODE

VR TUBE
(VOLTAGE REGULATION)

Fig. 11-17. Symbol for the PENTAGRID CONVERTER and special combination tubes.

tubes. Note that in some cases, two tubes are enclosed in one envelope. The name of each tube suggests its application.

GAS FILLED TUBES

The tubes discussed up to this point have been the high vacuum variety. In manufacturing these tubes, most of the air is removed from the glass or metal envelope. Any remaining air is removed by burning a small

amount of magnesium called a "GETTER" inside the tube after it has been sealed. The "getter" is ignited by a radio frequency current.

Other tubes are purposely filled with gases such as nitrogen, argon, neon and mercury vapor. The conduction in a gas filled tube is a result of the ionization of the gas. In a gas filled triode (thyratron) the grid can only control the point of ionization called the "ignition point" of the tube. When the tube begins to conduct, the grid has no control because it is surrounded by positive ions. To follow the conduction action in the gas filled tube, the electrons emitted from the cathode on their

THYRATRON
GAS FILLED TRIODE

Fig. 11-18. Gas-filled triode symbol. Note the black dot in the envelope.

way to the plate collide with the gas molecules and cause them to give up electrons and become ionized. The tube now contains electrons, positive ions and gas molecules. The energy required for ionization must be supplied from the power supply and a specific voltage is required to cause ionization in the tube. This is the "ignition voltage" or "ionization potential".

After the tube has started conduction, ionization can be maintained at lower voltages. However, a voltage may be approached which will no longer sustain the ionization and the tube will "go out" and conduction will stop. This is the "extinction voltage" or "deionization potential" of the tube.

Gas tubes may be identified on a schematic by the black dot in the tube. See Fig. 11-18.

Electricity - Electronics

Gas tubes are able to carry higher currents than vacuum tubes. However, there is danger of "arc back" or reverse current flow at high negative cathode voltages. This limitation is described as the "INVERSE PEAK VOLTAGE" rating of the tube. Gas tubes are found in many industrial electronic circuits such as rectifiers, voltage regulators, trigger and relay devices.

SPECIAL ASSIGNMENT

1. Prepare a special report for your class on the life and inventions of:
Dr. Thomas Edison
Dr. Lee DeForest

2. Discuss the reasons why the triode is not generally used for high frequency amplification.

3. Discuss the control grid action and conduction in a Thyratron.

4. For a class demonstration, secure a variable power supply, two voltmeters and an ammeter from the instrument room. Set up the tube characteristic circuit illustrated in Fig. 11-8 using the 6J5 tube.

Step I. Set grid voltage at zero and the plate voltage at zero. Now increase E_p in steps of 20 volts and record plate current for each step. Do not exceed 10 ma. Plot this information on a sheet of linear graph paper.

Step II. Set E_g at negative 2 volts and increase E_p from zero in 20 volt steps as in Step I. Record and plot the results.

Step III. Repeat previous steps using negative E_g of -4, -6, -8, -10, -12, and -14 volts and record and plot the results.

Step IV. Compare your graph with Fig. 11-11. Remember that 11-11 represents average curves for many tubes and your curves may appear different.

Step V. Compute:
Amplification Factor MU = _____
Plate Resistance r_p = _____
Transconductance g_m = _____

Compare answers with values given in Tube Manual.

TEST YOUR KNOWLEDGE

1. Draw the schematic symbols for:
Diode (directly heated cathode)
Diode (indirectly heated cathode)
Triode Pentode, Duo-diode
Thyratron, Duo-diode-triode, Twin Triode

2. Explain in your own words the meaning of the amplification factor of a tube.

3. Explain the meaning of Transconductance.

4. Explain the meaning of Dynamic Plate Resistance.

5. What materials are used as thermionic emitters?

6. Define:
A. Grid bias
B. Cut-off point
C. Saturation point

7. What is the purpose of the screen grid?

8. What is the purpose of suppressor gird?

9. What is the meaning of A, B, and C voltages?

10. Why is neutralization needed in a triode used as an rf amplifier? How is it accomplished?

11. State some advantages of the Pentode.

12. What is meant by "Inverse Peak Voltage?"

Chapter 12

POWER SUPPLIES

For the proper operation of electronic equipment, a variety of source voltages must be available. Alternating current must be supplied for the heaters of the tubes. High direct current voltages are needed for the B+ or plate and screens of the electron tubes. Negative voltages must be supplied for the C supply or grid bias. Although batteries may be used for all these requirements, the common source of electric power is that furnished by the local power company and is 115 volt alternating current at a frequency of 60 cycles per second.

The complete power supply circuit may be used to perform these circuit functions:

1. Step-up or step-down by transformer action the AC line voltage to required voltages.

2. Change the AC voltage to a pulsating DC voltage by either half-wave or full-wave rectification.

3. Filter the pulsating DC voltage so that a relatively pure DC is available for equipment use.

4. Provide some method of voltage division to meet the needs of equipment.

5. Frequently, the power supply includes circuitry and components to regulate its output in proportion to the applied load.

THE POWER TRANSFORMER

The first component in the Power Supply is the transformer. Its purpose is to step-up or to step-down the alternating source voltage to values needed for the radio, TV or electronic circuit. It would be wise at this time to review transformer action as dis-

cussed in Chapter 6. Since transformers of a variety of types and sizes may be found in almost all electronic devices, the student should be quite familiar with the basic theory and purposes of this valuable component.

LESSON IN SAFETY: Transformers produce high voltages which may be extremely dangerous. Proper respect and extreme caution must be practiced at all times when working with or measuring high voltages. Do not, under any circumstances, attempt to work with these high voltages until your instructor has given his approval.

HALF-WAVE RECTIFICATION

The process of changing an alternating current to a pulsating direct current is called RECTIFICATION. In the circuit of Fig. 12-1, the output of a transformer is connected to a

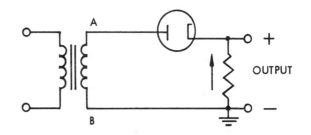

Fig. 12-1. Schematic of basic diode rectifier.

diode and a load resistor, in series. The input voltage to the transformer appears as a sine wave, which periodically reverses polarity at the frequency of the applied voltage. The output voltage of the transformer secondary also appears as a sine wave, the magnitude of which depends upon the turns ratio, and it is 180 deg. out of phase with the primary. The top of the transformer (point A) is connected to the diode plate. When point A is positive during the first half cycle, the diode conducts, producing a voltage drop across R equal to IR. During the second half cycle, point A is negative and the diode plate is negative. No conduction takes place and no IR drop appears across R. An oscilloscope connected across R would produce the wave form shown in Fig. 12-2. It is important to

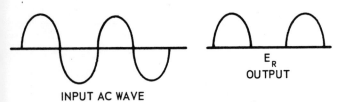

INPUT AC WAVE

E_R OUTPUT

Fig. 12-2. Wave forms of input and output of diode rectifier.

understand that the output of this circuit consists of pulses of current flowing in only one direction and at the same frequency as the input voltage. The output is a pulsating direct current. Since only one-half of the alternating current input wave is used to produce a useful output voltage, it is therefore named a HALF-WAVE RECTIFIER. The polarity of the output voltage should be observed. One end of resistor R is connected to ground. The electron or current flow is from ground to the cathode which makes the cathode end of R positive as indicated.

A negative rectifier may be made by reversing the diode in the circuit. See Fig. 12-3.

INVERTED DIODE

Fig. 12-3. Inverted diode produces a negative voltage.

The diode conducts when the cathode becomes negative, which is the same as making the plate positive. The current through R would be from plate to ground, making the plate end of R negative and the ground end of R more positive. Voltages taken from across R, the

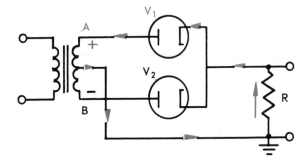

Fig. 12-4. Arrows show current in full-wave rectifier during first half-cycle.

output, would be negative in respect to ground. This circuit is called an inverted diode, and is used when a negative supply voltage is required.

FULL-WAVE RECTIFIER

The pulsating direct voltage from the half-wave rectifier is difficult to filter to a pure

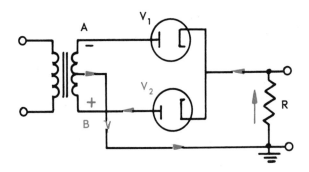

Fig. 12-5. Direction of current during second half-cycle.

DC voltage. The half-wave rectifier uses only one half of the input alternating current wave. By employing two diodes, as diagramed in Figs. 12-4 and 12-5, both half cycles of the input wave may be rectified. In order to do this, a center tap is made on the secondary winding which is attached to ground. In Fig. 12-4, point A is positive and diode plate of V_1 is

positive. Current flows as indicated by arrows. During the second half of the input
cycle, point B is positive, diode plate of V_2 is
positive, and current flows as indicated in
Fig. 12-5. Notice that, regardless of which
diode is conducting, the current through load
resistor R is always in the same direction.
Both positive and negative half cycles of the
input voltage cause current through R in the
same direction. Output voltage of this FULL-
WAVE RECTIFIER is taken from across R
and consists of direct current pulses at a
frequency of TWICE the input voltage. See
Fig. 12-6. In order to produce full-wave rec-

*Fig. 12-6. The wave forms of input and output of full-wave
diode rectifier.*

tification in this circuit, it was necessary to
cut the secondary voltage in half by means of
the center tap.

A variation of the full-wave rectifier circuit is drawn in Fig. 12-7. In this diagram a
duo-diode (two diodes in one envelope) is used
and the directly heated cathode is supplied by

*Fig. 12-7. Full-wave rectifier using a duo-diode which
produces both negative and positive voltages in respect to ground.*

a separate 5 volt secondary winding. The load
resistor R is replaced by two resistors and
the tap between R_1 and R_2 is grounded. The
transformer center-tap is connected to the

bottom of R_2. This circuit operates exactly
like the previous circuits. The reference point
for the output voltage which is ground has
been moved. Now point B is positive in respect to ground but point C is negative with

Fig. 12-8. Current in bridge rectifier during first half-cycle.

respect to ground. Both negative and positive
voltages may be supplied by this circuit.

THE BRIDGE RECTIFIER

It is not always necessary to use a center-
tapped transformer for full-wave rectification. The full secondary voltage can be
rectified by using four diodes in a BRIDGE
RECTIFIER CIRCUIT. See Figs. 12-8 and
12-9. Two circuit drawings are illustrated so

Fig. 12-9. Current in bridge rectifier during second half-cycle.

Fig. 12-10. Selenium rectifiers.
(International Rectifier Corp.)

that current flow may be observed on each half cycle. In Fig. 12-8, point A of transformer secondary is positive and current flows in direction of arrows. When point B is positive, current flows as shown in Fig. 12-9. Again, notice that the current through R is always in one direction. Both halves of the input voltage are rectified and the full voltage of the transformer is used.

METALLIC RECTIFIERS

Electron tubes used as rectifiers have some disadvantages. They are fragile, relatively more expensive and a heater voltage is necessary which consumes power. Research engineers discovered early in the development of electronic circuitry that certain combinations of materials exhibited unilateral (one direction) conduction of current. One such device employs a base plate, a SELENIUM layer and a counter-electrode of metal alloy. See Fig. 12-10. Several of the basic sections may be assembled in series for more effective rectification. This device, as might be suspected, has a <u>low forward resistance and a high reverse resistance</u>. The selenium rectifier, when inserted in a rectifier circuit

in place of the electron tube, performs a similar function.

Another combination used in the metallic disc rectifier is copper and copper oxide. The copper oxide coating is quite thin, so several of these rectifiers are placed in series for high power applications. Metallic rectifiers find wide use in many kinds of electrical and electronic equipment. They are efficient, inexpensive and are capable of handling high power requirements.

The full wave rectifier illustrated in Fig. 12-4 has been redrawn in Fig. 12-11, using metallic rectifiers in place of the diodes.

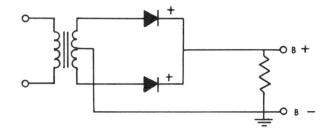

Fig. 12-11. Full-wave rectifier circuit using metallic rectifiers.

180

Notice the symbol used for the metallic rectifier. The positive or plate side of the rectifier should be connected to the positive side of the circuit. Electron flow is in the direction indicated in Fig. 12-12.

ELECTRON FLOW

Fig. 12-12. Symbol and direction of electron flow through metallic rectifier.

FILTERS

The resulting output of either the half-wave or full-wave rectifier is a pulsating voltage. Before it can be applied to the electron tubes in a radio or television receiver, the pulsations must be removed to a negligible amount. Pure direct current is desirable. This is accomplished by means of a FILTER NETWORK. Referring to Fig. 12-13, the out-

Fig. 12-13. Average value of full-wave rectifier output.

put waveform of a full-wave rectifier is shown. The average voltage of this pulsating wave is designated by the line E_{av} and is equal to .637 x the peak voltage. The shaded portion of the wave above the average line is equal in area to the shaded portion below the line. The fluctuation above and below the average voltage is called the AC RIPPLE. It is the ripple that requires the filtering. The PERCENTAGE OF RIPPLE to the average voltage must be limited to small value. Math-

ematically, the ripple percentage may be found by:

$$\%\text{Ripple} = \frac{E_{rms} \text{ of Ripple Voltage}}{E_{average}} \times 100$$

A capacitor connected across the rectifier output, as shown in Fig. 12-14, provides some filtering action. The capacitor has the ability to store electrons. When the rectifier tube is conducting, the capacitor charges rapidly to approximately the peak voltage of the wave,

Fig. 12-14. Filtering action of a capacitor.

limited only by the resistance of the rectifier tube and the reactance of the transformer windings. As the voltage from the rectifier drops, between the pulsations in the wave, the capacitor then discharges through the resistance of the load. The capacitor, in effect, is a storage chamber for electrons which accepts electrons at peak voltage and supplies them to the load when the rectifier output is low. A comparison of input and output wave forms may be seen in Fig. 12-15. Capacitors used for this purpose are the electrolytic types, because large capacitances are needed

Fig. 12-15. Input and output of capacitor filter showing change in wave form.

in a limited space. Customary values range from 4 to 50 microfarads or more with working voltages in excess of the peak voltage from the rectifier.

The filtering action may be improved by the addition of a choke in series with the load. This filter circuit appears as in Fig. 12-16. The filter choke consists of many turns of wire wound on a laminated iron core. In our earlier studies of magnetism and inductive reactance, it was learned that inductance was

Fig. 12-16. *Further filtering is produced by the choke in series with the load.*

that property of a circuit which resisted a change in current. A rise in current induced a counter emf which opposed the rise; a decrease in current induced a counter emf which opposed the decrease. So, as a result, the choke continually opposes any fluctuation in current, yet offers very little opposition to a direct current. Chokes used in radios have values from 8 to 30 henrys with current ratings from 50 to 200 milliamperes. Larger chokes may be used in transmitters and other electronic devices. The additional filtering action as a result of the filter choke may be observed in Fig. 12-17.

Fig. 12-17. *Wave forms show filtering action of capacitor and choke.*

A second capacitor may be used in the filter section after the choke, to provide additional filter action. See Fig. 12-18. The action of this capacitor is similar to the first capacitor. The circuit configuration appears

Fig. 12-18. *Pi (π) section filter configuration.*

as the Greek letter π and the filter is called a pi-section filter. Since the first filtering component is a capacitor, it is referred to as a capacitor input filter. In Fig. 12-19 the choke is the first filtering component, so it is called a choke-input filter. The circuit configuration now appears as an inverted L and is therefore called an L section filter. Several of these filter sections may be used in series to provide additional filtering.

Fig. 12-19. *Choke input L filter.*

In the capacitor input filter, the capacitor charges to the peak voltage of the rectified wave. However, in the choke input, the charging current for the capacitor is limited by the choke and the capacitor does not charge to the peak voltage. As a result, the output voltage of the power supply using the capacitor input filter is higher than one using the choke-input filter. Because the choke does not limit the charging current in the capacitor input filter, this type of filter should be used with vacuum tubes for rectifiers. The increase in the plate resistance of the vacuum tube limits the surge of current. The capacitor input filter should not be used with the mercury vapor rectifier tube, as these instantaneous high currents will destroy the tube. The choke input filter should be used in circuits employing mercury vapor rectifier tubes.

VOLTAGE REGULATION

The output voltage of a power supply will usually decrease when a load is applied. This is not a desirable effect and should be eliminated. The voltage decrease under load, to the power supply voltage with no load, when expressed as a percentage, is called the PERCENTAGE OF VOLTAGE REGULATION. It is a factor considered in the quality of a power supply. Expressed mathematically,

$$\% \text{ Voltage Regulation} = \frac{E_{nl} - E_{fl}}{E_{fl}} \times 100$$

where,

E_{nl} = voltage with no load
E_{fl} = voltage with full load

Example: If a power supply has a no load voltage of 300 volts and this voltage drops to 250 volts when a load is applied, what is its percentage of regulation?

$$\% \text{ Regulation} = \frac{300\,v - 250\,v}{250\,v} \times 100$$

$$= \frac{50}{250} \times 100 = 20\%$$

LOAD RESISTOR

To complete the basic power supply circuit a load resistor is connected across the supply as in Fig. 12-20. This resistor serves a three-fold purpose.

1. As a BLEEDER. During operation of the power supply, peak voltages are stored in the capacitors of the filter sections. These capacitors remain charged after the equipment is turned-off, and can be dangerous if accidentally touched by the technician. The load resistor serves as a "bleeder" and allows these capacitors to discharge when not in use. The wise technician will always take the added precaution and short-out capacitors to ground with an insulated screwdriver.

2. To Improve Regulation. The load resistor acts as a pre-load on the power supply and causes a voltage drop. When equipment is attached to the supply, the additional drop is relatively small and the regulation is improved. An example will clarify this point. Assume the terminal voltage of the power supply is 300 volts with no load resistor and no equipment connected to it. When the equipment is connected and turned on, the voltage drops to 250 volts and the regulation is 20 per cent. (See previous example under voltage regulation.) If the resistor across the power supply produces an initial drop to 260 volts, then the output voltage is considered as 260 volts. If the equipment now connected to the supply causes the voltage to drop to 250 volts, then the power supply regulation may be considered as,

$$\% \text{ Regulation} = \frac{260\,v - 250\,v}{250\,v} \times 100$$

$$= \frac{10\,v}{250\,v} \times 100 = 4\%$$

The usable voltage of the supply has only varied four percent. A further advantage of preloading the supply is an improvement in the filtering action of the choke. The resistor allows a current to flow in the supply at all

Fig. 12-20. Complete power supply circuit with load resistor.

times. A choke has better filtering action under this condition of current than when it varies between a low value and zero.

3. <u>As a Voltage Divider.</u> The load resistor provides a convenient method of obtaining several voltages from the supply. By replacing the single load resistor by separate resistors in series as in Fig. 12-21, several fixed

Fig. 12-21. *Voltage divider across power supply output.*

DC voltages are available. A sliding tap resistor may be used, if intermittent adjustments of voltage are required. This is called a VOLTAGE DIVIDER and takes advantage of Ohm's Law which states that the voltage drop across a resistor equals current times resistance, $(E = I \times R)$. In Fig. 12-21, the three resistors are equal. The voltage drop divides equally between them and their sum equals the applied voltage. Other values of resistors may be used, if other voltages are required.

The beginning student sometimes neglects the effect of connecting a load to one of the taps on a voltage divider. This load is in parallel to the voltage divider resistor, decreases the total resistance, and therefore changes the voltage at that particular tap. This is illustrated in Fig. 12-22. The divider is made up of three 50 K resistors. The 300 volts of the supply divides to 100 volts, 200 volts and 300 volts at terminals C, B and A respectively. If a load of 50 KΩ is now connected to terminal C as shown, it is in parallel with R_3 and resistance becomes:

$$R_T = \frac{R_3 R_L}{R_3 + R_L} = \frac{50,000 \times 50,000}{50,000 + 50,000} = 25,000Ω$$

Now the total series resistance across the power supply is only, 50KΩ + 50KΩ + 25KΩ = 125KΩ and the current through the divider is:

$$I = \frac{E}{R} = \frac{300}{125 \, KΩ} = .0024 \text{ amps}$$

and the voltage at point C is:

$E = I \times R = .0024 \times 25,000 \, Ω = 60 \, v$
and the voltage at point B is 180 volts.
If another load were connected to Point B, a further change of voltage division would result.

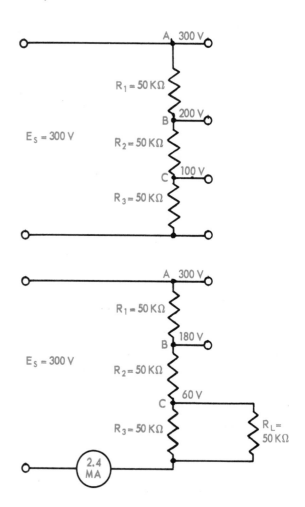

Fig. 12-22. *Diagrams show change in resistance in a voltage divider when a load is attached.*

VOLTAGE REGULATORS

It is apparent that some means should be provided to assure a constant voltage output at the power supply under varying load conditions. The theory of this circuit takes advantage of the fact that a voltage drop across a resistor is equal to the product of current and resistance. The fundamental circuit is diagramed in Fig. 12-23. The total output of the supply is applied to terminals A and B, and the voltage is divided between the load and variable resistor R in correct proportion. If the voltage of the supply increases, the

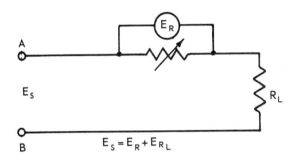

Fig. 12-23. Basic circuit shows theory of voltage regulation.

voltage across the load would tend to increase. If the resistance of R is manually increased, the voltage drop across R would increase and offset the increase of voltage from the supply, leaving a constant voltage for the load. To do this manually would be impossible, so sensitive electronic circuits have been devised to give excellent voltage regulation.

A simplified regulator circuit employs a neon glow tube. See Fig. 12-24. The glow tube conducts a current as a result of ionization

Fig. 12-24. Circuit of neon glow tube regulator.

of gas, and a fairly constant voltage drop appears across the tube. As the current increases, the internal impedance of the tube decreases because of increased ionization. In

Fig. 12-24 the resistance R is connected in series with the glow tube and the load in parallel. If the voltage of the power supply increases, the voltage across the glow tube increases, which increases the current through the tube and decreases its internal resistance. This increases the current through R and increases the voltage drop across R. As a result, the increasing voltage of the power supply appears as an increased voltage across R. The increase does not appear across the load. The load voltage remains relatively constant within the limitations of the values of R and the glow tube used. Tube types OA3/VR75, OC3/VR105 and OD3/VR150 are examples of glow tube regulators designed to regulate voltages within their specified ranges.

An electron-tube voltage regulator is diagramed in Fig. 12-25, which uses the glow tube to provide a bias voltage for the grid of the electron regulator. When the power supply voltage increases, the output voltage tends to increase, making the cathode of V_1 more

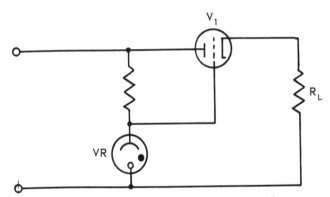

Fig. 12-25. Circuit diagram of an electron tube voltage regulator.

positive and increasing the bias. This increased bias increases the resistance of V_1, the voltage drop across V_1 increases, which counteracts the rise in supply voltage and the load voltage remains constant.

VOLTAGE DOUBLERS

Up to this point in the study of power supplies it has been assumed that the convenient source of power was 115 volt AC found in homes and schools. The transformer was used to step up or step down the voltages required for the electronic circuits. Because transformers are heavy and expensive, voltage multiplying circuits have been devised to raise voltages without the use of transformers. A study of Figs. 12-26A, and 12-26B, will explain the action in a half-wave voltage

Fig. 12-26A. *During first half-cycle C_1 charges through conduction of rectifier CR_1.*

Fig. 12-26B. *During second half-cycle applied line voltage is in series with charge on C and current flows through CR_2.*

doubler circuit. In Fig. 26A, the input AC voltage is on the negative half cycle, making point A negative and current flows from point A, through the metallic rectifier CR_1 and charges capacitor C_1 to the polarity shown. During the positive half cycle, point A is positive and the applied voltage is in series with the charged capacitor C_1. In the series connection the voltages add together so the output from the doubler is the applied voltage plus the voltage of C_1. Current cannot flow through the rectifier CR_1 due to its unilateral conduction. (See section on metallic rectifiers.) The output wave form shows half-wave rectification with an amplitude of approximately twice the input voltage. Metallic rectifier CR_2 permits current to flow in only one direction to the load.

A full-wave voltage doubler is drawn in Figs. 12-27A and 12-27B. During the positive peak of the AC input, point A is positive and current flow is from point B, charging C_1 in the polarity shown, through CR_1 to point A. (Follow arrows.) During the negative cycle of the input, point A is negative and current flows through CR_2 to C_2 and charges it to indicated polarity, to point B. Notice that during one cycle of AC input, capacitors C_1 and C_2 have been charged so that the voltages across C_1 and C_2 are in series. The output is taken from across these capacitors in series and the out-

Fig. 12-27A. *C_1 charges during first half-cycle.*

Fig. 12-27B. *C_2 charges during second half-cycle. Output voltage equals $C_1 + C_2$ in series.*

put voltage is the sum of both voltages or twice the input voltage.

Voltage doubler circuits are useful in producing high voltages for circuits requiring low currents. As the output voltage depends upon charged capacitors the voltage regulation is poor. Conventional filter circuits are added to smooth out the ripple voltage as in the transformer rectifier circuits. It is not necessary to use the metallic rectifiers in the doubler circuits, for the usual vacuum tube diodes serve equally as well.

Fig. 12-28. AC-DC Power Supply Circuit.

AC-DC SUPPLY

In Fig. 12-28 a common type of the AC-DC power supply is illustrated. It is used in many small table model radios. Compare this circuit to the half-wave rectifier in Fig. 12-1. It is the same, except that the transformer has been omitted. When used with AC, the output is the pulsating DC which must be filtered. The capacitor input filter is used to secure the higher voltage. Generally in a radio using this supply, the negative of B- is grounded to the chassis. If the AC plug is inserted the wrong way in the wall receptacle, it is possible to get a severe shock if you are grounded and accidentally touch the chassis.

When this supply is used on DC, the positive side of the DC line must be connected to the plate of the diode. The set will not operate otherwise. Current will only flow from cathode to plate. An interesting addition to this circuit is the use of the <u>series filament string</u>. Note that the heaters of all tubes are in series. When the series heaters are used, the sum of the voltage drops across each heater must equal the applied voltage. If this is not possible, a series voltage dropping resistor R is used to take up the remaining voltage. In this circuit if one tube burns out, the set is inoperative.

LESSON IN SAFETY: The AC-DC radio described in Fig. 12-28 is very dangerous if the AC plug is connected the wrong way. One

wire of your house wiring system is grounded to a water pipe, which will ground your radio only if the plug is inserted correctly. If the plug is reversed, an accidental contact between the radio and a water faucet would give a severe shock across your body. If the radio came in contact with any grounded table or appliance sparks would fly with the possible danger of fire.

Fig. 12-29. AC-DC supply with floating ground.

FLOATING GROUND

To avoid some of the hazzards of the AC-DC supply the radio chassis may be isolated from ground by a buffer capacitor. The chassis is not used as a common ground. The negative terminals are wired together in a "floating ground" system. See Fig. 12-29.

Test Your Knowledge

1. State four functions of the power supply.
2. State three purposes of the load resistor across the power supply.
3. The terminal voltage of a power supply is 300 volts. When a load is applied, the voltage drops to 280 volts. What is the percentage of regulation?
4. The average DC value of the output of a power supply is 250 volts. The ripple voltage has a peak value of 2 volts. What is the percentage of ripple?
5. Why does the output wave form of the capacitor filter approximate a saw tooth wave?
6. Why is the output from a capacitor-input filter higher than a choke-input filter?
7. When using a mercury vapor rectifier tube, which type of filter should be used?
8. A power supply has a 10KΩ load resistor. Its terminal voltage is 300 volts. What wattage rating should this resistor have?
9. A voltage divider is needed in place of the load resistor in problem 8 to give 75 volts, and 150 volts. What values of resistors should be used?
10. Draw a bridge rectifier circuit and place arrows showing current direction during each half cycle.

Chapter 13

ELECTRON TUBE AMPLIFIER

The growth of radio communication and electronic circuitry was made possible by the discovery of the control grid for the electron tube, by Dr. Lee DeForest. The function of this control grid permits the use of the tube as an amplifier, which is one of the more common applications of this device. Radio frequency waves develop only minute voltages in the antenna system of your radio. These voltages must be amplified to a level which will operate a speaker system so that you may hear the program. By definition, the word "amplify" means to produce a relatively large output signal by a small input signal. The "signal" may be a DC or AC voltage.

HOW THE ELECTRON TUBE AMPLIFIES

In Chapter 11, the operating characteristics of the vacuum tube were studied. The ability of an electron tube to amplify a voltage or signal is called its AMPLIFICATION FACTOR or "Mu" and represents the ratio between the change in plate voltage to a change in grid voltage when the plate current is held at a constant value. The amplification factor of any tube may be found by consulting a Tube Manual.

The following diagrams and examples explain the theory of vacuum tube amplification:

$R_T = 10,000\,\Omega$

$I_T = .02$ amps

$E_{R_1} = 100$ v and $E_{R_L} = 100$ v

Fig. 13-1.

$\underline{R_1 \text{ is reduced to } 4000\,\Omega}$

$R_T = 9000\,\Omega$

$I_T = .022$ amps

$E_{R_1} = 88$ v and $E_{R_L} = 112$ v

Fig. 13-2.

Fig. 13-3.

R$_1$ is increased to 6000 Ω

R$_T$ = 11,000 Ω

I$_T$ = .018 amps

E$_{R_1}$ = 110 v and E$_{R_L}$ = 90 v

The three simple series resistor circuits demonstrate a principle. In all cases R$_L$ is held constant. As R$_1$ is varied above and below 5,000, the voltage drops across R$_1$ and R$_L$ vary. When R$_1$ is increased, a larger proportion of the total voltage, 200 v, appears across R$_1$ When R$_1$ is decreased, a smaller proportion appears across R$_1$. Consider the case of R$_1$ with infinite resistance:

Fig. 13-4.

R$_1$ increased to infinite resistance

R$_T$ = infinity Ω

I$_T$ = 0

E$_{R_1}$ = 200 v and E$_{R_L}$ = 0

Since no current is flowing in the circuit, the voltage drop across
$$E_{R_L} = I \times R_L = 0 \times 5000 = 0$$

R$_1$ is reduced to zero resistance

R$_T$ = 5000 Ω

I$_T$ = .04 amps

E$_{R_1}$ = 0 and E$_{R_L}$ = 200 v

Fig. 13-5.

A vacuum tube may be considered as a variable resistance and its resistance depends upon the bias voltage applied to its grid. Refer back to Fig. 11-11 showing the characteristic curves of the 6J5 tube. When the plate voltage is 200 volts and the negative bias is -6 volts, the plate current is 7.5 ma. If the bias is changed to -8 volts, the current decreases to 3.5 ma. The tube appears as more resistance when the grid is made more negative.

Electron Tube Amplifier

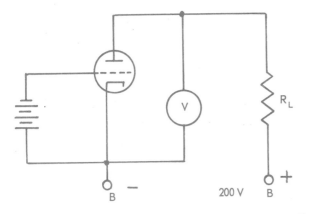

Fig. 13-6.

Tube V_1 is substituted for R_1

If V_1 is made more resistive by making the grid more negative, then E_p increases and E_{R_L} decreases.

If V_1 is made less resistive by making grid less negative, then E_p decreases and E_{R_L} increases.

Special cases are:

When V_1 is biased to CUT-OFF, it has infinite resistance, and E_p = B+ voltage of 200 volts.

When V_1 is biased positively to SATURATION, it has minimum resistance and E_p = approx. 0.

A varying voltage, therefore, applied to the grid of the tube, produces varying voltages E_p and E_{R_L}. This characteristic of a tube explains its ability to amplify an input voltage. For example: If a one volt change in grid bias produced a 20 volt change in plate voltage, E_p, the tube has amplified the input, and a GAIN of 20 times results.

$$\text{(Gain)} \quad A = \frac{\text{Output } E}{\text{Input } E} = \frac{20}{1} = 20$$

The GAIN of the tube is a result of both the amplification factor of the tube and the resistance R_L selected. They are related in the following formula:

$$A = \mu \times \frac{R_L}{R_L + R_p}$$

where,

μ = amplification factor

R_L = Load resistance

R_p = Plate resistance

Notice that as R_L is made larger, the gain A approaches the amplification factor, but it can never exceed it. The overall gain of several stages will equal the product of individual gains resulting from tubes and other devices, including transformers and tuned circuits.

The basic amplifier circuit is drawn in Fig. 13-7. For this example the grid bias voltage is fixed at negative four volts, and a

Fig. 13-7. Basic amplifier circuit with input and output signals.

two volt peak AC signal is also applied to the grid. The instantaneous grid bias voltage is equal to the algebraic sum of the fixed voltage and the signal voltage.

When signal is maximum positive then:

(+2) v + (-4) v = -2 volts

When signal is maximum negative then:

(-2) v + (-4) v = -6 volts

The grid voltage is varying between the limits of -2 and -6 volts. The output voltage wave form is also shown in Fig. 13-7 as the plate voltage of the tube. Observe that the output signal has been inverted or is 180 deg. out of phase with the input signal. This will be explained by a careful review of the previous discussion on "How a tube amplifies." The inverted amplified output voltage may be coupled to another tube or circuit for further amplification.

GRID BIAS VOLTAGE

The term "grid bias voltage" has been defined as the voltage applied between the grid of a tube (usually negative) and its cathode. Three common methods are used to supply this voltage and each should be thoroughly understood:

1. FIXED BIAS. This bias is supplied by a C battery or negative power supply. Cir-

cuits used for this purpose were described in Chapter 12. The fixed supply has wide application in radio transmitters and other equipment. Refer to Fig. 13-7 in which a C battery is used.

2. THE GRID LEAK. In Fig. 13-8 a capacitor has been inserted in series with the control grid. When the incoming signal is positive, the grid of the tube is driven positive. Some of the electrons emitted from the cathode will be attracted to this positive grid. When the incoming signal is negative, the grid becomes negative, but the grid is a cold element in the tube and cannot give up its electrons. As a consequence, more electrons are collected by the grid with each positive swing of the signal, until the grid becomes so negative that the tube will become CUT-OFF. To overcome this objectionable behavior, a resistor, called a "leak" is placed in parallel to the capacitor as in Fig. 13-9. This leak re-

Fig. 13-9. Resistor in parallel with C provides an electron "leak" and permits C to discharge.

sistor allows the capacitor to partially discharge, and maintain a level or charge for satisfactory operation. The function of the leak may be better understood by referring to Fig. 13-10. In this diagram, the bucket containing water may be considered the capacitor C. The hole or leak in the bucket is R and the supply pipe is the source of water or the grid. If the leak is too large, the level of water will decrease; if the leak is too small, the level will increase. Proper selection of values of R and C will permit the correct voltage level or bias to be maintained on the grid. It is important to note that no

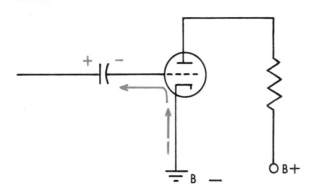

Fig. 13-8. Capacitor is connected in series with grid to establish a bias voltage.

bias will be developed for the tube, unless there is an incoming signal to drive the grid positive. Circuits similar to these were used as the grid-leak detector of early radios. They

Fig. 13-10. Leak action is compared to maintaining water level in a bucket.

now find application in limiting circuits and oscillators.

3. CATHODE OR SELF-BIAS. One of the more common methods of supplying the bias for proper operation of a vacuum tube is the cathode resistor, as diagramed in Fig. 13-11. When the tube conducts, a voltage drop develops across R_K and the cathode end of R_K

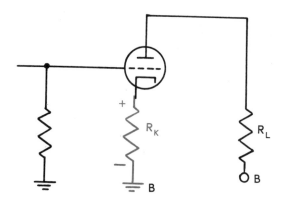

Fig. 13-11. Resistor R_K in cathode circuit causes cathode end of R_K to be more positive than ground.

becomes more positive than ground. But the grid is connected to ground, so the cathode is more positive than the grid. Is this not the same as applying a negative voltage to the grid? It means exactly the same. Either the grid may be more negative than the cathode, or the cathode may be more positive than the

grid. The voltage drop E_R determines the bias on the tube.

PROBLEM: A vacuum tube is designed to operate with a plate current of 6 ma with a bias voltage of negative 4 volts. What value cathode resistor should be used?

SOLUTION:

$$R = \frac{E}{I} \qquad R = \frac{4v}{.006} = 666\,\Omega$$

See diagram in Fig. 13-12.

Fig. 13-12. Resistor of 666 ohms creates a -4 bias.

PROBLEM: In the diagram in Fig. 13-13, the resistance and current values are given. Find the B+ voltage, the plate voltage and the grid bias.

SOLUTION Since the total current is 20 ma and 10 ma is flowing through the tube, then 10 ma must be flowing through R_2. So the voltage drop across R_2 is:

$$E_{R_2} = I \times R =$$
$$.01 \times 20,000\,\Omega = 200 \text{ volts, B+ supply}$$

Since 10 ma is flowing through the tube and R_K is in series, the voltage drop across R_K is:

$$E_{R_K} = .01 \times 2,000\,\Omega = 20 \text{ volts}$$

The cathode is 20 volts more positive than

ground to which the grid is connected, and the tube has a <u>negative 20 volt bias.</u> The plate voltage E_p must equal <u>200 v</u>, measured between plate and ground.

Fig. 13-13. Schematic diagram of problem in text.

DEGENERATION BY CATHODE BIAS

It is apparent from previous studies that the current flow in a vacuum tube is controlled by the incoming signal and the bias voltage on the grid. As the signal swings positive, the bias on the tube is less negative and the current through the tube increases. But the self-biasing cathode resistor produces a voltage drop in direct proportion to the current. As a result a positive signal increases the voltage drop and thus makes the grid more negative in respect to the cathode. These two effects are opposing each other and result in a decrease in gain in the tube. If part of the output of the tube is fed back to the input grid circuit, so that it opposes the input, (180 deg. out of phase) it is called DEGENERATION. This is undesirable in many circuits, so a method must be employed to maintain the voltage drop across the cathode resistor. A capacitor of the correct value, called a cathode bypass capacitor, is connected in parallel with R_K in Fig. 13-14. The capacitor provides a low reactance path for a varying or

AC current around the resistor, thus leaving a relatively constant voltage drop across R_K

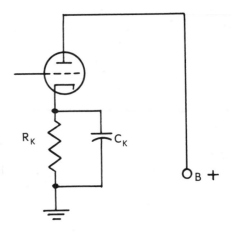

Fig. 13-14. Cathode bypass capacitor is used to limit degeneration.

due to the direct current. The value of C depends upon the frequency of the signals being amplified and should have a reactance of one-tenth or less of the value of the cathode resistor.

PROBLEM: A tube used to amplify audio frequencies down to 100 cps has a cathode resistor of 1200 ohms. What value bypass capacitor should be selected?

SOLUTION: Since R_K equals 1200 ohms, C should have a reactance of one-tenth or 120 ohms or less at 100 cps. Now:

$$X_C = \frac{1}{2\pi fC} \quad or \quad C = \frac{1}{2\pi fX_C}$$

Then:

$$C = \frac{1}{6.28 \times 100 \times 120}$$
$$= \frac{1}{75360} = .000013 \text{ f.} = 13 \ \mu\text{f.}$$

Capacitors are manufactured in 10 and 16 μf sizes, so the 16μf would be selected for this circuit and X_C would be less than 120Ω. A capacitor of this value would effectively short circuit the variation in voltage at a frequency of 100 cps and when used as a cathode bypass, it would reduce degeneration to an allowable minimum.

Electron Tube Amplifier

If the tube were used to amplify radio-frequency signals at 1000 kc for example, then the bypass capacitor value would be,

$$C = \frac{1}{6.28 \times 1000 \times 10^3 \times 120} \quad \text{or} \quad .0013\,\mu f$$

A .001 μf capacitor would be used.

CLASS A AMPLIFIERS

One convenient method of classifying vacuum tube amplifiers is by the operating point as determined by the fixed grid bias. Referring to the characteristic curve of a common vacuum tube in Fig. 13-15, the operating point is set at negative four volts by a fixed voltage source. The curve shows that a plate current of 8 ma will flow with a plate voltage of 160 volts. A one volt peak signal applied to the grid causes the grid voltage to vary between -3 and -5 volts and the plate current to

Fig. 13-15. Tube is operating around center of linear portion of characteristic curve as Class A.

vary between 5 ma and 11 ma. Both the input and output wave forms are shown in Fig. 13-15. A tube operated in this manner is classified as a Class A amplifier and may be identified by:

1. The operating point is near the center of the straight line portion of the curve or it is operating on the linear portion of the curve.

2. The output wave form is a faithful reproduction of the input wave form except that it is amplified.

3. Plate current is always flowing in the circuit, whether an input signal is applied or not.

4. The average plate current is the same whether an input signal is applied or not.

5. Considering one cycle of the input signal as 360 deg., then current flows in the plate circuit during 360 deg. of the input cycle.

Characteristics of a Class A amplifier may be summarized as:

1. Low distortion, faithful reproduction. Such an amplifier enjoys wide usage in audio amplifiers when high fidelity reproduction is required.

2. Low power output and low efficiency. The tube is conducting at all times, thus allowing no time for cooling.

3. High power amplification.

It should be noted that the grid in the above mentioned amplifier is not driven positive by the input signal. This is usually the case. In special applications, the signal does drive the grid positive and the grid collects electrons which causes a grid current to flow. Amplifiers have a further designation by a subscript number such as:

Class A_1 - grid is not driven positive

Class A_2 - grid is driven positive and grid current flows. If no subscript is used, it is assumed to be Class A_1.

CLASS B AMPLIFIERS

On the characteristic curve in Fig. 13-16, a tube is biased at its cut-off point of negative 8 volts. A peak input signal of 4 volts causes the grid voltage to vary between -4 volts and -12 volts. The tube conducts only between -8 volts and -4 volts. During the negative half cycle of the input signal the tube does not conduct and plate current is zero. The tube acts as a half-wave rectifier and produces plate current only during the positive half of the input signal. A tube operated in this manner, is called a CLASS B amplifier and may be identified by:

1. The tube is biased at approximately cut-off, which is its operating point.

2. Plate current flows only during one half the input signal or 180 deg. of the cycle.

3. Considerable distortion results, be-

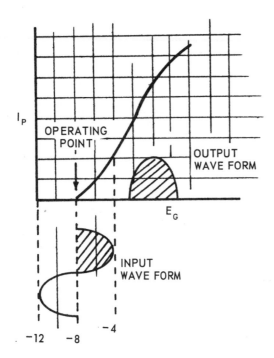

Fig. 13-16. *Tube biased at cutoff is operating Class B.*

cause one half of the input wave form has been removed.

The amplifier may be further characterized by:

1. Medium power output and efficiency. The tube is resting (not conducting) one half of the time.

2. Medium power amplification.

Again, if the input signal drives the grid positive, the subscript $_2$ is used, as Class B$_2$.

PUSH-PULL AMPLIFIERS

The medium power and efficiency characteristics of the Class B amplifier may be used to advantage to produce a high fidelity output by a push-pull circuit. Two tubes are used.

Each tube amplifies faithfully one half of the input signal. Fig. 13-17 shows the circuit configuration. The input signal is applied to the grids of V$_1$ and V$_2$ by coupling transformer T$_1$. During the positive half of input cycle, the upper end of the secondary of T$_1$ is positive, making grid V$_1$ more positive and driving it into conduction. As a result, both halves of the input signal combine in the output as a relatively true reproduction of the input wave form.

It should be noted that the design of a push-pull amplifier requires the division or separation of the input signal into positive and negative half cycles. These half signals are fed respectively to the grids of the tubes. This was accomplished in the previous example by means of an input or driver transformer.

Transformers which will give a satisfactory frequency response in a circuit of this nature are expensive. Other circuits have been designed which are more economical. In Fig. 13-18 is a diagram of a triode amplifier using equal load resistors in both the cathode and plate circuits. The varying current in the tube causes an equal voltage drop across both R$_1$ and R$_2$. However, the signal taken from the plate of the tube is 180 deg. out of phase with the input signal and the signal taken from across the cathode resistor is in phase with the input signal. These two signals are coupled by means of capacitors to the respective grids of the push-pull amplifier. This circuit is called a PHASE SPLITTER.

In order to provide greater gain as well as phase splitting or inversion, two triodes may be used as diagramed in Fig. 13-19. A duo-triode may be used. The tube used in this schematic is a 12AX7. Both triodes are enclosed in one glass envelope. To trace the action of this circuit, it must be remembered that both triodes have equal amplification factors. Assuming a voltage gain of 10, a one volt signal will produce a ten volt change at the plate of V$_{1A}$. This signal is fed to the grid on one push-pull amplifier tube. The load resistor in the plate circuit of V$_{1A}$ consists of two resistors in series. One of these resis-

Fig. 13-17. Basic diagram of a push-pull power amplifier.

Fig. 13-18. Basic diagram of a phase splitter.

Fig. 13-19. Basic diagram of a phase inverter. V_{1A} and V_{1B} drawn as separate tubes to clarify the explanation of circuit.

Fig. 13-20. Commercial high fidelity amplifier employing a push-pull amplifier. (Allied Radio)

fied to produce a ten volt change at the plate of V_{1B}. This signal is coupled to the grid of the other push-pull amplifier tube. The phase of each signal in the circuit should be carefully studied as indicated on the schematic.

SUMMARIZING: A positive signal at the grid of V_{1A} produces a negative signal or 180 deg. phase shift at the plate of V_{1A}. One tenth of this negative signal is fed to the grid of V_{1B} which produces a positive signal at the plate of V_{1B}. This circuit is frequently called a PHASE INVERTER, or a PARAPHASE AMPLIFIER.

A commercial high fidelity amplifier which uses the phase splitter and push-pull amplifier is illustrated in Figs. 13-20 and 13-21. Refer to the circuit diagram and compare to Figs. 13-17 and 13-18.

tors is valued at one tenth and the other nine tenths of the total load resistance. The voltage drop across the load can then be divided to one volt and nine volts respectively. The one volt signal is fed to the grid of V_{1B} and ampli-

Fig. 13-21. Schematic of Hi Fi amplifier pictured in Fig. 13-20.

NOTES

RESISTORS INDICATED IN OHMS
K = 1,000 OHMS
MEG = 1,000,000 OHMS
⏚ = CHASSIS GROUND

CAPACITORS INDICATED IN MICROFARADS UNLESS OTHERWISE SPECIFIED

VOLTAGE MEASUREMENTS ARE DC FROM POINTS INDICATED TO CHASSIS GROUND UNLESS OTHERWISE SPECIFIED

ALL MEASUREMENTS MADE WITH A VTVM

VOLTAGE TOLERANCE ±10%

CLASS AB AMPLIFIERS

This class of amplification should be considered because it represents a compromise between the high fidelity characteristics of the Class A amplifier and the higher efficiency of the Class B amplifier. The tube is biased at some point between cut-off and the center of the linear portion of the characteristic curve, usually close to the knee or bend in the curve as shown in Fig. 13-22. The current in the

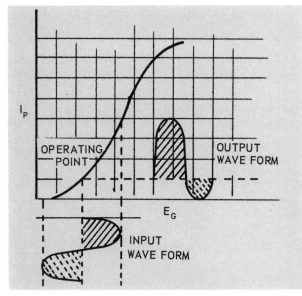

Fig. 13-22. *Tube is biased between Class A and B which combines some characteristics of both. It is Class AB.*

tube flows more than half the time, or for more than 180 deg. of the input signal. If the signal drives the grid positive, it is classified as AB_2, otherwise it is AB_1 or simply Class AB.

CLASS C AMPLIFIERS

This important classification of amplifiers is used extensively as radio-frequency amplifiers. The tube is biased at a point considerably beyond cut-off. Current flows in the tube for less than one half the time of the input signal or less than 180 deg. of the input signal. The graph in Fig. 13-23 illustrates the operation characteristics and a visual comparison of input and output signals. The output does not resemble the input and there is high distortion in this class of amplifica-

tion. Consequently, it cannot be used for the amplification of audio signals. However, a radio frequency signal can be amplified because the wave form in the output can be restored to its original shape by means of a tuned-tank circuit. This will be discussed in a later chapter. The Class C amplifier may be summarized as:

1. The tube is biased to a point beyond cut-off.

2. High efficiency since the tube is operating only a fraction of the time.

3. High distortion in output, not suitable for audio frequency amplification.

4. High power output and low power amplification.

METHODS OF COUPLING

One tube or stage of amplification is usually insufficient to amplify the small signal voltages normally found in radios, amplifiers and other electronic equipment. Several stages may be connected together in CASCADE to secure the necessary voltage levels.

Fig. 13-23. *Characteristic curve shows a Class C amplifier.*

This involves coupling or connecting the output of one tube to the input of another. Four methods are commonly used:

1. RC (resistance-capacitance) coupling
2. Transformer coupling

3. Impedance coupling
4. Direct coupling

Coupling circuits should provide optimum response for frequencies to be used, with low distortion of the wave form.

RC COUPLING

The most common method of coupling

tubes in cascade is by resistance and capacitance. This is an economical method involving low cost components, with the added advantage of light weight and compactness. Such coupling provides good frequency response and is especially adaptable to many tubes used as amplifiers. Because of the importance of this method, it will be discussed in detail and certain basic principles of electronics should be reviewed. Follow each diagram and its explanation:

Capacitor C charges to 150 volts with the indicated polarity. When C is fully charged, the voltage E_c will equal the applied voltage of 150 volts. During charging a voltage drop will appear across R_g and is equal to I x R. When C has reached its full charge, current will no longer flow and no voltage drop will appear across R_g.

Fig. 13-24.

If the voltage at point A is now decreased to 140 volts, capacitor C will discharge to this new voltage. Discharge current flows in direction of arrow and produces voltage drop across R_g during discharge.

Fig. 13-25.

Conversely, if voltage at point A is increased to 160 volts, capacitor C will charge to this new voltage. Charging current flows in direction of arrow and produces voltage drop across R_g during charging.

Fig. 13-26.

At this point, some important observations should be made. Refer to diagrams.

1. <u>When C is fully charged, no voltage appears between G and ground.</u>

2. If the voltage at point A is changed, the capacitor charges or discharges to the new value and this current produces a voltage between G and ground equal to I x R_g. When the capacitor has changed its charge to the new value, no voltage will appear between G and ground.

3. The voltage at point A will not appear at point G because a <u>capacitor blocks a DC voltage.</u>

4. However, <u>any change in the voltage at point A will appear as a voltage at point G, because a capacitor passes a change in voltage.</u>

If a 10 volt peak AC voltage is applied to point A, then the voltage at point A will vary between +160 v and +140 v at the frequency of the AC signal voltage. At the same time, a varying voltage of the same frequency will appear across R_g equal to I x R or 10 volts plus or minus.

Fig. 13-27.

Fig. 13-28.

In this diagram, two tubes are coupled in cascade by the resistance-capacitance method. Let's apply what we have learned. The incoming signal on the grid of V_1 causes the conduction of V_1 to vary which produces an amplified change in the plate voltage of V_1 or at point A. Capacitor C charges and discharges as the voltage at point A changes. A voltage drop is produced across R_g equal to the <u>change in voltage at point A.</u> This voltage across R_g is connected to the grid of V_2 which controls the conduction of V_2. Several

tubes may be coupled in this manner and each tube contributes a voltage gain to the circuit. The total gain is equal to the product of the individual tube gains. For example: If V_1 has a voltage gain (A) of 20 and V_2 has an A of 20, then the cumulative gain of both tubes would equal 20 x 20 or 400 times.

In this simplified discussion of RC coupling, mention should be made of the frequency response of this coupling circuit. It is a design problem to assure maximum signal response at desired frequencies, which means that the change in plate voltage should appear across the grid resistor R_g. Therefore, the reactance of C must be low at the desired range of frequencies. As X_c increases when frequency decreases, low frequencies may be severely attenuated. The response of the amplifier and coupling network will be distorted. Likewise at higher frequencies, the reactance of C becomes so low that it acts as a shunt across the load (R_L) of the previous tube and decreases the gain of the tube.

A typical response curve for an amplifier is drawn in Fig. 13-29. The curve shows that the gain of the circuit between certain frequency limits is the same or "flat." At each end of the range, the gain falls off, producing frequency distortion in the output.

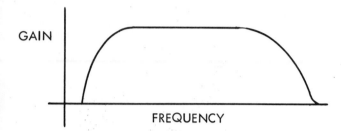

Fig. 13-29. Typical frequency response curve of an audio amplifier.

TRANSFORMER COUPLING

A circuit using transformer coupling is shown in Fig. 13-30. Certain advantages may be realized with this method:

1. Amplification of a signal voltage may be accomplished due to transformer action, which can be used to step-up the voltage in proportion to its turns ratio. Amplification then is the result of both the tube and the transformer.

2. The use of a transformer blocks the DC plate voltage from the grid of the next tube,

Fig. 13-30. Schematic of transformer coupled amplifier.

yet couples the change in voltage or signal voltage. (This function was performed by C in the RC coupling.)

3. When the transformer is used, it is not necessary to use a plate load resistance,

thereby avoiding this voltage loss.

4. The transformer may be used as a driver for a push-pull amplifier and provides the phase inversion.

5. The transformer may be used as an impedance matching device. This will be discussed in a later chapter.

Disadvantages of the transformer include its added weight, expense, and the necessity for excellent design to provide for high and low frequency response.

The transformer primary is matched to the output impedance of the selected tube for the range of frequencies to be used. At center frequencies in the range, the impedance of the primary and distributed capacitance is high and appear almost as an open circuit. As a result little signal voltage is lost. As the frequency is lowered, the reactance of the primary winding also decreases and the gain of the amplifier decreases. At a point representing 70.7 per cent of the gain at center frequency, the impedance of the transformer primary is equal to the plate resistance of the tube. This may be mathematically expressed as:

$$f = \frac{r_p}{2\pi L_p}$$

where:

f = frequency at which gain is 70.7 per-cent of gain at middle range

r_p = plate resistance of tube used

L_p = inductance of primary of transformer in henrys

EXAMPLE: The amplification factor of a tube is 10 and has a plate resistance of 10,000 ohms. A transformer used in coupling has a step-up ratio of 3 to 1 and a primary inductance of 40 henrys. What is the low frequency limit when used as an amplifier?

SOLUTION:

$$f = \frac{r_p}{2\pi L_p} = \frac{10,000}{6.28 \times 40} = 39.7 \text{ cps}$$

The gain at middle frequencies is the amplification factor times the turns ratio of 3 to 1. In this example it is:

$$10 \times 3 = 30$$

so at a frequency of 39.7 cps the gain falls off to 70.7 per cent of 30 or 21.2.

At high frequencies in the range the reactance of the transformer primary is high, which would have a tendency to increase the gain of the amplifier. However, the reactance of the distributed capacitance in the circuit decreases and has a shunting effect across the output voltage. The gain falls off rapidly.

IMPEDANCE COUPLING

Impedance coupling is similar to RC coupling except that the load resistor R_L is replaced by an inductance. This circuit is diagramed in Fig. 13-31. Since the resistance of the load is only the resistance of the wire used

Fig. 13-31. Diagram showing impedance coupling.

to wind the inductance, very little DC voltage drop appears across it, thereby leaving higher voltages for the plates of the tube. The load for the tube is developed by the reactance (X_L) of the inductance. So that some reactance may be present at low frequencies, large values of inductance may be used. The gain of an amplifier using impedance coupling increases as the frequency increases, because X_L increases with frequency. In the high frequency range, the decreasing reactance of the distributed capacitance shunts the signal voltage. Magnetic fields around load impedance

can also cause undesirable coupling to other circuits and must be overcome by specially designed inductances.

DIRECT COUPLED AMPLIFIERS

In the previous methods of coupling, the DC voltage on the plate of the tube has been blocked from the grid of the following tube either by a capacitor or transformer. Only the AC voltage has been coupled. The technician may look at a radio signal as having two parts; the DC component and the AC component. The DC component may represent the level or axis about which the AC voltage varies. Reference to Fig. 13-32 shows the DC

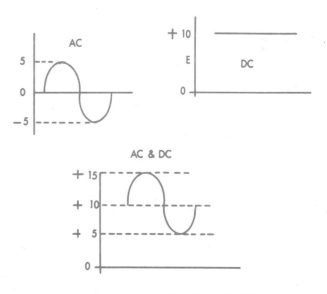

Fig. 13-32. Graphs show: 1, AC voltage. 2, DC voltage. 3, Combined AC and DC voltage.

and AC components separately and then combined. Frequently the DC component must be amplified together with the signal variation, so that some reference level may be maintained to determine the average signal strength. One such application is the overall brightness of the picture on your television. Night pictures appear dark and daylight pictures relatively lighter. The average brightness of the television picture is transmitted to your home as part of the video signal or its average DC component. This DC component cannot be lost, so video amplifiers employ directly coupled circuits, or other means to restore the DC component before the signal enters the picture tube.

The chief disadvantages of the direct-coupled amplifier is the necessity of providing a series of increasing voltages. These are made possible by the voltage divider in Fig. 13-33. Note that the plate of the first

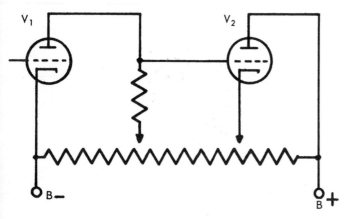

Fig. 13-33. A two-stage DC amplifier circuit.

tube V_1 is connected directly to the grid of V_2. In order to have the proper bias on tube V_2, the cathode voltage of V_2 must be higher than its grid. The plate voltage of V_2 must also be relatively higher. The whole circuit is rather complex and requires careful adjustment of voltages for elements of the tubes. Generally not more than two tubes are connected in this manner. When properly designed and adjusted, the amplifiers provide excellent frequency response and fidelity. Because of its low distortion and rapid response at low frequencies, direct-coupled amplifiers are common in pulse circuits used in industrial and military electronic devices.

FEEDBACK CIRCUITS

Feedback, as the word implies, means the feeding of a part of the output signal of an amplifier back to the input of the amplifier. In other words, part of the signal from the plate circuit of the tube is fed back to its grid circuit. If the feedback signal is in phase with the incoming signal and reinforces it, it is called REGENERATION or POSITIVE FEEDBACK. If the feedback signal is 180 deg.

out of phase with the incoming signal and cancels part of it, it is called DEGENERATION or NEGATIVE FEEDBACK.

Degeneration has already been discussed in reference to the cathode bypass capacitor. It is not undesirable in many cases, even though the gain of the amplifier is decreased. Negative feedback improves the fidelity of the output by removing distortion. Distortion present in the output, when fed back to the input, will cancel because it is 180 deg. out of phase. Loss of gain has its compensation by improved output.

Regeneration will be discussed in detail later during explanations of oscillators and detectors.

Negative feedback may easily be understood by examination of Fig. 13-34, which represents a simple RC coupling from the plate of the tube to the grid. As the plate volt-

Fig. 13-34. Degeneration is caused by coupling part of the plate signal back to the grid.

age is 180 deg. out of phase with the incoming signal, the feedback is also 180 deg. out of phase. The amount of feedback is determined by the ratio between R_1 and R_g which acts as a voltage divider for the feedback voltage. Usually about one tenth of the plate voltage is sufficient. The capacitor C acts as a DC blocking capacitor as well as a control of the frequency of the feedback voltages. If voltages in the audio range (20-20,000 cps) are being amplified, C should have a value which gives a low reactance path for these

Fig. 13-35. Degeneration is caused by feeding part of the signal at the speaker back to the cathode of the previous stage.

frequencies. Smaller capacitors would feed-back voltages of higher frequencies.

The relationship between output and feedback voltages is expressed as the Greek letter β (beta),

$$\beta = \frac{E_{feedback}}{E_{output}}$$

and is usually between .1 and .2.

In Fig. 13-35 is another circuit, showing feedback from the loudspeaker output back to the cathode of an amplifier. The resistance R_1 determines the correction proportion of the feedback voltage.

Feedback has only been briefly discussed at this point in our studies. We will meet degeneration again when a study is made of neutralizing circuits in radio transmitters. We will also study how a radio signal controls itself by feedback systems such as automatic volume and gain controls (AVC and AGC) circuits.

DISTORTION

The term distortion has been used frequently in our previous studies. It may be defined as an irregularity or difference in form between the input and output of an amplifier or circuit. It may appear in several types.

AMPLITUDE DISTORTION

Amplitude distortion may result from operating a tube non-linear or on the curved portion of its characteristic curve. This may be caused by improper bias or over-driving

Fig. 13-36. A commercial audio amplification system used at football games, fairs, amusement parks, dances and many other places where it is desired that hundreds of people may hear the program. (Stromberg-Carlson)

the tube. If the tube is driven to either saturation or cut-off, the resultant wave form is clipped-off and its amplitude is not a reproduction of the input.

Fig. 13-37. Telephone amplifier.

FREQUENCY DISTORTION

A properly designed amplifier should have sufficient gain for all frequencies for which it is intended. If some frequencies are amplified more, while others are attenuated, frequency distortion results. A common example of this type of distortion is the TONE CONTROL on your radio. Most people prefer the rich low tones in music, so provisions are made to remove high frequency tones for your listening pleasure.

HARMONIC DISTORTION

A harmonic frequency is the number of the harmonic times the fundamental frequency. For example, the 2nd harmonic of 1000 cps is 2000 cps; the 3rd harmonic of 5000 cps is 15,000 cps. Harmonic tones are desirable as a part of voice or music and identify the quality of the music. But harmonics, unrelated to music, generated within an amplifier are a form of distortion. If an amplifier is over-driven and its output wave is clipped either by cut-off or saturation, the resulting wave is no longer a sine wave of a fundamental frequency. It is a composite wave representing the fundamental and several harmonics. These harmonics were not present in the original sound, and this is harmonic distortion.

TRANSISTORIZED TELEPHONE AMPLIFIER

How many times have you wished that everyone in the room might hear the voice of friends or family over a long distance telephone call. The amplifier shown in Figs. 13-37, 13-38, and 13-39 is a practical device and may be permanently attached to your telephone. A flick of the switch will activate the transistorized amplifier and you may then have a family telephone visit.

The telephone pickup T_4, Fig. 13-38, is connected to two, transformer-coupled, common emitter stages which drive a push-pull power amplifier. Potentiometer R_7 is a gain control to adjust the volume of the amplifier. In the layout of the parts, keep transformers T_1 and T_2 as far from the input as possible to prevent possible feedback. Keep leads short. C_2, C_3 and C_5 are bypasses to prevent oscillation. If the circuit should oscillate, reverse the connections to the secondary of T_1.

In Fig. 13-39, the parts have been mounted on a small sheet of 1/8 inch plastic. The amplifier may be placed in a case of your own design.

Fig. 13-38. Wiring diagram for telephone amplifier.   (Sylvania Electric Corp.)

Fig. 13-39. Telephone amplifier, breadboard style.

PARTS LIST, TELEPHONE AMPLIFIER

B_1	9 V battery		R_4	4.7 K Ω, 1/2 watt
C_1, C_4	2 mfd, electrolytic, 15 V		R_5	68 Ω, 1/2 watt
C_2, C_3	8 mfd, electrolytic, 15 V		R_6	12 Ω, 1/2 watt
C_5	0.01 mfd, ceramic disc or mica, 100 V		R_7	100 K Ω, 1/2 watt potentiometer
LS_1	3-6 ohm loudspeaker		T_1	Argonne AR-104, Stancor TA-27 or equivalent
Q_1, Q_2, Q_3, Q_4	Sylvania 2N1265 Transistor		T_2	Argonne AR-109, Stancor TA-35 or equivalent
R_1	470 K Ω, 1/2 watt		T_3	Argonne AR-119, Stancor TA-21, or equivalent
R_2	150 K Ω, 1/2 watt		T_4	Telephone pickup coil, Lafayette MS-16, Shield M-133,
R_3	270 K Ω, 1/2 watt			or equivalent.

Fig. 13-40. Paging amplifier.

A PAGING AMPLIFIER

Many times the electronics experimenter requires a small audio amplifier to connect to a microphone. We call such a device, Fig. 13-40, a paging or announcing amplifier, because it works well with a lapel microphone. It will boost your voice so that it may be heard in crowds for some distance. The circuit, Fig. 13-41, has sufficient power to drive the small speaker. A gain control is provided by R_3.

In the paging amplifier three grounded emitter stages are connected in cascade. The last stage is a push-pull power amplifier. In the physical layout of parts, it is wise to keep R_3 some distance from transformer T_2 to prevent feedback.

These parts have been mounted on an 1/8 in. plastic sheet. It is advisable to construct a new circuit in breadboard style and test it before final assembly and soldering. This project represents several hours of recreation and education. You will have much satisfaction from the completed project. Try designing a modern case for it.

PARTS LIST FOR PAGING AMPLIFIER

B_1	9 V battery
$C_1 C_2$	10 mfd electrolytic, 15 V
LS_1	any 4, 8, or 16 ohm loudspeaker
Q_1	Sylvania 2N1265 transistor
Q_2, Q_3, Q_4	Sylvania 2N1266 transistor
R_1	68 K Ω, 1/2 watt
R_4	120 K Ω, 1/2 watt
R_2, R_6, R_8	560 Ω, 1/2 watt
R_3	5 K Ω, 1/2 watt potentiometer
R_5	6.8 K Ω, 1/2 watt
R_7	100 Ω, 1/2 watt
R_9	10 K Ω, 1/2 watt
T_1	Stancor TA-5 or equivalent
T_2	Stancor TA-10 or equivalent

Electron Tube Amplifier

Fig. 13-41. Wiring diagram for paging amplifier.
(Sylvania Electric Corp.)

FOR DISCUSSION

1. Why does a tube using the grid leak depend upon an input signal for its bias?
2. What are some of the characteristics of a good high fidelity sound system?
3. What is the purpose of feedback in an amplifier?
4. Discuss the relative merits of RC coupling vs. transformer coupling.
5. Discuss the several kinds of distortion possible in an amplifier.

TEST YOUR KNOWLEDGE

1. State three methods used to bias a tube.
2. Name four types of coupling used to cascade amplifiers.
3. A tube has MU of 20 and r_p of $7,000\,\Omega$. What is the voltage gain when R_L = $5,000\,\Omega$; when R_L = $10,000\,\Omega$; and when R_L = $50,000\,\Omega$.

4. A tube requires a negative 4 volt bias. I_p = 5 ma. What value cathode resistor should be used?
5. What value bypass capacitor should be used in question 4 for 100 cps?
6. Identify a Class A amplifier.
7. Name four characteristics of a Class A amplifier.
8. Identify a Class B amplifier.
9. Name four characteristics of a Class B amplifier.
10. Identify a Class C amplifier.
11. Name three characteristics of a Class C amplifier.
12. Draw circuit diagrams of the following.
    A. Two stages - RC coupled.
    B. Two stages - transformer coupled.
    C. Two stages - impedance coupled.
    D. A push-pull amplifier using transformers.
    E. A push-pull amplifier using splitter.
    F. A push-pull amplifier using inverter.

Electronics in a Paper Mill. From this console many of the processes of manufacturing paper are controlled. (Minneapolis-Honeywell Regulator Co.)

Chapter 14

VACUUM TUBE AS AN OSCILLATOR

The pendulum on a grandfather's clock which swings to and fro, marking the seconds of time as they become moments in history, should stimulate the inquiring mind of the young scientist. Why does the pendulum swing? The question is answered as the keeper of the clock restores its energy by winding the main spring with the familiar key. Has it kept a correct record of the passing time? The keeper makes adjustments on the length of the pendulum so the period of time required for one complete swing is synchronized with the fleeting seconds. The pendulum may be described as OSCILLATING.

A brief review of Chapter 5 will rediscover how an alternating current or voltage is generated. In the study of electricity, we can consider an oscillating current as a current which is flowing back and forth, or varying first in one direction and then the other, from a common reference point or mean. A comparison of the clock pendulum and an oscillating voltage is graphically illustrated in Fig. 14-1. The amplitude of the volt-

age may be followed as it starts from its reference line and rises to maximum potential in one direction and falls to zero, then rises to maximum potential in the opposite direction and returns to zero. One CYCLE or chain of events has been completed. A continuation of the oscillation would be more of the same, a repetition of these cycles. The period of time which elapses during this cycle is called the PERIOD of cycle, and the number of these cycles occurring per second can be measured and described as the FREQUENCY in cycles per second. In our studies in Chapter 5 we discovered that the electricity used in our homes and factories is an alternating or oscillating current at a frequency of sixty cycles per second. This alternating current is generated by dynamos driven by steam, water or atomic power.

In the study of electronics, voltages and currents of much higher frequencies are used and are generated by the VACUUM TUBE USED AS AN OSCILLATOR. Actually the vacuum tube does not oscillate, but merely acts as a valve, which feeds energy to a tuned circuit to sustain oscillation. The oscillatory action in the tuned circuit was explained in Chapter 8. Now is a good time to turn back and review these pages.

Two conditions must exist to sustain oscillations in the tuned circuit:

1. The energy fed back to the tuned circuit must be in phase with the first excitation voltage. The oscillator depends upon REGENERATIVE or POSITIVE feedback.

2. The amplitude of the feedback voltage must be sufficient so that the energy dissi-

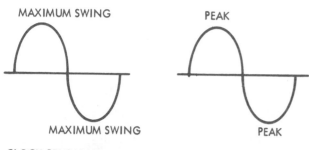

MAXIMUM SWING   PEAK

MAXIMUM SWING   PEAK

CLOCK PENDULUM

Fig. 14-1. A comparison between a swinging clock pendulum, and an oscillating current.

pated by the resistance of the circuit is re-placed. Perpetual motion has not yet been discovered.

THE ARMSTRONG OSCILLATOR

The simple circuit of the Armstrong oscillator is diagramed in Fig. 14-2. From this circuit the basic theory of oscillators may be understood. Notice the tuned-tank circuit L_1C_1 which determines the frequency of the oscillator. Follow the sequence of events in the theory of this circuit.

Fig. 14-4

STEP II. When V_1 reaches its saturation point, there is no longer a change of current

Fig. 14-2. Schematic of Armstrong Oscillator.

Fig. 14-3.

STEP I. When the voltage is applied to circuit, current flows from B-, through tube, through tickler coil L_2 to B+. L_2 is closely coupled to L_1 and the expanding magnetic field of L_2 makes the grid end of L_1 positive and the grid of V_1 positive. C_1 charges to the polarity shown. The grid of V_1 also collects electrons and charges C_2 in the indicated polarity.

in L_2 and the magnetic coupling to L_1 drops to zero. The negative charge on the grid side of C_2, no longer opposed by the induced voltage in L_1, drives the tube to cut-off. This rapid reduction of current through the tube and L_2 causes the grid end of L_1 to become negative which INCREASES the negative bias on V_1. C_1 also starts its discharge through L_1 as the first half cycle of oscillation. C_2 bleeds off its charge through R_1.

STEP III. The tube V_1 is held at cut-off until the charge on C_2 is bled-off to above cut-off at which time the tube starts conduction and the cycle is repeated.

Points to remember in this theory of the ARMSTRONG oscillator include:

1. The voltage developed across L_1 first opposes and then adds to the bias developed by the RC_2 combination.

2. The energy added to the tuned-tank cir-

cuit L_1C_1 by the tickler coil L_2 is sufficient to offset the energy lost in the circuit due to resistance. The coupling between L_1 and L_2 is adjustable.

3. The combination RC_2 has a relatively long time constant and establishes the operating bias for the tube. V_1 is operated Class C.

An examination of the voltage wave form in Fig. 14-5 on the grid of V_1 will give further clarification. The shaded portion represents tube conduction. At point B the bias

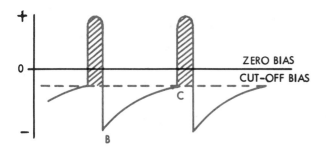

Fig. 14-5. Voltage wave form on grid of oscillator. Compare it to steps 1, 2, and 3 previously discussed.

is very negative as the result of the charge on C_2 plus the induced voltage across L_1. Interval B to C represents the time that C_2 is discharging through R until the cut-off point is reached and tube begins conduction for the next cycle.

THE HARTLEY OSCILLATOR

A very common oscillator used in radio receivers and transmitters is the HARTLEY oscillator. It has better stability than the Armstrong and the theory of operation is similar. The component parts in Fig. 14-6 are labeled to correspond to similar parts used in the description of the Armstrong oscillator in Figs. 14-4 and 14-5. Notice that the L_2 section of the coil is in series with the cathode-plate circuit and carries the total plate current. Follow the operation:

STEP I. When voltages are applied to V_1, current flows from B-, through coil L_2, to cathode, to plate, to B+. Since L_2 is inductively coupled to L_1, a voltage will be in-

duced in L_1 so that its grid end is positive. This increases the positive bias on the grid and drives the tube to its saturation point. During this time C_2 is also charging and trying to make the grid negative. The induced voltage and the charge on C_2 oppose each other.

STEP II. When the tube reaches saturation and there is no longer any change in current, the magnetic coupling between L_2 and L_1 falls to zero and the magnetic field around L_1 and L_2 will collapse and charge C_1 so that the grid end of the tank-circuit is negative. Since this charge now adds to the charge on C_2, the tube is quickly driven to cut-off. The decreasing current in L_2 induces a voltage in L_1 so that its grid end is negative. This increases the negative bias on V_1 to an even larger value.

STEP III. The tube is held at cut-off during the discharge time of C_2 through R. Current oscillates in tank-circuit $C_1L_1L_2$ as C_1 charges in first one polarity and then the other. The frequency of oscillation depends

Fig. 14-6. Hartley Oscillator. Compare it with the Armstrong Oscillator.

upon the value of L in henrys and C in farads. When C_2 discharges to above cut-off, the tube again conducts and the cycle is repeated. The RC_2 combination is used to set the operating point of the tube. It is Class C.

Fig. 14-7 shows a typical oscillator coil, used as the local oscillator in a radio receiver. The coil is wound continuously on a single form. The coil L_2 is formed by tapping at a specified point on the coil. In all cases the feedback or tickler coil L_2 supplies energy to the tuned circuit to overcome the resistance and sustain oscillations.

The capacitor C_3 in Fig. 14-6 bypasses the alternating current in the plate circuit of the tube around the power supply.

SERIES AND SHUNT FED OSCILLATORS

Series and shunt or parallel feeding an oscillator circuit describes the method of connecting the B+ voltage. A circuit is

Fig. 14-7. Typical oscillator coil used in the superheterodyne receiver. (J. W. Miller)

series-fed if the direct current from the B+ supply flows through the tank circuit. If the direct current is blocked by means of a capacitor and only the oscillating currents flow in the tuned-tank, then it is shunt fed. The Hartley oscillator in Fig. 14-6 is series-fed. Fig. 14-8 is a diagram of the same oscillator using a shunt-fed connection. The shunt-fed oscillator prevents a possible

dangerous high voltage shock in case the technician should accidentally touch the tank coil.

THE COLPITTS OSCILLATOR

Another widely used oscillator circuit employs a split capacitor, rather than the tapped coil, to obtain its feedback voltage. This Colpitts circuit is diagramed in Fig. 14-9. The operation of this circuit is similar

Fig. 14-9. Colpitts oscillator schematic.

to the Hartley. Its frequency is determined by the values of L_1, C_1 and C_2. The amount of feedback or excitation is adjusted by varying C_1. The operating bias is controlled by the RC_3 network. C_4 is a bypass capacitor as previously explained. This Colpitts oscillator is shunt-fed.

TUNED-GRID TUNED-PLATE OSCILLATOR

Another type of oscillator, called the tuned-grid tuned-plate (TGTP) is diagramed in Fig. 14-10. The feedback to the grid

Fig. 14-8. Shunt-fed Hartley oscillator diagram.

Fig. 14-10. Tuned-Grid-Tuned-Plate oscillator diagram.

tank circuit to sustain oscillations is accomplished through the interelectrode capacitance of the tube, as shown by the dotted component C in the schematic. The operating bias is again set by the grid-leak RC_3 and the voltage across the oscillating grid tank is either adding to or subtracting from the charge on C_3. The output is taken from the tuned-plate circuit tank. Both tank circuits are tuned to almost the same frequency. The output is slightly lower than the resonant frequency of either tuned circuit.

CHARACTERISTICS OF OSCILLATORS

The primary consideration in the design of any oscillator is frequency stability. Once

Fig. 14-11. Electron-coupled oscillator (ECO). Notice the Hartley oscillator circuit, using a grid for its plate.

it is adjusted to a frequency, it should remain at that frequency. When a load is applied to an oscillator by removing radio frequency energy from the tank, it has a tendency to change the frequency of the oscillator. Methods of isolating the load from the oscillator will be considered in the ELECTRON-COUPLED OSCILLATOR.

Temperature changes, vibration and changes in supply voltage also have adverse effects upon frequency stabilization and are problems which the design engineer must solve.

THE ELECTRON COUPLED OSCILLATOR

As previously mentioned, the changing load on an oscillator causes its frequency to change. The schematic diagram in Fig. 14-11 is that of a Hartley oscillator which

uses the SCREEN GRID of a pentode as a PLATE. Otherwise, the circuit is exactly the same as described before. The plate in the pentode V_1 is connected to the output tuned tank circuit. The only coupling between the grid and plate circuits is by means of the electron stream in the tube. It is therefore called the ELECTRON COUPLED OSCILLATOR or ECO. Capacitors C_3 and C_4 serve as bypass capacitors, keeping the screen grid at RF ground potential and the RF from the power supply respectively. The resistor R_2 is a voltage divider to provide a lower voltage for the screen grid.

An interesting built-in frequency control of this circuit results: If the screen voltage is increased, the frequency of the oscillator is decreased. If the plate voltage is increased, the oscillator frequency increases. Therefore, any variation of the supply voltage, which would ordinarily change the frequency, is cancelled due to these opposite effects.

CRYSTAL-CONTROLLED OSCILLATORS

A circuit which exhibits a very high frequency stability is the crystal-controlled oscillator. Radio communications, broadcasting stations and other equipment demanding a fixed frequency with little drift or variation depend upon the crystal as a frequency stabilizer. In our earlier studies of the Sources of Electricity, the phenomena of producting an EMF by mechanical pressure and/or distortion of certain crystalline substances were discussed. The opposite is also true. A voltage applied to the surfaces of a crystal will produce distortion. These effects are called PIEZOELECTRIC EFFECTS. When an electrical pressure is applied to a crystal, it will respond or oscillate at a frequency depending upon the size, thickness and kind of crystal used. The method of originally cutting the crystal also has a very important influence upon its behavior. These cuts are illustrated in Fig. 14-12. These small crystals are cut from a natural quartz crystal. The surfaces of an X cut crystal are perpendicular to the X or electrical axis of the crystal or perpendicular to a line drawn from the corners of the hexagonal crystal. A crystal cut so that its faces are perpendicular to the Y or mechanical axis is called a Y-cut crystal. A crystal cut at an angle of 35 deg. to the Z or optical axis is called an AT cut crystal. Each of these crystals responds to

Fig. 14-12. *Frequency characteristics of a crystal are determined by method of cutting.*

temperature changes in the following manner:

X-cut - negative temperature coefficient. As temperature increases, its frequency decreases.

Y-cut - positive temperature coefficient. As temperature increases, its frequency increases.

AT-cut - zero temperature coefficient. Very slight change of frequency with change of temperature.

A crystal is used in Amateur Radio to control the frequency of the transmitter. These crystals may be purchased for fixed frequencies used in the amateur bands. At a commercial broadcasting station, crystals used to control the transmitter frequency are placed in <u>crystal ovens</u> which are very

accurately maintained at an even temperature.

The simple crystal oscillator circuit is diagramed in Fig. 14-13. This circuit operates on the theory that if a small amount of energy from the plate circuit is fed back to the grid circuit which contains the crystal, the crystal will maintain oscillation in the circuit. The frequency of the oscillator is accurately controlled by the natural frequency of the crystal. The output or plate tank circuit is tuned to a frequency slightly above the crystal frequency so that the tank circuit is slightly inductive and will provide positive feedback.

In the crystal oscillator diagram a milliammeter has been inserted in the plate circuit in series with the tuned tank. To properly adjust the oscillator, C_1 should be varied until there is a <u>minimum</u> or "dip" in the plate current. This indicates that the tank circuit

Fig. 14-13. *Crystal oscillator circuit.*

is in resonance at the natural frequency of the crystal and the tank circuit has a <u>maximum impedance</u> Z to plate current at this frequency. Turning the capacitor C_1 very slightly in a reducing direction will adjust the tuned tank above the crystal frequency and result in stable operation. The plate current will rise slightly. The previous discussion on <u>tuning the tank circuit</u> is a very important lesson and should be thoroughly understood. There are many tuned circuits in electronic equipment.

Fig. 14-14. Block diagram representing various stages of basic radio transmitter.

THE RADIO TRANSMITTER

We will now discuss the building of a radio transmitter. Any of the oscillators which have been discussed will produce a radio frequency wave, which if properly connected to an antenna system, would radiate energy into space. However, more powerful signals are desired, so some stages of amplification are needed to increase the amplitude of the oscillator wave so that it will drive a final power amplifier. The block diagram of a simple continuous wave transmitter is drawn in Fig. 14-14. The first block is the conventional crystal oscillator, followed by two stages which act as BUFFERS or FREQUENCY MULTIPLIERS and then the final power amplifier. Three power supplies are provided: One for the oscillator and intermediate amplifiers, a higher voltage supply for the final power amplifier and a bias supply.

What is the purpose of a BUFFER STAGE? We have already learned that if a load is applied to an oscillator, it loses its frequency stability. It may change frequency. The buffer stage is a Class A amplifier, so designed that the grid is never driven positive by the oscillator signal and therefore the oscillator does not supply any power to the circuit. In other words the buffer stage places no load on the oscillator. A load may be applied to the output of the buffer stage, without affecting the oscillator frequency. The buffer isolates the load from the oscillator. An analogy, in everyday life, of a buffer may be observed in the construction of new developments of suburban homes. Shopping centers and commercial businesses

are usually not built right next to residential homes. Several apartments or multiple-family units are generally constructed to act as a buffer between business and residential living.

A typical buffer amplifier is drawn in Fig. 14-15. Although it does not differ from amplifier circuits already studied, it might

Fig. 14-15. Circuit diagram of a typical buffer amplifier.

serve as a practical review to identify and describe the purpose of each component in the circuit.

C_1 serves as a coupling capacitor to couple the signal from the oscillator to the grid of the buffer.

$C_2 R_2$ network provides the self bias for the tube. R_2 is selected to bias the tube for Class A operation and C_2 is the bypass for the radio frequency current.

R_1 is the grid load resistor.

R_3 serves to reduce the B+ voltage for the screen grid of the tube.

C_3 is an RF bypass capacitor to keep the screen grid at RF ground potential.

RFC is a radio frequency choke to keep the radio frequency signal from the power supply. It also provides an operating load for the tube.

C_5 couples the amplified signal to the tuned circuit.

$L_1 C_4$ is the tuned tank circuit. If it is tuned to the same frequency as the oscillator, it is called "straight through" operation.

What is a FREQUENCY MULTIPLIER? Crystals which are ground to oscillate at very high frequency must be very thin and consequently are fragile. So that high frequencies may be generated by using low frequency crystals, a frequency multiplier stage or stages may be used. In the frequency multiplier, the output tuned tank circuit is tuned to the second or third harmonic of the fundamental oscillator frequency. Since the oscillator output contains harmonics as well as the fundamental frequency, the tank circuit of the multiplier responds to the selected harmonic and attenuates other frequencies. The output of the multiplier may therefore be either two or three times the frequency of the input. If the frequency is twice as great it is called a DOUBLER, if three times greater, it is a TRIPLER. Several multiplier stages may be used to increase the frequency many times. Some power is lost, however, by the multiplication process.

THE POWER OR FINAL AMPLIFIER

Assuming that the oscillator wave has been sufficiently amplified and multiplied to the desired transmitting frequency, it then is used to control or "drive" a final power amplifier. In high powered transmitters an inter-

mediate power amplifier stage may be necessary to drive the large final tubes.

The major consideration of any power amplifier is its ability to handle large currents. It is characterized by its high cathode emission and relatively large plate surfaces. In low powered transmitters the Tetrode or Pentode may be satisfactory, but as power is increased the Triode with the directly heated cathode finds wide application. It may be either air or water cooled.

For the low powered transmitter, a single tube may be used as a single ended amplifier. The schematic is drawn in Fig. 14-16. For the continuous wave transmitter, this

Fig. 14-16. Schematic of a single-ended power amplifier.

final tube is usually operated Class C. This is possible since the wave may be restored to its original shape by the flywheel action of the tuned tank circuit in the output of the amplifier.

The student may better understand this action by comparing it to a child on a playground swing. A slight push on the swing as it moves from its maximum backward position will keep it swinging indefinitely. The push restores the energy lost by friction. The Class C amplifier has only pulses of energy in its output. These pulses are used to keep the tank circuit oscillating or swinging back and forth. A review of Class C operation in Chapter 13 may be necessary.

Now compare this circuit in Fig. 14-16 to the circuit of the TGTP oscillator in

Fig. 14-10. It is very similar, is it not? This circuit could act as an oscillator. If energy is fed back from the plate circuit to the grid circuit in phase or regenerating, the final oscillator would break into oscillation. Very unstable conditions would result in spurious radiation. But the TGTP oscillator sustained its oscillation through feedback due to the interelectrode capacitance between plate and grid. This capacitance also is present in the final amplifier and must be cancelled by a process known as NEUTRALIZATION. If a small voltage from the plate circuit is fed back to the grid circuit 180 deg. out of phase with the voltage fed back by the interelectrode capacitance, the two voltages will cancel. As a result the circuit will not oscillate. In Fig. 14-17 a center tapped coil is used in the final tank circuit. The voltage at point A is 180 deg. out of

diagramed in Fig. 14-18. The operation is similar to the circuit in Fig. 13-17. The neutralization is accomplished by using two capacitors. A part of the output voltage of one tube is used to neutralize the other tube. Since the outputs of the tubes are 180 deg. out of phase, the proper degeneration is possible.

KEYING

Up to this point the output of the transmitter has been a continuous radio fre-

Fig. 14-18. Push-pull power amplifier.

Fig. 14-17. Neutralization is accomplished by feedback through C$_n$.

phase with the voltage at point B, in respect to ground. The voltage at point A or at the plate of the tube is the troublesome voltage which causes the feedback through the interelectrode capacitance. The voltage at point B, which is 180 deg. out of phase, is fed back to the grid through the variable capacitor C$_n$. This capacitor is adjusted so that the degenerative feedback equals the regenerative feedback. If you are operating a transmitter, you should be familiar with procedures used for neutralization as outlined in the Manual.

To increase the power of the transmitter, frequently two or more tubes are used in parallel in the final amplifier. Another common type is the PUSH-PULL amplifier

quency wave, abbreviated to c.w. It contains no information for communication purposes. Early in the art of radio communications, methods were provided to interrupt the continuous wave into a series of short and longer bursts of radiated energy representing dots and dashes or dits and dahs. The familiar Morse Code which assigns the dits and dahs

to letters in the alphabet and numbers is still a popular and very dependable method of communication. In order to transmit these bursts of energy, a means of turning the transmitter "on and off" by means of a switch or KEY is necessary. Fig. 14-19 illustrates a key in common use. Learning to send and receive Morse Code is like learning a new language. In order to qualify for a Novice License in Amateur Radio, a code speed of five words per minute is required. For a General Class License one must copy thirteen words per minute.

Several methods of keying the transmitter

are in use today. Sometimes only one tube is keyed or several tubes may be keyed simultaneously. A common method is keying the plate circuit of a tube. Actually this means

Fig. 14-19. Key used with cw transmitter for sending Morse Code. (E. F. Johnson Co.)

turning the plate voltage on and off. A diagram of "plate keying" a final amplifier is shown in Fig. 14-20. Notice the KEY-CLICK FILTER in the circuit. When the circuit is suddenly interrupted by opening the key, large surges of energy are present which tend to oscillate and arc across the key contacts. This creates undesirable radiation in the form of clicks which may be heard by a nearby radio receiver. The filter absorbs this energy and minimizes radiation. In large transmitters employing heavy plate currents

Fig. 14-20. Final amplifier is keyed in plate circuit. Note key click filter.

in the final amplifier, a "keying relay" is used. This is a familiar use of a relay, i.e. to use a small voltage to control a high voltage, high current circuit. This circuit is schematically drawn in Fig. 14-21.

A third common method and a very satisfying one is called GRID-BLOCK KEYING. This system takes advantage of the cut-off characteristic of a vacuum tube. A high negative bias is applied to the grid of the tube to be keyed. It therefore is cut off and inoperative. When the key is depressed, a positive voltage is applied to the grid which raises the bias voltage up to its normal operating point. Fig. 14-22 illustrates this circuit.

When the key is up or open the negative bias supply cuts the conduction of the tube to zero. When the key is closed, the bias supply is short circuited and the tube operates in its normal manner and the transmitter radiates its radio frequency output.

Fig. 14-21. Relay used to key transmitter.

MODULATION

When you turn on the radio or TV, you expect to hear music and the voices of your

Fig. 14-22. Circuit is keyed by "grid blocking."

favorite program. The "dits and dahs" of the CW transmitter would have no meaning to the inexperienced operator. The process of combining or superimposing an audio wave on a radio frequency wave is called MODULATION. Sound waves must first be converted into electrical waves, amplified, and combined with the radio wave.

In one method, used in commercial broadcasting, the amplitude of the radio wave is

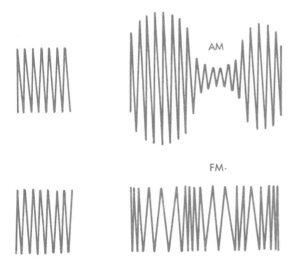

Fig. 14-23. Wave forms show Amplitude & Frequency Modulation.

made to vary at an audio frequency rate. This is amplitude modulation or AM. In a second method, the frequency of the radio

wave is made to vary at an audio frequency rate called frequency modulation or FM. Both of these methods are illustrated in Fig. 14-23, showing first the RF and AF waves separately and then the modulated waves.

MICROPHONES

The first problem in our study is the conversion of sound waves to electrical waves. The nature of a sound wave must be explored. Physicists describe a sound wave as condensations and rarefactions of the air. Your vocal cords set up vibrations in the air and these waves radiate out to all persons within hearing range. A device, called a MICROPHONE, is used to convert these sound waves to electrical audio waves of the same frequency and relative amplitude. In Fig. 14-24 three types of microphones are illustrated to familiarize the student with the interior of these devices.

A relatively simple and economical microphone takes advantage of the resistance of carbon granules. The theory may be followed by the sketch in Fig. 14-25. Granules of carbon are packed in a small container and electrical connections are made to each side. A transformer and a small battery are connected in series with the carbon. To one side of the container, called a "button," a diaphragm is attached. Sound waves striking the

Fig. 14-24. Microphones used in broadcasting and general communications. (Shure Bros., Inc.)

diaphragm cause varying degrees of compression to the carbon granules which <u>vary the resistance</u> of the carbon. The varying resistance causes a varying current to flow through the carbon button and the transformer primary. The output is a current which varies at the same frequency as the sound waves acting on the diaphragm. The carbon microphone is a very sensitive device and has a

Fig. 14-25. In carbon microphone sound waves change resistance of circuit.

frequency response up to about 4000 cps. This is quite satisfactory for voice communication, but would reproduce music rather poorly. It does provide a good response for its intended

Fig. 14-26. Mechanical pressure produces electrical energy. The crystal microphone takes advantage of piezoelectric effect.

frequencies and it is non-directional. This means it will pick up sound from all directions.

A second type of microphone takes advantage of the piezoelectric effect of certain crystals. When sound waves strike a diaphragm, mechanical pressure is transferred to the crystal. The flexing or bending of the crystal produces a small voltage between its surfaces. This voltage is of the same frequency and relative amplitude as the sound wave. The microphone may be connected

directly to the grid of an amplifier tube. Crystal "mikes" have a frequency response up to 10,000 cps. They are rather sensitive to shock and vibration and should be handled with care. This "mike" is sketched in Fig. 14-26.

The dynamic or moving coil microphone is sketched in Fig. 14-27. As sound waves strike the diaphragm, they cause the voice coil to move in and out. The voice coil is surrounded by a fixed magnetic field. When the coil moves, a voltage is induced in the coil, (Faraday's discovery). This induced voltage will cause a current to flow at a frequency and amplitude similar to the sound wave causing the motion. It has a frequency response up to 9,000 cps. It is directional. It requires no external voltage for operation.

A very high quality microphone, called the VELOCITY MICROPHONE, is constructed with a corrugated ribbon of metal suspended

Fig. 14-27. Dynamic microphone. Electrical audio waves are produced by coil moving in magnetic field.

in a magnetic field. Sound waves striking the ribbon directly cause the ribbon to vibrate. As the ribbon cuts the magnetic field a voltage is induced. Suitable connections at the ends of the ribbon bring the voltage out to terminals. This voltage varies according to the frequency and amplitude of the impinging sound waves. It is a relatively delicate "mike" and has a response above 12,000 cps. When speaking into this microphone, one should either speak across its face or stand about 18 inches away or a "booming" effect is created. This microphone requires a transformer to match its impedance to the grid of an amplifier tube.

THE AUDIO AMPLIFIER

An amplifier, consisting of several stages of voltage amplifiers, is necessary to bring the level of the voltage from the microphone up to a satisfactory level to operate either a loud speaker system or to modulate a radio transmitter. The stages of voltage amplification are followed by either a single-ended or push-pull power amplifier. In Fig. 14-28 the schematic of a low powered modu-

Fig. 14-28. Schematic of a low-powered modulator using plate modulation.

lator is shown. The principles of operation of this push-pull amplifier have been discussed in Chapter 13.

However, the audio power output is connected to a modulation transformer, the secondary winding of which is in series with the plate circuit of the RF Power Amplifier. The audio voltage developed across the secondary winding of the modulation transformer either aids or opposes the B+ supply voltage. Since the plate power input to the RF Amplifier depends upon the B+ voltage, the

series aiding or opposing modulation voltage will change the amplitude of the RF output and at a frequency of the audio wave. It is apparent that a larger audio voltage would produce a greater change in the RF Amplifier plate voltage, which brings us to the term of PERCENTAGE OF MODULATION. In Fig. 14-29 a modulated RF wave is sketched. Notice that the modulating voltage causes the RF wave to rise to twice its height on positive peaks and to drop to zero at its negative peak. The peaks, therefore, vary 100 per cent above and 100 per cent below the average

Fig. 14-29. Wave form shows 100 per cent modulation.

unmodulated RF wave. This case illustrates 100 per cent modulation. Examples of under-modulated (less than 100 per cent) and over-modulated (over 100 per cent) are shown in

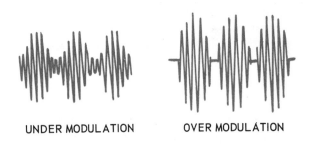

Fig. 14-30. Under and over modulation wave patterns.

Fig. 14-30. Percentage of modulation may be expressed mathematically as:

$$\% \text{ Modulation} = \frac{E_m}{E_c} \times 100$$

where: E_m equals the maximum value of modulating signal.

E_c equals the value of unmodulated carrier wave.

Electricity - Electronics

SIDEBANDS

When an audio modulating voltage is applied to a carrier RF wave, new frequencies appear in the output called SIDEBANDS. Note in Fig. 14-31 that an RF carrier occupies only a single frequency space (assume 1,000 kc). When modulated by a one kc audio wave, sideband frequencies appear which represent the sum and difference between the two waves:

1000 kc + 1 kc = 1001 kc
1000 kc - 1 kc = 999 kc

The modulated wave then is considered as having three parts:
1. The carrier wave
2. The Upper Sideband
3. The Lower Sideband

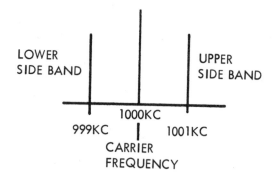

Fig. 14-31. This graph represents the position of sidebands and carrier of a 1000 kc wave modulated by a 1 kc wave.

Since the modulation caused these sidebands, it is correct to assume that the intelligence of the radio signal is contained in the sidebands. Also, in order to transmit intelligence, some space must be used from the frequency spectrum. In this example, a space 2 kc wide (1001 kc to 999 kc) was necessary. Higher modulating frequencies expand the sidebands. Commercial AM broadcasting stations are allowed a 10 kc space in the radio frequency spectrum for the transmission of their signals.

Since both the upper and lower sidebands contain the audio information necessary for communications, recent designs in transmitters remove one sideband by filtering circuits before it leaves the transmitter. This is called single-sideband transmission. Since the SSB occupies only one half the spectrum space used by the double sideband, a more economical allotment of available space in radio frequency bands may be enjoyed and many more stations may transmit without interference to each other.

MODULATION POWER

Theoretically, the modulator must add 50 per cent more power to the radiated energy from the transmitter to produce 100 per cent modulation of the radio frequency carrier wave. Since the carrier wave remains unchanged, the additional power added must therefore be in the sideband frequencies.

Assume that a transmitter is rated at 100 watts. When this transmitter is modulated to 100 per cent, the power input will rise 50 per cent or to 150 watts of the total radiated energy. The carrier wave contains 100 watts, and the sidebands contain 50 watts. One third of the total power is in the sidebands. Since the modulated signal has both an upper and a lower sideband, it would be reasonable to assume that one half of the sideband power would be in each respective sideband or 25 watts in each sideband.

Examination of Fig. 14-29 shows that the audio power must cause the rf wave to vary between zero and twice its value, for 100 per cent modulation. At peaks then, the voltage will be 2E and the current 2I and the peak power will be 2E x 2I or 4EI. Peak power with 100 per cent modulation will be four times the power of the carrier.

When 50 per cent audio power is required for 100 per cent modulation, it is assumed that the audio wave will approximate a sine wave. Complex audio waves containing many frequencies and amplitudes will require less power, usually limited to 25 per cent of the carrier wave power, for 100 per cent modulation. The advantages of 100 per cent modulation are stronger signals and more complete readability. Lower percentages of modulation produce a marked decrease in radiated power.

Amateur Radio, better known as "Ham

Radio" offers one of the most interesting and educational hobbies for the beginner as well as for the "old timer" in electronics. In order to qualify for a Novice License issued by the FCC, it is necessary to send and receive a minimum of five words per minute in the Morse Code. A basic examination in radio theory is also required. For further information consult any "ham" or write directly to the Amercian Radio Relay League, West Hartford, Conn.

The novice transmitter appearing schematically in Fig. 14-31A offers a simple and inexpensive way to get "on the air." It is presented here through the courtesy of the ARRL and appears in the Radio Amateurs Handbook. It is not necessary to follow the exact layout as pictured. In fact, you may create an attractive and individual front panel. The transmitter is constructed on a 11 x 7 x 3 in. aluminum chassis.

CONSTRUCTION NOTES

R_1 consists of three 33 K, one watt resistors soldered together in parallel.

R_2 consists of two 100 K resistors soldered together in parallel.

The transformer, tube sockets, crystal socket and pilot light appear on top of the chassis. The switches, meter and tuning capacitors are mounted on the front side of the chassis or may be mounted on a front

Parts List for Novice Transmitter

C_1	470 $\mu\mu$f mica capacitor
C_2, C_7,	.01 μf ceramic disc capacitor
C_3	250 $\mu\mu$f variable capacitor (Hammarlund MC 250 M)
C_4	365 $\mu\mu$f per section dual variable capacitor, broadcast replacement type. (Allied Radio 60H725) sections connected in parallel.
C_5	680 $\mu\mu$f mica capacitor
C_6	1,000 $\mu\mu$f, 1200 volt mica
C_8, C_9,	20-20 μf, 500 volt, dual section
R_1	11,000 Ω, 3 watts (See text)
R_2	50,000 Ω, 2 watts (See text)
R_3	27,000 Ω, 1/2 watt
R_4	100 K Ω, 5 watt (See text)
RFC_1,	1 mh rf choke (National R-50)
RFC_2,	1 mh rf choke (National R-50)
RFC_3,	1 mh rf choke (National R-50)

Fig. 14-31A. Schematic diagram for Novice Transmitter.

RFC_4	2.5 mh, rf choke (National RIDOS)
S_1	single pole-two position switch (Centralab 1460)
S_2	single pole-single throw toggle switch
T_1	Transformer-750 volts, ct, 150 ma, 5 volts, 3 amp., 6.3 volts 4.5 amps. (Stancor PC 8411)
I_1	Dial Lamp 2 volts, 60 ma., No. 48 or 49
J_1	Key Jack, open circuit.
J_2	Coax Connector
L_1	35 turns No 20, 1 1/4 inch dia., 16 t.p.i., tapped 15 turns from the C_4 end. (B&W 3019)
L_2	9 h, 125 ma., filter choke. (Triad CIDX)
M_1	Meter 0-200 ma. (Shurite 850)
V_1	5U4GB
V_2	6146

panel. General parts layout may be observed in Fig. 14-32.

Coil L_1 is self supporting when soldered between the stators of C_3 and C_4. The bleeder resistor for the power supply R_4 is made up of three $33\,K\Omega$ 2 watt resistors in series.

Pilot light I_1 is mounted in a 1/2 in. rubber grommet next to the crystal. The crystal socket may be a regular octal socket (AMPHENOL MIP) or a special crystal socket. V_1 and V_2 are also octal sockets.

No attempt has been made to show you how to build or wire this transmitter. The chassis layout in Fig. 14-32 is a start in the right direction. Carefully plan your layout and wiring. Check and recheck against the schematic drawing.

BOTTOM VIEW OF CHASSIS

Fig. 14-32. Suggested layout plan for transmitter. Be sure to make the changes necessary to fit your parts.

CODE PRACTICE OSCILLATOR

For "fun and learning," the oscillator shown in Figs. 14-34 and 14-35, produces a variable tone which may be keyed for practicing the Morse Code. It will be useful to young men interested in radio communications, ham radio and Boy Scouts. Simple musical tunes may be played with only a little practice by varying the tone control knob.

Once again the "shadow cabinet" is used in this project and the finished product looks like a commercial unit. The cabinet is made of 20 ga. galvanized iron and covered with imitation leather. Glue the leatherette to the metal. See Fig. 14-33.

Parts List for Code Practice Oscillator

C_1 - Capacitor .5 μf
R_1 - Potentiometer 25 K Ω
R_2 - 6800 Ω, 1/2 w
T_1 - Transistor Output Transformer AR 119

  or Thordarson TR 27

Q_1 - CK 722 transistor
PM - Speaker 1 1/2" Philmore
S_1 - Switch, SPST
Binding Posts or phono jack, knob and small hardware

Fig. 14-33. Finished Audio Code Oscillator in a shadow cabinet.

Fig. 14-34. Schematic diagram for Code Practice Oscillator.

THE SQUAWKER
SOMETHING NEW IN "HOT ROD HORNS"

An individualized horn is something that has a lot of appeal to the youth with his own car. This transistorized horn was first designed as a "fog horn" but has an equally startling effect on the customized car. See Fig. 14-35.

The circuit uses power transistors in a multivibrator configuration, Fig. 14-36. The amplifier stages are also used to generate the audio frequency oscillation by feeding the output of one transistor to the base of the other transistor. Feedback is accomplished by C_1 and C_2. S_1 may be replaced by wires

Fig. 14-35. Completed Hot Rod Horn.

Fig. 14-36. Schematic diagram for transistorized Hot Rod Horn.

to the horn button. B_1 is the 12 volt battery in the car.

Any metal or wooden box may be used to house the horn. It is advisable to use a weatherproofed speaker if installed on a car or protect it against the weather by a plastic covering. No difficulty should be experienced in building the project, if the circuit diagram is carefully followed.

Parts List for The Squawker

B_1	12 volt battery (1 ampere drain) conventional auto or boat battery, or 2 Burgess F4P1 batteries wired in series.
C_1, C_2	2.0 mfd, electrolytic, 25 volt
LS_1	8 ohm tweeter, Lafayette HK-3 or equivalent
Q_1, Q_2	Sylvania 2N307 power transistor
R_1, R_2	220 Ω, 1w
S_1	Single-pole, single-throw pushbutton switch, normally open
T_1	Lafayette TR-94 or equivalent
LS_2	for alternate connection - 45 ohm paging trumpet; University CMIL-45, University MIL-45, or equivalent

Fig. 14-37. The Electroluminescent Night Light in a shadow cabinet.

ELECTROLUMINESCENT NIGHT LIGHT

A useful project, inexpensive and fun to own is shown in Figs. 14-37 and 14-38.

The electroluminescent light you will need in making this project may be purchased at your local hardware store. They are widely used as night lights and produce a warm and friendly greenish glow when plugged into the ordinary 115-volt AC outlet. This project has its own power supply, which is the con-

Vacuum Tube as Oscillator

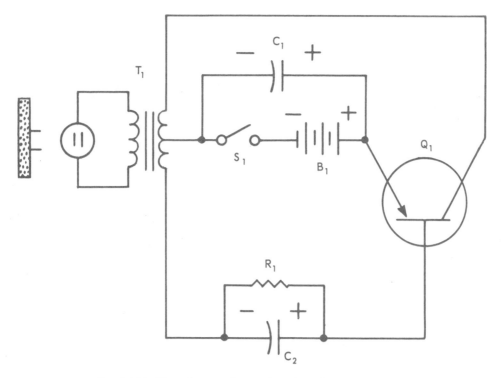

Fig. 14-38. The schematic diagram for Electroluminescent Night Light

ventional Hartley oscillator circuit you have studied. The output of the oscillator is transformer coupled to the light and is sufficient to operate the device without other sources of power.

The "shadow" cabinet used to house this light is a popular design. This one is made of 20 ga. galvanized iron on which an imitation leather is glued. This method of construction is easy and produces a "commercial look" to a project. The same methods may be used to build cabinets for radios, amplifiers and other projects. Try it! You will be rewarded by a project with a pleasing appearance.

Parts List for Night Light

T_1 - Filament Transformer 6.3 V CT, Triad F16X
S_1 - Switch SPST Toggle
C_1 - Capacitor 50 μf-25 V electrolytic
C_2 - Capacitor 8 μf-15 V electrolytic
R_1 - Resistor 2700 Ω, 1/2 w
Q_1 - Transistor 2N241A Sylvania
B_1 - Battery 9 V Eveready 264 or equivalent.
       Sylvania Panelescent Light 120 V -.02 w
       Receptacle - Amphenol 61F1.

FOR DISCUSSION

1. A measured negative voltage on the grid of a vacuum tube used in an oscillator signifies that the circuit is functioning. Explain.
2. Explain the theory of "dipping the final" in a radio transmitter. What does it indicate?
3. What is meant by side-bands? Relate side-bands to space occupancy in the frequency spectrum.
4. Why is 100 per cent modulation desirable in the AM transmitter?
5. Check the requirements for a General Class Amateur Radio License and report to class.

TEST YOUR KNOWLEDGE

1. Define cycle, period and frequency.
2. What two conditions must be satisfied to produce continuing oscillations?
3. A vacuum tube used in an oscillator is operated in which Class?

4. Draw a diagram of:

   Armstrong Oscillator

   Hartley Oscillator

   Crystal Oscillator

   Colpitts Oscillator

   ECO

5. What advantage does the ECO have over other basic oscillators.

6. What advantages does the AT cut crystal have over the X or Y cut crystals?

7. What is a frequency multiplier?

8. What is the purpose of Neutralization?

9. Name three methods of keying a transmitter.

10. Describe AM and FM.

11. A device used to convert sound waves into electrical audio waves is called a
_____.

12. Name and describe four types of microphones discussed in the text.

13. Draw wave forms of AM wave showing,
    A. 100 per cent modulation.
    B. Undermodulation
    C. Overmodulation (Use sine wave pattern)

14. How much power must the modulator supply to modulate the carrier 100 per cent.

Chapter 15

RADIO WAVES AND DETECTION

In our previous studies many references have been made to waves of certain frequencies. Mention has been made of power frequencies, audio and radio frequencies. It might be wise at this point to look over the frequency spectrum shown in Fig. 15-1 and satisfy our scientific curiosity. This spectrum, although not in detail, will indicate the <u>bands</u> of frequencies used for communication by the many services including radio broadcasting, amateur radio, FM, TV, police and industry.

It must be remembered that the use of

space in communications must be rigidly controlled, not only by our own Federal Communications Commission, but also by conferences involving other countries. There are only so many frequency allocations available. These must be assigned to satisfy the needs of all of the people for industrial, military and entertainment purposes and at the same time minimize any interference between the services.

Another general classification of waves is according to frequency. This will prove use-

Fig. 15-1. An abbreviated frequency spectrum chart showing locations of several communications services.

ful to you when discussing ranges of frequencies. See Table 15-1.

60 cps	Power Frequency
20-30,000 cps	Audio Frequency
Below 30 kc	VLF Very Low Frequencies
30-300 kc	LF Low Frequencies
300-3000 kc	MF Medium Frequencies
3000-30,000 kc	HF High Frequencies
30,000 kc-300 mc	VHF Very High Frequencies
300 mc-3,000 mc	UHF Ultra High Frequencies

Table-15-1

In this table of frequencies you will recognize the location of several familiar services. Notice that the AM broadcast stations use the HF range, whereas television may be found in the VHF and UHF ranges. A Hi-Fi operates in the audio frequency range. Electricity for the home is 60 cps, or at the power frequency.

A radiated wave into space may be visualized as waves rolling toward the ocean beach. A frequent comparison of the descriptions of radiating waves suggests the use of a calm lake. Throw a stone into the water. From the point where the stone entered the water, small waves radiate outward making concentric circular patterns. The stone created a disturbance, or set a wave in motion, which moved outward decreasing in amplitude as the distance from the center became greater. Consider this wave of water for a moment. Does the water move as a wave? No. The water moves UP to a crest and DOWN in a hollow or trough as the wave passes. The water has acted as the medium for transmitting the wave.

Scientists have discovered that radio waves travel through space at a speed of 300,000,000 meters per second or 186,000 miles per second. This is approximately the speed of light. Picture a wave at a frequency of one cycle per second originating from point A in Fig. 15-2 and traveling at the speed of 300,000,000 meters per second. At the be-

ginning of the second cycle, the first wave has moved 300,000,000 meters away. If the frequency of the generated wave was 1000 cps, then the first wave would be 300,000 meters away by the time the second wave started. Continuing this explanation, the frequency is

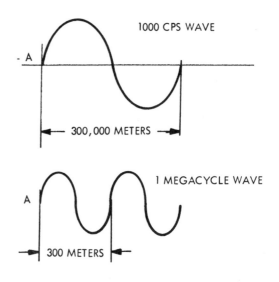

Fig. 15-2. A comparison between the distance, travelled during one cycle, of a 1000 cps and a one megacycle wave.

increased to 1,000,000 cps or 1 megacycle, then the first wave would have moved only 300 meters before the start of the second cycle. It seems, then, that a wave might be described not only by its FREQUENCY but also by its LENGTH. This is true, as shown in Fig. 15-3. The distance between the crests of the waves is termed the WAVE LENGTH. This conclusion may also be accepted: As the frequency increases, the wave length decreases. The Greek letter λ (lambda) signifies wave length in electronics and the

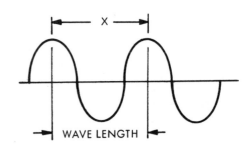

Fig. 15-3. Waves may be identified by their length or their frequency.

mathematical relationship may be stated as:

$$\lambda \text{ (in meters)} = \frac{300{,}000{,}000}{f \text{ (in cps)}}$$

$$f \text{ (in cps)} = \frac{300{,}000{,}000}{\lambda \text{ (in meters)}}$$

EXAMPLE I. An amateur radio transmits on a frequency of 3.9 mc. What is the wave length of the radiated waves?

$$\lambda = \frac{300{,}000{,}000}{3.9 \text{ mc}}$$

3.9 mc is converted to 3,900,000 cps, then

$$\lambda = \frac{300{,}000{,}000}{3{,}900{,}000} = \frac{3000}{39} \text{ or } 77 \text{ meters}$$

Observe how the mathematics is simplified by using "powers of ten"

$$\lambda = \frac{3 \times 10^8}{3.9 \times 10^6} = \frac{3 \times 10^2}{3.9} = .77 \times 10^2 = 77 \text{ meters}$$

EXAMPLE II. What is the frequency of a transmitter operating on 40 meters?

EXPLANATION:

$$f = \frac{3 \times 10^8}{4 \times 10} = .75 \times 10^7 = 7{,}500{,}000 \text{ cps or } 7.5 \text{ megacycles}$$

A more practical statement of the above formula may be made, since the foot is the common unit of measure and radio frequencies are usually in megacycles, so,

$$\lambda \text{ (in feet)} = \frac{984}{f \text{ (in mc)}}$$

It would be wise to memorize this formula. It is used a great deal in the design of antennas for special frequencies.

RADIO WAVE PROPAGATION

In the study of electromagnetism, we learned that a conductor carrying an electric current was surrounded by a magnetic field. If the current were an alternating current, the magnetic field would periodically expand and collapse and change its polarity. Some of these magnetic lines of force will lose the influence of the conductor and radiate into space. These

radiated electromagnetic waves are perpendicular to the direction in which they travel. Associated with any electromagnetic field is an electrostatic field which is perpendicular

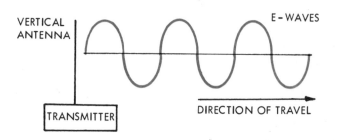

Fig. 15-4. *The angular relationship between electrostatic and electromagnetic waves. They are perpendicular to each other and both are perpendicular to the direction of travel.*

to the electromagnet field, and is also perpendicular to the direction of radiation or travel. As a result, the radio wave consists of electromagnetic and electrostatic fields. Fig. 15-4 shows the relationship between these fields and direction of travel. The position in which these waves radiate in respect to the earth is called POLARIZATION. In Fig. 15-5

Fig. 15-5. *A vertical antenna radiates a vertically polarized wave.*

the waves are radiated from a vertical antenna. Note that the electrostatic or E waves are in the same plane as the antenna yet perpendicular to direction of travel. The vertically polarized waves are perpendicular to the surface of the earth. In Fig. 15-6, the wave is radiated from a horizontal antenna. It is still perpendicular to the direction of travel, but is parallel to the surface of the earth. Generally speaking, the antenna which receives these waves should be oriented the same as the transmitting antenna. At high frequencies the polarization changes during propagation to some extent.

Fig. 15-6. A horizontal antenna radiates a horizontally polarized wave.

The beginning student may ask a meaningful question, "Does the transmitting antenna radiate two waves?" The answer is found by the fact that without one there cannot be the other. A moving electrostatic field produces a moving electromagnetic field; and a moving electromagnetic field produces a moving electrostatic field. These conditions are true whether an actual conductor is present or not.

GROUND WAVES

The radiated waves from an antenna may be divided into two types. First, let us consider the GROUND WAVE, so called because it follows the surface of the earth to the radio receiver. The GROUND WAVE may be considered as having three parts:
1. The surface wave.
2. The direct wave which follows a direct path from the transmitter to the receiver.
3. The ground reflected wave which strikes the ground and then is reflected to the receiver.

These last two waves are combined and called the SPACE wave. The direct and reflected waves that constitute the space wave may or may not arrive at the receiver in proper phase. They may add together or cancel each other depending on distances travelled by each wave. Broadcast stations depend on the surface wave for reliable communications. As the surface wave travels along the surface of the earth, it will induce currents in the earth's surface which use up the energy contained in the wave. The wave becomes weaker as the distance over which it travels increases. An interesting sidelight is the conductivity of salt water which is about 5000 times better than the earth. Overseas communication is very reliable when transmitters are near the coastline. These stations use high power and operate at lower frequencies than the familiar broadcast band.

SKY WAVES

The second radiated wave from an antenna is toward the sky. It is called the SKY-WAVE. The sky-waves strike a heavily ionized layer

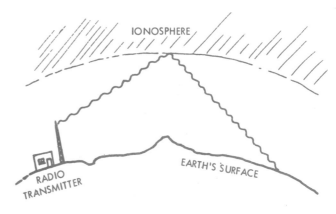

Fig. 15-7. Radio waves may be bounced back to the earth's surface.

of the earth's atmosphere. This layer, called the IONOSPHERE, is located from 40 to 300 miles above the earth's surface, and is believed to consist of large numbers of positive and negative ions. This ionization is dependent upon the earth's position in relation to the sun and "sun spot activity." When radio waves strike the ionosphere, a part may be absorbed and a part may be refracted or bent back to the earth's surface. See Fig. 15-7. One of the fascinations of amateur radio results from the use of reflected waves as a method of communication. The "ham op-

Fig. 15-8. A block diagram of a TRF (tuned radio frequency) receiver.

erator" calls "CQ," which is the general inquiry call to establish communication. His reply may come from a distant station in another part of the world.

THE RADIO RECEIVER

The radio wave transmitted through space also carries information, such as voice and music, which has been combined with the carrier wave at the transmitter by the modulation process. These radiated electromagnetic waves cut across the receiving antenna and induce a small voltage in the antenna. The small radio frequency voltages are coupled to a tuned circuit in the receiver which selects the desired signal to be heard. After the selection, the voltages may be amplified and then demodulated. DEMODULATION means DETECTION or the separation of the audio portion of the signal from the carrier wave. The audio signal is then amplified to sufficient strength to drive a loudspeaker. A block diagram of this receiver is shown in Fig. 15-8. The modulated rf wave is shown as it passes the antenna; the audio wave is illustrated as the output of the detector. The increase in amplitude of the waves between the blocks is the result of stages of amplification. This type of receiver was once quite popular and is called the TRF or TUNED-RADIO-FREQUENCY receiver. For satisfactory operation of the circuit it was necessary to tune each stage to the correct incoming frequency of the signal. Some of the early radios had a series of tuning dials on the front panel which required skill and patience for proper adjustment. The development of the SUPERHET-

ERODYNE receiver, which is used today, overcomes these early undesirable characteristics.

THE TUNING CIRCUIT

It has been stated that one of the functions of any radio receiver must be that of selection of the desired radio signal. Details of the "tank circuit" and flywheel action have been discussed in Chapter 8. Fig. 15-9 shows a schematic of the first stage of the TRF Receiver. Following the signal of the antenna to the output of this circuit will materially aid

Fig. 15-9. The tuning or station selector section of the radio receiver.

the understanding of the operation. Radio signals of many frequencies from many radio transmitters are passing by the antenna. The induced voltage in the antenna causes small currents to alternate from antenna to ground and from ground to antenna through coil L_1. Since L_2 is closely coupled to L_1, the magnetic field created by the antenna current in L_1 transfers energy to L_2. The combination coils L_1 and L_2 are usually called the AN-

TENNA COIL and are wound on a common cylinder of cardboard. Fig. 15-10 illustrates two types used in transistor radios. Variable capacitor C_1 is connected across the terminals of L_2 and forms a tank circuit. C_1 may be adjusted to vary the RESONANT frequency of the tank. When the resonant frequency of the tank circuit is the same as

Fig. 15-10. Typical antenna coil used with transistorized receivers.
(J. W. Miller Co.)

the incoming signal, relatively high circulating currents develop in the tank. In other words, the tank circuit may be adjusted to give maximum response for only one frequency. The $L_2 C_1$ combination may only cover a certain range or band of frequencies. Most of our home radios cover only the broadcast band. For other groups of frequencies, such as short wave, another coil is switched in place of L_2, which changes the resonant fre-

quency range of the circuit. This type of circuit is called a BAND-SWITCHING circuit.

The ability of a radio receiver to select a single frequency and only one frequency is called SELECTIVITY. The ability of a receiver to respond to weak incoming signals is called SENSITIVITY. Both of these characteristics are highly desirable and special circuits and components have been devised to improve selectivity and sensitivity.

RF AMPLIFICATION

The voltage developed across the tuned circuit is maximum for the selected frequency. This voltage is connected to the grid of the first RF amplifier stage. Pentodes are more satisfactory for this amplifier because of their high gain and neutralization is not required. The circuit in Fig. 15-11 follows the familiar configuration as studied in previous lessons. R_1 is the cathode bias resistor and C_2 is the cathode bypass. The screen voltage for the pentode is secured from B+ supply through dropping resistor R_2. The screen is bypassed to ground by C_3. The coupling method to the next stage is by means of T_1 and the impedance of the primary of T_1 is the plate load for tube V_1. Across the secondary of T_1 is another variable capacitor C_4 which forms a second tuned tank circuit. The dotted line between C_1 and C_4 indicates that both capacitors are controlled by a single shaft. The illustration in Fig.

Fig. 15-11. A typical circuit of an RF amplifier.

15-12 shows a double section capacitor. The RF stage amplifies the incoming signal. The second tuned circuit increases the selectivity of the circuit. So that both C_1 and C_4 will tune to the same frequency at all settings of the dial, small variable TRIMMER CAPACITORS, C_5 and C_6, are connected in parallel. These small trimmers are adjusted so that C_1 and C_4 will TRACK at the same frequency.

For further amplification of the radio signal, additional stages may be added which will be similar to the rf stage just discussed. Two other components R_2 and C_7 which appear on

Fig. 15-12. A double section tuning capacitor.
(J. W. Miller Co.)

the diagram need some explanation. This is called a DECOUPLING NETWORK. R_2 is an isolation resistance and is not part of the plate load of V_1 since C_7 is selected for a low impedance for the rf signal to ground. As a result the rf signal is shunted to ground through C_7 and does not enter the power supply B+.

This prevents any feedback from one stage to another through the common impedance of the power supply. All rf stages will be decoupled in a similar manner.

DETECTION

Assuming that the modulated radio frequency signal has been amplified by several stages of rf amplification, it now has sufficient amplitude for detection. Detection is the process of rectification and the removal of

the rf wave, leaving the af wave only. See Fig. 15-13 which shows: 1. The rf carrier within the modulation envelope. 2. The rectified rf wave. 3. The audio wave when the rf wave has been removed. Detection is nec-

MODULATED RF WAVE   DETECTED WAVE   AUDIO WAVE

Fig. 15-13. The appearance of the wave forms as they are demodulated or detected.

essary to recover the audio signal from the modulated rf carrier wave.

THE DIODE DETECTOR

One of the more common and quite satisfactory methods of detection employs the diode as a unilateral conductor (one direction). The characteristics of the diode were discussed in Chapter 11 and may be summarized again for purposes of review. When the plate of the diode is driven positive, electrons flow through the tube from cathode to plate. The tube conducts. When the plate is driven negative, the tube does not conduct. The schematic drawing in Fig. 15-14 represents the diode detector in its simplified

Fig. 15-14. The basic diode detector circuit.

form. The amplified modulated signal is supplied to the detector from the previous amplifier stage. When the input signal is positive, the diode conducts and a voltage is developed across the diode load resistor R_1. Conversely, when the incoming signal is negative, there is no current in the diode circuit. The diode has rectified or converted the modulated rf signal into pulses or waves of DC voltage which have a frequency and amplitude of the audio wave. This half-wave rectification may be understood by examination of the input and output wave forms in Fig. 15-15.

MODULATED
WAVE

DETECTED
SHOWING
AVERAGE VALVE

DETECTED
WITH
FILTER C_1

Fig. 15-15. The average value of the DC component is represented by the dotted line. The DC average is raised by adding the filter capacitor.

The dotted curve in the output of the diode represents the AVERAGE DC value of the rectified voltage. In order to raise the average DC output voltage and cause it to conform to a more faithful reproduction of the input signal, a filter capacitor of the correct value C_1, is shunted across R_1. This capacitor charges to the peak value of the signal and prevents the voltage across R_1 from dropping to zero when the diode is not conducting. The improved output wave form as a result of filtering is also shown in Fig. 15-15. The time constant of $R_1 C_1$ should be long when compared to the rf cycle, so that C_1 will not dis-

charge to a low value. Conversely this time constant should be short when compared to the af cycle, so the voltage variations across the $R_1 C_1$ network will follow the audio frequency cycle.

A more complete detector circuit using a twin diode-triode tube (6AV6) is drawn in Fig. 15-16. This dual function tube includes the diode detector and a triode voltage amplifier. Several new components have been added which require some explanation. The diode load resistor R_1 has been made a potentiometer, which serves as a volume control for the receiver. The desired amount of af voltage is selected and coupled through C_1 to the grid of the amplifier. C_2 is a small trimmer capacitor across the transformer secondary, which is adjusted during alignment for maximum response of the tuned circuit. Note that when the diode conducts, point A in Fig. 15-16 becomes negative in respect to ground. If the amplitude of the signal increases, point A will be correspondingly more negative. This voltage, which varies according to signal strength, may be used to automatically control the volume of the receiver and is called the automatic volume control (AVC) voltage. The voltage is coupled, after proper filtering to remove the audio wave, to the grids of previous amplifier stages. If the incoming signal is strong, a strong negative AVC voltage decreases the gain of the amplifier stages. As a result, after one setting of the volume control on the receiver, the program re-

Fig. 15-16. The diode detector and 1st AF audio stage contained in one tube. A volume control has been added.

ception remains fairly constant without further adjustment. AVC circuits are used in most radio receivers manufactured today.

THE GRID LEAK DETECTOR

The theory of establishing a bias on an amplifier tube by means of the "grid leak" was discussed in Chapter 13 and should be reviewed at this time. The grid leak detector may be compared to the diode-triode circuit of Fig. 15-16. In Fig. 15-17, the capacitor

Fig. 15-17. The circuit of the grid-leak detector.

C_1 charges when the incoming signal drives the grid positive and the grid collects electrons from the electron stream in V_1. The grid would therefore become increasingly

Fig. 15-18. These graphs compare the incoming signal, the grid current charging C and the negative bias voltage.

more negative, since electrons cannot return to the electron stream in V_1 because the grid is cold and does not emit electrons. The tube would quickly become so negatively biased that it would cut-off if it were not for the leaking resistor R_1. The time constant of R_1C_1 is selected to be long in comparison to the rf signal, yet short in respect to the audio wave. As a result the negative bias on the tube follows the pattern of the audio modulation of the modulated carrier wave. The greater the amplitude of the signal, the greater bias. A low amplitude of signal produces a less negative bias. This is shown graphically in the wave forms of Fig. 15-18. The audio portion of the modulated carrier wave has been recovered and the cathode-grid circuit of tube V_1 may be considered as a diode detector.

The bias on the tube V_1 controls the plate current. The plate current varies as the audio portion of the modulated signal. It is also amplified by the tube. The rf variations are still present in the output of the tube. Capacitor C_2 may be considered as a filter so the rf variations do not appear across the load resistor R_L. The output of the grid-leak detector is taken from across R_L and coupled to the next stage by C_3. The sensitivity of the grid-leak detector is very good for weak signals, but has a tendency to load and distort high level signals with a decrease in selectivity.

THE PLATE DETECTOR

In the PLATE DETECTOR circuit drawn in Fig. 15-19, the modulated rf signal is applied directly to the grid of tube V_1. Detection of the audio signal may be considered as taking place in the plate circuit. Resistor R_1, the cathode resistor, is selected with a value which will maintain a self bias on the tube at approximately cut-off. Review Chapter 13. C_1 bypasses the audio variations around R_1 so that a constant bias is maintained. The tube is operated similar to a Class B amplifier. A positive signal on the grid causes conduction in the plate circuit of the tube. A negative signal only increases the bias of the tube beyond cut-off and therefore does not

Fig. 15-19. *The basic plate detection circuit. The tube is biased as a Class B amplifier.*

cause conduction. Rectification has been accomplished and the output wave form from the plate detector appears in Fig. 15-20. As in the grid-leak circuit, the output of the tube

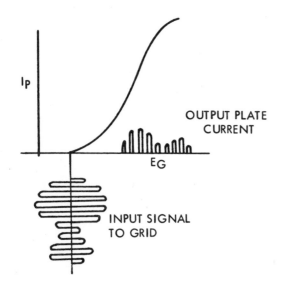

Fig. 15-20. *The output wave form as a result of plate detection.*

is filtered by C_2 and the audio voltage appears across R_L.

THE REGENERATIVE DETECTOR

The principles of regeneration and degeneration have been discussed in previous chapters. By taking a part of the output signal of the detector and feeding it back to a previous stage so that the signals are in phase or reinforcing each other, a detector may

be built which is extremely sensitive to weak signals. Fig. 15-21 diagrams a circuit using regeneration. The output signal present in the plate circuit passes through the TICKLER COIL L_1 which is inductively coupled to the antenna tank circuit coil L_2, in such a way that the signal in L_1 reinforces the input signal in L_2. The amount of feedback may be manually controlled by varying the coupling between L_1 and L_2. If the feedback is excessive, this circuit will break into oscillation. This may be desirable for the reception of Morse Code. The oscillation will produce an audible tone for the earphones or speaker. For reception of music and voice, the receiver should be adjusted at a point just before oscillation for maximum sensitivity and selectivity.

THE SUPERHETERODYNE RECEIVER

To overcome many of the disadvantages of the tuned-radio frequency receiver, the superheterodyne circuit was developed. This heterodyning or mixing of signals provides a means of converting all incoming signals to a single INTERMEDIATE FREQUENCY which can be amplified with minimum loss and distortion. A block diagram of a Superheterodyne Receiver is illustrated in Fig. 15-22. The signal picked up by the antenna is first fed to a stage of radio frequency amplification (RF Amp.). The output of the RF Amp. is then fed to the MIXER or CONVERTER TUBE. Also the output of a LOCAL OSCILLATOR is fed to the converter. When two signals are

Fig. 15-21. The basic circuit of the regenerative detector
sometimes called a "Regen."

Fig. 15-22. The block diagram of the Superheterodyne Receiver.

mixed together, four signals will appear in the output. These will include the original two signals, the sum of the two signals and the difference between the two signals. For example: A 1000 kc signal is mixed with a 1455 kc oscillator signal. Appearing in the output then will be:

1000 kc	original signal
1455 kc	original oscillator frequency
2455 kc	the sum of both frequencies
455 kc	the difference between both frequencies

The BEAT frequency of 455 kc is of major importance in the study of the superheterodyne receiver. The desired station is selected by the tuning circuits of the receiver by turning the tuning knob, on the front panel, which varies the capacitance of the tuning circuit. Mechanically attached to the shaft of the tuning capacitor is another tuning capacitor which adjusts the frequency of the local oscillator. These capacitors, operating in step with each other, provide a change in oscillator frequency as the tuned frequency is changed, always maintaining a fixed difference or beat

frequency of 455 kc, called the INTERMEDIATE FREQUENCY or IF. The IF output is then amplified by two stages of voltage amplification and fed to the DETECTOR. The output of the detector is an audio frequency voltage which is amplified sufficiently to operate the power amplifier and speaker. The wave forms at each stage are shown in Fig. 15-22.

The schematic diagram of a complete superheterodyne receiver is drawn in Fig. 15-23. This circuit uses a PENTA-GRID CONVERTER tube which means FIVE GRIDS. An analysis of the tube's operation shows its dual function. In Fig. 15-24, only the oscillator section is shown. Compare this diagram to Fig. 14-2 in Chapter 14. Is it not the conventional HARTLEY oscillator circuit? Grids number 2 and 4 are connected together and serve as the PLATE for the oscillator. The incoming signal from the RF stage is fed to grid 3. Grid 5 acts as the suppressor grid. The tube serves as an oscillator and a mixer-amplifier. The amplified output of the heterodyned signals appears in

Electricity - Electronics

Fig. 15-23. The schematic diagram of a Superheterodyne Receiver. (RCA)

SUPERHETERODYNE RECEIVER
MATERIAL LIST

C_1 C_5 C_8 = Ganged tuning capacitors, 10-365 $\mu\mu$f
C_2 C_6 C_9 = Trimmer capacitors, 4-30 $\mu\mu$f
C_3 C_{13} = 0.05 μf, paper, 50 V.
C_4 = 0.05 μf, paper, 400 V.
C_7 = Oscillator padding capacitor - follow oscillator-coil manufacturer's recommendation
C_{10} = 56 $\mu\mu$f, mica
C_{11} C_{12} C_{14} C_{15} = Trimmer capacitors for if transformers
C_{16} C_{17} = 180 $\mu\mu$f, mica
C_{18} C_{22} = 0.01 μf, paper, 400 V.
C_{19} C_{20} = 20 μf, electrolytic, 450 V.
C_{21} = 120 $\mu\mu$f, mica
C_{23} C_{24} = 0.02 μf, paper, 400 V.
C_{25} = 20 μf, electrolytic, 50 V.
C_{26} = 0.05 μf, paper, 600 V.
L = Loop antenna, 540-1600 Kc
R_1 R_5 = 180 ohms, 0.5 watt
R_2 = 12000 ohms, 2 watts
R_3 = 22000 ohms, 0.5 watt

R_4 R_6 = 2.2 megohms, 0.5 watt
R_7 = 100000 ohms, 0.5 watt
R_8 = Volume control, potentiometer, 1 megohm
R_9 R_{13} = 10 megohms, 0.5 watt
R_{10} = 1800 ohms, 2 watts
R_{11} R_{12} = 220000 ohms, 0.5 watt
R_{14} R_{16} = 470000 ohms, 0.5 watt
R_{15} = 8200 ohms, 0.5 watt
R_{17} = 270 ohms, 5 watts
R_{18} = 15000 ohms, 1 watt
S = Switch on volume control
T_1 = RF transformer, 540-1600 Kc
T_2 = Oscillator coil for use with 10-365-$\mu\mu$f tuning capacitor and 455-Kc if transformer
T_3 T_4 = Intermediate-frequency transformers, 455 Kc
T_5 = Power transformer, 250-0-250 volts rms, 120 ma. dc
T_6 = Output transformer for matching impedance of voice coil to a 10000-ohm plate-to-plate tube load

242

the plate circuit. The IF transformer, which couples the signal to the grid of the first IF amplifier, is sharply tuned to 455 kc and provides maximum response at that frequency.

Fig. 15-24. The penta-grid converter showing the oscillator section.

The other frequencies are rejected and by-passed to ground. An IF transformer is illustrated in Fig. 15-25.

The RF amplifier stage before the converter serves a dual purpose. Not only does it amplify the incoming signal but the rf stage provides greater selectivity and IMAGE REJECTION. In the discussion of the heterodyning principle, it was explained that the incoming signal and the local oscillator signal were mixed together to produce a beat IF of 455 kc. Using the same frequencies, study this example:

Incoming signal	1910 kc
Local Oscillator	1455 kc
IF	455 kc

It appears that the receiver could be tuned to 1000 kc and yet respond to a frequency of 1910 kc, if the tuning circuit were sufficiently broad to accept a part of this 1910 kc signal. This is referred to as the IMAGE FREQUENCY and may be found by:

Desired station frequency ± 2 x IF

frequency = Image frequency

Preselectivity of the RF amplifier reduces the response to the image frequency to a mini-

mum. Images may be very troublesome problems to designers of receiver circuits.

The second purpose of the RF stage is its ability to act as a buffer between the local oscillator and the antenna. The oscillator is, in fact, a small radio transmitter and will radiate an rf signal into space. Undesirable interference to other radio receivers nearby

Fig. 15-25. Typical IF transformers.

will result. The rf stage isolates the oscillator from the antenna, thereby reducing radiation.

Usually broadcast band receivers employ an IF frequency of 455 kc. This is not always true, however. Some communications receivers use other IF frequencies. Frequently, a double conversion is made which requires two IF frequencies. The technician should refer to the manuals to discover the IF frequencies used in the equipment he is planning to service.

REPRODUCERS

The purpose of the reproducer is to convert the electrical energy at audio frequencies in the final stage of the radio receiver into sound energy. Such a device is the LOUD-SPEAKER or HEADPHONES.

One of the more common types of

Fig. 15-26. A typical loudspeaker used in a radio.
(Stromberg-Carlson)

constructed with a permanent magnet is called a PM speaker. Such speakers are manufactured in a variety of sizes and types.

In the electrodynamic type speaker, the permanent magnet is replaced with an electromagnet, Fig. 15-28. The action is similar to the PM type. A strong source of direct current must be supplied to the electromagnet.

Fig. 15-28. In the electrodynamic speaker the permanent field is replaced by an electromagnetic field.

SPEAKERS is illustrated in Figs. 15-26 and 15-27. In this type a strong magnetic field is produced between the poles of a fixed permanent magnet. A small voice coil is suspended in the airgap and is attached to the speaker cone. When the audio alternating currents are connected to the voice coil, the interaction be-

Fig. 15-27. This sketch shows the principle of operation of the permanent magnet (PM) Speaker.

tween the fixed field and the moving field causes the voice coil to move back and forth. This motion also causes the speaker cone to move back and forth, resulting in the alternating condensations and rarefactions of the air in the form of sound energy. A speaker

This may be secured from the power supply. A common method is the use of the field coil of the speaker as the filter choke in the supply.

Due to increased interest in speakers by high-fidelity music enthusiasts, special sizes and novel types of speakers have been developed. These provide optimum response for specified bands of audio frequencies. Examples of these types are shown in Fig. 15-29. Low frequency speakers are described as WOOFERS; high frequency speakers are TWEETERS. The middle range is reproduced by the INTERMEDIATE speaker. Special filters and cross-over networks have been devised so that signals within specified ranges of frequencies are channeled to the speaker designed to reproduce the sound with maximum fidelity.

A cross-over network in its simplified form is diagramed in Fig. 15-30. Note that coil L is connected to the woofer. As the frequency of the sound increases, the reactance of L increases by the formula, $X_L = 2\pi fL$. However, the tweeter is connected through C

SP8B   SP12B   SP12

SP15B   SP15

T3500   T35B   T35

T350

Fig. 15-29. An assortment of speakers designed for high-fidelity reproduction. (Electro-Voice)

and as the frequency increases, the reactance of C decreases as, $X_C = \dfrac{1}{2\pi fC}$. By this circuit the frequencies are divided and reproduced by the speaker designed for best reproduction. Values of L and C may be selected for the desired cross-over point, usually between 400 and 1200 cps. It is interesting to note that at one frequency X_L equals X_C and the response is equal for

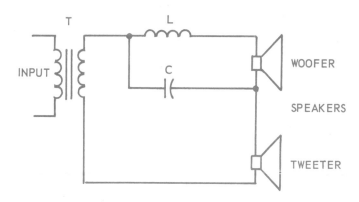

Fig. 15-30. A basic design of the cross-over network.

both speakers at this cross-over frequency.

The HEADPHONES illustrated in Fig. 15-31 still remain as a popular and useful method of sound reproduction for private listening. The principle of operation is not too

Fig. 15-31. The headphones provide private listening for communications receivers and a wide variety of other purposes.

different from the speaker and may be understood by following the diagram in Fig. 15-32. On the poles of a small horseshoe magnet are wound coils of fine wire. The incoming audio signal is attached to these windings. Mechanically suspended before this magnet is a flexible soft-iron diaphragm. The magnetic force of the permanent magnet holds the diaphragm under tension. The varying signal current through the coils either adds or subtracts from the magnetic field, and the diaphragm moves in and out as the magnetic

attraction varies. The moving diaphragm creates sound energy of the same frequency and amplitude as the incoming audio signal within the limitations of the device.

TONE CONTROLS

People differ in respect to the amount of high or low frequencies preferred in their

Fig. 15-32. The diagram shows the construction of a typical headphone.

music. Most radios, TVs and audio amplifiers incorporate a front panel adjustment, so the desired tone may be selected for listening pleasure. The schematic diagram in Fig. 15-33 shows a common circuit used for this purpose. Capacitor C_1 has a low reactance for high audio frequencies and would bypass only the desired amount as selected by the listener. The value of C_1 is usually $.05 \mu f$ and R_1 is 50,000 ohms. A tone switch may also be used providing three positions of tone control. Each position depends upon the reactance of its capacitor as a means of filtering or removing the high frequencies. Fig. 15-34 diagrams the tone switch control system, using three capacitors.

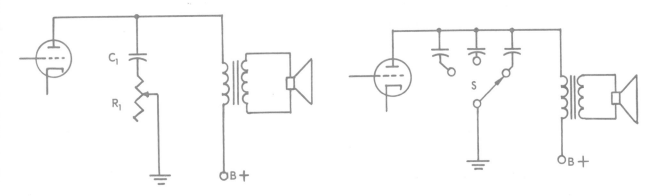

Fig. 15-33. A basic tone control circuit removes the higher frequencies from the speaker output.

Fig. 15-34. This tone control has three positions only. The tone may be selected by the listener.

ALIGNMENT

The superheterodyne receiver contains several tuned circuits, including the primary and secondary windings of the IF transformers, which must be tuned to resonance or maximum response for those signals which must be passed. Variable trimmer capacitors connected in parallel with these coils provide the adjustment, which is called ALIGNMENT. Receivers generally need alignment after parts or tubes have been replaced in the service shop. Also the effect of gradual deterioration of parts due to age may be minimized by an occasional "peaking" or aligning the receiver. The basic instruments needed for the job include the SIGNAL GENERATOR and an output indicator such as an AC VOLTMETER. (Test instruments are discussed in Chapter 20.) Briefly, a signal generator produces either a modulated or unmodulated rf wave which may be slected by the controls on the panel. When an alignment job must be done, it is always best to consult the technical manual for that particular radio or TV. Consequently any discussion of alignment procedures must be general and refer only to the basic theory.

In Fig. 15-35, a diagram of only the signal circuit has been drawn of a superheterodyne receiver. The AC voltmeter is connected to the plate of the final power amplifier tube through a .1 μfd-600 v capacitor. This is the indicating device. The signal generator is set up to produce a 455 kc modulated RF wave and is connected to the input grid of the converter tube, through a .001μf capacitor. The local oscillator must be disabled by connecting a "jumper lead" between the rotor and stator plates of the oscillator tuning capacitor. Turn the attenuation control on the

Fig. 15-35. This diagram shows only the signal path through a superheterodyne receiver. Connections for instruments are made for IF alignment.

Fig. 15-36. A practical crystal radio, using commercially manufactured parts.

generator so that only a faint tone is heard in the speaker. Starting with the output of the last IF transformer, adjust the trimmer capacitor, using a special alignment tool, for maximum reading on the voltmeter. Proceed toward the front end of the receiver by adjusting, in order, the secondary and primary of all IF transformers for maximum output response. This completes the IF alignment.

The oscillator section of the diagram in Fig. 15-35 contains both a trimmer capacitor and a series padder capacitor called the "600 PADDER." To adjust the oscillator, the generator is set at a modulated frequency of 600 kc and attached to the antenna input terminals through a 250 $\mu\mu f$ capacitor. The receiver is tuned to 600 kc and the 600 padder is adjusted for maximum response. Now the generator and receiver are tuned to the high frequency end of the band around 1400 kc and the trimmer capacitor is carefully adjusted for maximum response. More complete instructions for the alignment of a particular radio will be found in the manual and will include antenna trimmer tuning and more precise oscillator adjustments.

CRYSTAL RADIO

Crystal radios have been built at home and in school for many years. The first experience of hooking a few parts together and hearing a local broadcast program may become a lifetime memory. To many young people, the home built crystal radio is the first step toward a life long interest in electronics. The little radio, Figs. 15-36 and 15-37, demonstrates some of the principles

Fig. 15-37. Schematic diagram for crystal radio.

Fig. 15-38. Left. Pocket size transistor radio with loudspeaker. Fig. 15-39. Right. Rear view of transistor radio showing parts placement.

PARTS LIST FOR CRYSTAL RADIO

T_1 Antenna Coil   Miller 20A
C_1 Variable Capacitor $365\mu\mu f$ Philmore 1946 G
CR_1 IN34 Crystal Diode
Headphones $2000\,\Omega$
Binding Posts or Terminals

we have studied, such as tuning and detection.

Commercial parts have been used in this project because its construction is an introduction to more sophisticated circuits. Early familiarization with components and construction practice will pay dividends in more advanced projects. The radio may be built on a plastic sheet or a wooden base. It will require a good antenna for satisfactory operation.

FOUR TRANSISTOR RADIO

A four transistor radio that gives good reception on local stations and is relatively inexpensive to build is shown in Figs. 15-38 to 15-40 incl.

Station selection is accomplished by tuned-circuit $L_1 C_1$. The signal is detected by crystal CR_1 and amplified by four transistor stages to drive the loudspeaker. This amplification also increases the sensitivity of the detector. The grounded-emitter configuration is used by Q_2, Q_3 and Q_4. C_4, C_5 and C_6 provide interstage coupling.

Referring to the photographs you will notice that tiny electrolytic capacitors are

Fig. 15-40. Schematic diagram of transistor radio. (Sylvania)

249

Fig. 15-41. Completed experimental superheterodyne receiver. Each stage is interconnected by octal plugs.

used, also the transistor tuning capacitor C_1 and midget speaker LS_1 permit a compact assembly. All parts have been mounted on a sheet of 1/16 in. plastic, but printed circuitry may be used.

FOUR TRANSISTOR RADIO PARTS LIST

B_1 - 6 volt battery
C_1 - 0-365 mmfd tuning capacitor
C_2, C_3 - 0.02 mfd ceramic disc or paper
C_4, C_5, C_6 - 1.0 mfd electrolytic, 15 V
C_7 - 25.0 mfd electrolytic, 15 V
CR_1 - Sylvania 1N64 or 1N34 diode
L_1 - Ferri-loopstick antenna coil
LS_1 - 3-6 ohm loudspeaker
Q_1, Q_2, Q_3, Q_4 - Sylvania 2N1265 transistor
R_1, R_8 - 470 k, 1/2 w
R_2, R_4, R_6 - 220 k, 1/2 w
$R_3, R_5, R_7,$ - 2.2 k, 1/2 w
R_9 - 100 Ω, 1 w
T_1 - Argonne AR-133 or equivalent

It is advisable to build the radio first by using parts mounted on a breadboard. After satisfactory tests have been completed, a case may be designed to hold the radio.

AN EXPERIMENTAL SUPERHETERODYNE RECEIVER

Even a relatively simple electronic circuit may seem confusing to the beginner in electronics. The experienced technician will study individual stages and determine the relationship of each stage to the total circuit. It is the purpose of this project (actually five projects) as shown in Figs. 15-41, and 15-42, to give the student experience in the construction and function of each stage of the common superheterodyne receiver. A complete radio receiver is then assembled.

If students using this text have previously used the elementary texts on ELECTRICITY and ELECTRONICS published by Goodheart-Willcox Co., they will find this receiver to be a continuation of the block system project method of understanding the reception and transmission of radio signals as well as numerous industrial applications. For example: The Power Supply and Audio Amplifier are interchangeable with all projects.

This small radio is built on separate chassis which represent the block diagram of an operating superheterodyne receiver. A demonstration type is illustrated in the photograph Fig. 15-41 and the schematic diagram for each block in Fig. 15-42. You may wish to "breadboard" the radio and be assured that it is properly aligned and operating. This is a practical radio and satisfactory for permanent assembly in a case of your own design. Follow the diagrams carefully.

Fig. 15-42. Individual schematic diagrams for block stages of Superheterodyne Receiver.

Electricity - Electronics

SUPERHETERODYNE RECEIVER PARTS LIST

Pentagrid Converter

T_1 - Antenna Coil Miller 73A
L_1 - Oscillator Coil Miller 73-OSC
C_1, C_2 - Ganged tuning capacitor 10-365 $\mu\mu$f Double Section
C_{1a}, C_{2a} - Trimmer Capacitors (a part of C_1 and C_2)
C_3 - 50 $\mu\mu$f ceramic capacitor
C_4 - 470 $\mu\mu$f ceramic capacitor
C_5 - .05 μf paper capacitor, 400 V
R_1 - 22 KΩ, 1/2 w resistor
R_2 - 10 KΩ, 1/2 w resistor
V_1 - 6BE6

IF Amplifier

T_2, T_3 - Intermediate frequency transformers, 455 kc
R_3 - 100 Ω, 1/2 w
R_4 - 2.2 Meg. Ω, 1/2 w
V_2 - 6BA6

Detector - 1st AF Amplifier

R_5 - 500 KΩ Potentiometer, 1/2 w
R_6 - 5.6 meg Ω, 1/2 w
R_7 - 470 KΩ, 1/2 w
C_6 - .005 μf paper capacitor
C_7 - 220 $\mu\mu$f ceramic capacitor
V_3 - 6AV6

Audio Amplifier

R_8 - 500 KΩ potentiometer, 1/2 w
R_9 - 1000 Ω, 1/2 w
R_{10} - 47 KΩ, 1 w
C_8 - .01 μf paper capacitor, 400 V
C_9 - 1 μf electrolytic, 25 V
C_{11} - .01 μf paper capacitor, 400 V
V_4 - 6J5

Power Supply

C_{12}, C_{13} - Dual capacitor, electrolytic 20/20 μf, 450 V
L_2 - Choke 8.5 h - 50 ma
R_{13} - 25 KΩ - 25 w Wire Wound resistor with adjustable slider
S_1 - Single-Pole Toggle Switch
Line cord
T_4 - Power Transformer 480 V CT, 50 ma; 5 V - 2 amps; 6.3 V - 2 amps
V_6 - 5Y3

Audio Power Amplifier

R_{11} - 100 KΩ, 1/2 w
R_{12} - 270 Ω, 1/2 w
C_{10} - 8 mf Electrolytic, 50 V
T_5 - Audio Output Transformer 7600 Ω - 3.2 Ω
Speaker, PM
V_5 - 6V6

ALIGNING THE "SUPERHET" RADIO

Equipment needed:
RF signal generator
VTVM and alignment tools
Procedure:

1. Connect the VTVM to the plate of V_5 through a .1 μf-600 v capacitor. Set VTVM on AC range.

2. Short capacitor C_2 from stator to rotor with a jumper lead so that local oscillator is inoperative.

3. Connect signal generator to grid 3 (pin #7) of the pentagrid converter through a .001 μf capacitor. Set rf generator to 455 kc with modulation. Keep output only high enough to obtain a reading on the output meter (VTVM).

4. First tune T_3 secondary and then T_3 primary for maximum response on the meter.

5. Tune the secondary of T_2 and then the primary for maximum response. Reduce output of generator so that only a readable indication appears on meter.

Note: If IF transformers are badly out of adjustment, it may be necessary to tune them individually. To tune T_3, connect generator to the control grid of V_2 (pin 1) and adjust T_3 for maximum indication.

6. Remove the short across the oscillator and set signal generator to 1400 kc. Connect to antenna terminal through a 250 $\mu\mu$f capacitor.

7. Turn tuning dial to receive a 1400 kc signal and adjust trimmer C_{2a} for maximum response. The modulation tone (400 cps) should be heard from the speaker. Adjust for loudest tone.

8. Now adjust tuner trimmer C_{1a} for maximum sound.

Most radios also have a "padder" capacitor in series with the oscillator tuning capacitor. (It is not included in this demonstration radio.) Further alignment adjustments are made by this "padder" at the low frequency end of the tuning range at 600 kc.

FOR DISCUSSION

1. Are the waves radiated to your TV antenna, horizontally or vertically polarized?
2. How is it possible for a ham radio operator to talk to distant countries?
3. How does the tuning circuit select a desired frequency?
4. Explain the process of heterodyning signals.
5. Relate cross-over networks to high fidelity sound.

TEST YOUR KNOWLEDGE

1. What is the length of a wave which has a frequency of 1200 kc?
2. A short wave broadcasting station has a wave length of 40 meters. What is the frequency of this wave?
3. Name and explain the two fields in a radiated radio signal.

4. The process of removing the audio wave from the modulated rf wave is called _____ or_____ .
5. Name three types of detectors and draw basic circuits of each.
6. What two characteristics determine the quality of a tuning circuit?
7. Name three purposes of an rf amplifier.
8. What is the purpose of the capacitor across the load resistor in the detector?
9. What is the purpose of the AVC circuits?
10. What is the usual IF frequency used in broadcast receivers?
11. What type of audio amplification is used in Fig. 15-23? Name the stages.

12. Draw a diagram and explain the operation of a PM Speaker.
13. Explain the action of a tone- control circuit.
14. What is the purpose of alignment?
15. State the purposes of trimmer and padder capacitors.

An example of modern electronic miracle of miniaturization . . 18 diodes, four transistors, eight resistors balanced on eye (magnified) of a 2 1/4 in. long needle. (Western Electric)

Chapter 16

TELEVISION

In a brief span of a few years, television has grown from its infancy to a giant in the field of communications. Today, entertainment, education, on-the-spot news and commercial advertising are channeled into millions of homes as television has become a popular addition to family living.

Although it is beyond the scope of this text to study the detailed electronic circuits involved in the production, transmission and reception of television signals, it is important for students interested in the science of electronics to have an overall picture of television and related information.

THE TELEVISION CAMERA

What is a black and white picture? A picture may be considered as an infinite number of black and white dots, and dots of varying degrees between black and white. These dots are called picture elements. Examine a photo in one of the local newspapers and these elements are clearly visible. As the television camera looks at a scene in the studio, it is looking at these many picture elements of varying intensities from black to white. The scene is focused on a photo-sensitive mosaic consisting of many photo-electric cells. Each cell responds by producing a voltage in proportion to the intensity of light. These voltages are amplified and used for modulation of the AM carrier wave, which is transmitted to the home receiver. A line drawing of an image orthicon is shown in Fig. 16-1. The scene before the camera is focused on the photo cathode by the conventional lens system used by cameras. The varying degrees of illumination cause electrons to be emitted on the target side of the cathode, actually forming an electron image of the scene before the camera. The target plate is operated at a high positive potential and the electrons from the cathode are attracted to the target. The target is made of low resistive

Fig. 16-1. A non-technical sketch showing the interior arrangement of the image orthicon tube used in the television studio.

glass and has a transparency effect. The electron image appears on both sides of the target plate.

At the right in Fig. 16-1 is the electron gun which produces a stream of electrons. The electron stream is accelerated by the grids. The beam is made to scan left to right and from top to bottom by the magnetic deflection coils around the tube. The moving electron beam strikes the target plate and the electrons return to the electron multiplier section. The intensity of the electron stream returning to the multiplier is in proportion to the electron image and provides the desired signal current for electronic picture reproduction.

SCANNING

Scanning may be defined as the point-to-point examination of a picture. In the picture camera the electron beam must scan the

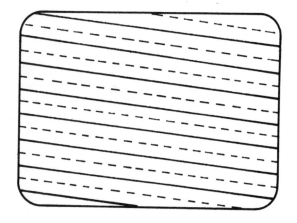

Fig. 16-2. The scanning pattern used in television in abbreviated form. There are actually 525 lines.

electron image and respond to the point-to-point brilliance of the picture. The system of scanning used by television in the United States is the interlace system and consists of 525 scanning lines. The beam starts at the top left hand corner of the picture and scans, from left to right, the odd lines of the scanning pattern, such as lines 1-3-5-7 etc. At the completion of 262-1/2 lines, the electron beam is returned to the beginning by vertical deflection coils and the beam then scans the even

numbered lines. One scan of 262-1/2 lines represents a FIELD and one set of the odd and even numbered fields represents a FRAME. The interlace system of scanning reduces picture flicker to a minimum. The scanning pattern is shown in an abbreviated form in Fig. 16-2.

The frame frequency has been set by the FCC as 30 cycles per second, which means that your TV receives 30 complete frames per second or 60 picture fields per second of alternate odd and even lines. A continuous, non-flickering picture is a result of your persistance of vision similar to your experience

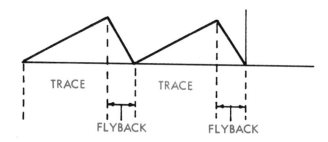

Fig. 16-3. The wave form of the voltages required for scanning and flyback. It is called a saw-tooth wave form.

with a motion picture which is a successive showing of individual scenes at a rapid rate.

In order to produce 525 lines per frame at a frame frequency of 30 cps, the horizontal deflection oscillator causing the electron beam to move back and forth must operate at a frequency of 525 x 30 or 15,750 cps. Likewise, the vertical deflection oscillator, which causes the beam to move from top to the bottom of the picture, must have a frequency of 60 cps. This is the field frequency.

Further examination of the scanning process reveals that the beam scans as it moves from left to right. After it has read one line, then it must quickly flyback to the left to start reading the next line, similar to the way you are reading this book. The FLYBACK time is very rapid, yet would show a visible retrace line in your picture. The picture must be BLACK during this retrace time. Also, when the beam reaches the bottom of the picture, the beam must be returned to the top in order to scan again. The picture must also be black during vertical flyback or trace lines would be visible.

The oscillators producing the scanning and flyback voltages for both the HORIZONTAL and VERTICAL SWEEP must produce a wave form as illustrated in Fig. 16-3. This is a saw-tooth wave form. Notice the relatively gradual increase in voltage during the sweep and then the rapid decrease during flyback. These voltages are applied to coils around the picture tube in the television called the DEFLECTION YOKE. The increase in the strength of the magnetic fields in the coils causes the electron beam to move. In Fig. 16-4 the schematic symbol and an illustration of the yoke are shown.

It is obvious that the scanning of the pic-

Fig. 16-4. A deflection yoke which fits around the neck of the television picture tube.
(Triad Transformer Corp.)

ture at the studio and the scanning of the picture in your home television must be in step. In order to accomplish this, a very accurate pulse generator is used to TRIGGER the horizontal and vertical oscillators at the studio. This same pulse is also sent over the air and received by the television set. This pulse, known as the SYNCHRONIZATION PULSE or SYNC PULSE, triggers the oscil-

lators in the receiver and keeps them at exactly the same frequency. The HORIZONTAL HOLD and VERTICAL HOLD controls on your TV are used to make slight adjustments so that the oscillators can lock-in with the SYNC pulses.

COMPOSITE VIDEO SIGNAL

The television signal received by your TV must therefore contain considerable information in addition to the picture (video) and

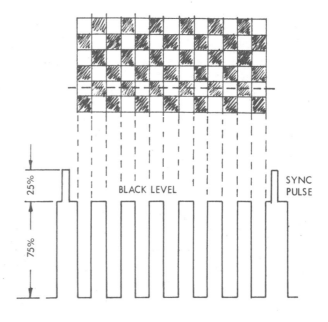

Fig. 16-5. The voltages developed as the camera scans one line across a checkerboard. The sync pulses are transmitted at the end of each line.

sound (aural) information. Perhaps the easiest way to understand the complete video signal will be to follow the formation of the signal as the camera scans a simple picture of a checker board in Fig. 16-5. Some standardization is necessary in the formation of the video signal so that your television may be used in any locality. These arbitrary standards are set up by the FCC and are used by all TV broadcasting stations. The amplitude of the modulation is divided into two parts. The first 75 per cent is used to transmit video information and the remaining 25 per cent for the sync pulses. Also a system of negative transmission has been adopted which means that the higher amplitudes of video information produce darker areas in the picture until at 75 per cent the picture is completely BLACK. In Fig. 16-5 the percentage of video is indicated on the scale at the left. As the beam scans the next black bar, a similar action takes place. At the end of the line, the screen is driven back to the BLACK PEDESTAL or BLANKING LEVEL. During this blanking pulse the beam flyback occurs and also a sync pulse is transmitted in the blacker-than-black or infrablack region (upper 25 per cent) for oscillator synchronization. A second line to be scanned would be a duplicate of the first unless the picture is changed. At the bottom of the picture a series of pulses trigger the vertical oscillator and keeps it synchronized. The illustration in Fig. 16-6 shows a composite video signal. The video information for one line between the

Fig. 16-6. The composite video signal of one line scanned by the television camera.

blanking pulses consists of varying degrees of illumination between black and white.

A comparison between the two video signals in Fig. 16-7 would disclose that signal

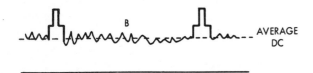

Fig. 16-7. A comparison of a dark and a light picture as it appears in the video signal.

A is made up of mostly light objects or a daylight scene. The average overall brightness of the scene is another part of the information sent to your TV receiver from the transmitter and may be detected from the composite video signal.

THE PICTURE TUBE OR CRT

The average television viewer has a limited knowledge of the "insides" of his receiver. His primary concern is with the picture appearing on the face of the picture tube. As students of electronics we will look behind the face of the cathode ray tube (CRT) and discover the mysteries of picture production. In Fig. 16-8 a sketch is produced which shows the functioning parts of the electron gun and deflection yoke. The theory of operation of the CRT is similar in most respects to the vacuum tube. Beginning at the left in Fig. 16-8 is the cathode and heater. Its purpose, of course, is the emission of a space cloud of electrons. Surrounding the cathode is a metal cylinder, closed at one end except for a small hole or aperture, which controls the flow of electrons in the CRT. It is the control grid with which we are familiar. It also serves to concentrate or electronically focus the emitted electrons through the small hole in the shape of a beam. Grid No. 2 is operated at a higher positive potential and its strong attraction for the negative electrons causes the electrons to accelerate or speed up. Grids No. 3, 4, and 5 serve as further accelerating and focusing elements which results in a narrow stream or beam of electrons. The beam is moved from left to right, successively scanning the face of the picture tube from top to bottom, by the magnetic deflection coils around the neck of the tube. The inside of the face of the picture tube is treated with special florescent materials. The electron beam causes these chemicals to glow as the electrons strike this florescent screen. The brilliance is in proportion to the intensity of the electron beam. The picture is observed through the glass front of the tube. The inside of the bulb of the tube is coated with a conductive coating. External connections to this coating are made from a high voltage power supply. When the electron beam strikes the florescent screen, electrons are knocked off, called secondary emission. These electrons are collected by the high potential anode or conductive inner coating and thus complete the circuit.

A LESSON IN SAFETY: Extremely high and dangerous voltages are present at the external connections to this anode, usually from 8,000 to 20,000 volts. Extreme caution must be observed by the technician when working close to these connections. A wise service man works with only one hand, so that an accidental shock will not be fatal. Keep one hand in your pocket!

Returning to the theory of vacuum tube operation, the control grid determines the flow of electrons through the tube. In the CRT this is also true. At zero bias the CRT is at maximum current and the screen, therefore,

Fig. 16-8. Sketch of a typical CRT showing the electron gun.
(RCA)

is bright or white. At cut-off bias the current is zero and the screen is black. The tube is operated at a selected bias on the control grid which may be controlled by a knob on the front of the TV called the BRIGHTNESS CONTROL. It adjusts the overall brightness level of the picture. When no picture is being received on the TV, the scanning electron beam may be observed by the lines on the TV screen called the RASTER. Turn your home TV to a vacant channel and observe this raster. Now adjust the brightness control from black to bright. The incoming detected video signal is applied to the grid of the CRT (sometimes to the cathode, depending on polarity of signal). The video signal adds-to or subtracts-from the bias on the tube resulting in a modulated or varying electron stream conforming to the picture information in the video signal. The picture is produced on the florescent screen.

The sharpness or focus of the electron beam may be adjusted by changing the voltages of the focusing grids. These controls are usually located on the rear of the TV and require occasional adjustment. Referring to Fig. 16-8 again, a centering magnet may be seen. Slight adjustments on this magnet may

be made in the service shop when the picture is off-center.

When the cathode in the CRT emits electrons, negative ions are also emitted. Since the ions have a greater mass than the electrons, they are not deflected as much, which could result in a brown spot about one-inch in diameter forming in the center of the picture tube because of ion bombardment. Several methods are used to eliminate the ION SPOT. Some tubes employ a tilted electron gun arrangement so that the ions hit the neck of tube. The electron beam is bent in its proper direction toward this screen by small magnets attached to the neck of the tube. These magnets are sometimes called an ION TRAP or BEAM BENDER. Aluminized picture tubes use an aluminum film on the electron gun side of the screen which protects the screen from ion bombardment as well as improving the sharpness of the picture.

THE TV RECEIVER

The block diagram in Fig. 16-9 represents the groups of components performing specific functions in the television receiver. This

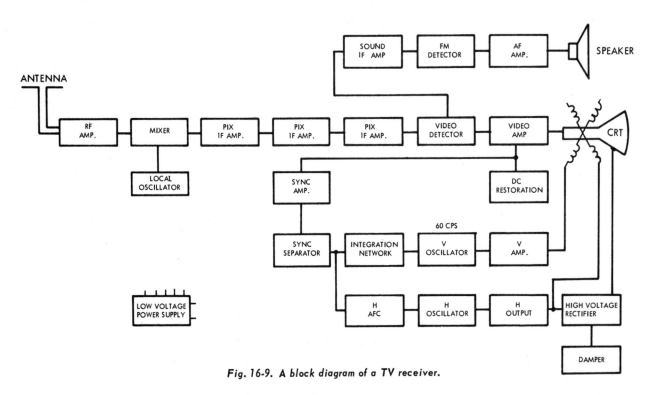

Fig. 16-9. A block diagram of a TV receiver.

block representation is used to familiarize the student with the interrelationships between various sections of the television. The signal path through the various stages may be traced and the purpose of each group of components to the total reception of the TV program may be understood. The name of each block suggests its purpose in the circuit.

RF AMPLIFIER: As the name suggests, this tube serves a function similar to that in the superheterodyne radio. The incoming television signal is selected by switching fixed inductors into the tuning circuit. These carefully tuned circuits are necessary to provide uniform gain and selectivity for each television channel. In this stage the video signal with all its information is amplified and fed to the mixer.

MIXER: In the mixer stage the incoming video signal is mixed with the signal from a local oscillator to produce an intermediate frequency. The common IF used in modern televisions is 45.75 megacycles. When the Channel Selector Switch is turned to a channel, not only is the tuning circuit changed, but also the frequency of the oscillator is changed, always producing the IF of the correct frequency. A FINE TUNING control is provided which changes the frequency of the oscillator slightly in order to provide the best response. The above three blocks in the diagram, namely the RF Amp, Mixer and Oscillator are combined in one unit called the TUNER or FRONT END of a television. These units are usually factory assembled and aligned. Adjustments should not be made on these units without correct instrumentation and thorough knowledge of procedures.

PIX-IF AMPLIFIERS: The output of the mixer stage, containing the 45.75 megacycle intermediate frequency with the video and aural information, is amplified by these stages. To provide a maximum frequency response of each stage up to 4.5 mc, each stage must amplify a broad band of frequencies. Consequently the voltage gain of each stage is reduced and more stages of IF amplification are required. In this system the aural information or sound is passed through the IF amplifier with the video signal. It is called the "intercarrier system."

VIDEO DETECTOR: The output from the last IF stage is fed to the detector or demodulator. The detection process is the same as in the radio. The video signal used to amplitude modulate the transmitted carrier wave is separated and fed to the next stage.

VIDEO AMPLIFIER: In these stages the demodulated video signal is amplified and fed to the grid (sometimes cathode) of the CRT. It is this signal which modulates or varies the intensity of the electron beam and thus produces the picture on the face of the CRT.

SOUND IF AMPLIFIER: Later in this chapter you will discover that the FM sound of the television program is separated from the video carrier wave by 4.5 megacycles. This produces a 4.5 mc FM signal at the output of the video detector which is coupled to the sound IF amplifiers. The FM sound signal is amplified in these stages.

Modern electronic equipment being used to control machinery which makes corrugated board sheets.
(Westinghouse)

FM AUDIO DETECTOR: This stage detects the frequency variations in the modulated signal and converts it to an audio signal.

AF AMPLIFIERS: These are the same as used in the conventional radio or audio system. The audio signal is amplified sufficiently to drive the power amplifier and the loudspeaker.

SYNC SEPARATOR: The output of the video amplifier is fed to this circuit which removes the horizontal and vertical sync pulses, which have been transmitted as part of the composite video signal. These sync pulses are used to trigger the horizontal and vertical oscillators and keep them "in step" with the television camera.

SYNC AMPLIFIER: This is a voltage amplifier stage to increase the sync pulses.

HORIZONTAL AFC: In this block the frequency of the horizontal oscillator is compared to the sync pulse frequency. If they are not the same, correction voltages are developed which change the horizontal oscillator to the same frequency.

HORIZONTAL OSCILLATOR: This oscillator operates on a frequency of 15,750 cps and provides the saw-tooth wave form necessary for horizontal scanning of the picture.

HORIZONTAL OUTPUT: This tube shapes the saw-tooth wave form correctly for the horizontal deflection coils and drives the horizontal deflection coils. It also provides power for the high voltage rectifier.

HIGH VOLTAGE RECTIFIER: The output of the horizontal oscillator is used to shock excite the HORIZONTAL OUTPUT TRANSFORMER (HOT). This autotransfromer develops a high AC voltage which is rectified and filtered for the anode in the CRT. See Fig. 16-10.

DAMPER: This stage dampens out the oscillations in the HOT after retrace and also rectifies part of the AC for a boosted B+ VOLTAGE. Part of this damper voltage is used in the horizontal scanning under the name of "reaction scanning."

VERTICAL OSCILLATOR: The output of the sync amplifier is fed through a vertical integration network to the vertical oscillator. The integrator, which is nothing more than a RC circuit, is designed with a time constant which

builds up a voltage when a series or group of closely spaced sync pulses occur. The transmitted vertical pulse is a wide pulse and occurs at a frequency of 60 cps. The vertical oscillator is triggered by this pulse and therefore keeps on frequency. The output of the vertical oscillator provides the saw-tooth voltage to the deflection coils which moves the beam from the top to the bottom of the screen and the "flyback" from bottom to top, at the end of each field.

Fig. 16-10. A typical horizontal output transformer (HOT). (Triad Transformer Corp.)

VERTICAL OUTPUT: An amplifier for the output of the oscillator to provide the proper currents in the deflection yoke for vertical scanning.

SPECIAL PURPOSE CIRCUITS

Many refinements have been made on the basic television circuit, including automatic controls for many functions which would be tedious for the TV viewer to manage. It might be well to mention and define a few of these. Detailed explanations and circuitry may be found in many television text books.

DC RESTORATION: The average darkness or brightness of the TV picture (night or day scenes) is transmitted as the average value of the DC component of the video signal. If

Television

Channel Number	Frequency Band (mc)	Video Carrier Frequency	Aural Carrier Frequency
2	54-60	55.25	59.75
3	60-66	61.25	65.75
4	66-72	67.25	71.75
5	76-82	77.25	81.75
6	82-88	83.25	87.75
7	174-180	175.25	179.75
8	180-186	181.25	185.75
9	186-192	187.25	191.75
10	192-198	193.25	197.75
11	198-204	199.25	203.75
12	204-210	205.25	209.75
13	210-216	211.25	215.75

Table 16-1, Frequency Allocations

the video amplifiers are RC coupled, the DC value of the signal is lost. In this case, the average value of the video signal is taken from the detector and used to establish the bias on the CRT.

AUTOMATIC GAIN CONTROL: The AGC in the television serves the same function as the AVC in the radio receiver. Its purpose is to provide a relatively constant output from the detector by varying the gain of the amplifiers in previous stages. This is accomplished by rectifying the video signal to produce a negative voltage. This voltage is applied to the bias of the previous amplifiers to change their gain.

THE TELEVISION CHANNEL

The Federal Communications Commission has assigned a channel or section of the radio frequency spectrum for each television channel. This channel is 6 mc wide. The limits of channels 2 to 13 are shown in Table 16-1. Let's examine Channel 4 in detail, Fig. 16-11. The video carrier frequency is 67.25 mc. Reviewing Chapter 14 you will recall that when an rf carrier wave is amplitude modulated, sideband frequencies appear which represent the sum and difference between the carrier frequency and the modulating frequencies. To transmit a real sharp video picture, frequencies up to 4 mc and more are necessary for modulation. These would combine in Channel 4 to give a band occupancy necessary for the modulated signal from 67.25 - 4 mc or 63.25 mc to 67.25 + 4 mc or 71.25 mc, or a total channel width of 8 mc. But the FCC only allows 6 mc and a compromise must be made. In commercial TV broadcasting the upper sideband is transmitted without attenuation. The lower sideband is partly removed by a vestigial-sideband filter at the transmitter. The curve in Fig. 16-11

Fig. 16-11. Location of picture carrier and sound in Channel 4. Channel is 6 mc wide.

represents the typical response characteristics of the TV transmitter. The sound is

Electricity - Electronics

transmitted as a frequency-modulated signal at a center frequency <u>4.5 above the video carrier</u>.

In Channel 4 the sound is at 71.75 mc.

FREQUENCY MODULATION

In the system of frequency modulation the frequency of the carrier wave is made to vary around a CENTER FREQUENCY at an audio frequency rate. The unmodulated and modulated FM wave is illustrated in Fig. 16-12. The modulation process at the transmitter

FM CARRIER WAVE

FREQUENCY MODULATED WAVE

Fig. 16-12. The carrier wave and the FM carrier wave.

involves the use of the audio voltage wave to change the frequency of the RF oscillator. Detailed explanations of modulation systems using a reactance tube may be found in advanced texts in communications. The block diagram of the simplified FM system is shown in Fig. 16-13.

In the FM system the carrier signal is transmitted at a constant amplitude. This is a decided advantage, since noise and interference are in the form of amplitude modulation and can be "clipped" or removed from the signal.

Further clarification of FM may be gained by studying the following definitions.
CENTER FREQUENCY: This is the assigned

frequency of the FM broadcasting station and represents the carrier frequency when NO MODULATION IS PRESENT.
FREQUENCY DEPARTURE: The amount of instantaneous frequency change from center frequency as a result of modulation. For example, if an audio modulating voltage causes an RF carrier at center frequency of 71.75 mc to change to 71.76 mc, the departure is 10 kc.
FREQUENCY DEVIATION: This represents the maximum frequency departure from center frequency during modulation. The amplitude or strength of the modulating audio voltage produces a greater deviation.

FREQUENCY SWING: This is equal to twice the deviation and represents the total change of frequency above and below center frequency.

PER CENT OF MODULATION: In FM broadcasting a frequency swing of ± 75 kc is considered as 100 per cent modulation. In television a swing of ± 25 kc is defined as 100 per cent modulation.

FM DETECTION

At the transmitter the frequency of the RF carrier wave is changed by the audio modulating voltage. At the receiver, the FM detector changes the frequency variation into an audio voltage which can be amplified and used to drive a speaker.
PHASE-SHIFT DISCRIMINATOR CIRCUIT: Fig. 16-14. In this circuit the amplified FM signal at IF frequency is inductively coupled to the tuned-tank circuit $L_1 C_1$. The signal is also coupled to the center of L_1 through capacitor C_2. The tank circuit $L_1 C_1$ is tuned to resonance at the CENTER FREQUENCY, and

Fig. 16-13. The block diagram of a simplified FM transmitter.

Fig. 16-14. The circuit diagram of a phase-shift discriminator.

Fig. 16-15. The circuit diagram of the Ratio Detector.

the voltages developed at the plates of V_1 and V_2 are equal. The voltage drops across R_1 and R_2 are therefore equal, but of OPPOSITE POLARITY. The voltage between point A and B is ZERO. At frequencies OTHER THAN CENTER frequency, the tank circuit is not at resonance and the voltages appearing at the plates of V_1 and V_2 will be UNEQUAL and the unequal conduction of the diodes produces unequal voltages across R_1 and R_2. The difference between these voltages appears as the output voltage of the detector and varies at an audio rate as a result of frequency change applied to L_1C_1. The RFC prevents the by-passing of the signal voltage while completing

the DC circuit for the diodes.

THE RATIO DETECTOR: Fig. 16-15. This circuit is similar in some respects to the discriminator. Note that one of the diodes is reversed. The incoming signal at center frequency produces equal voltages across C_2 and C_3 and the sum of these voltages charges stabilizing capacitor C_4, which is a relatively large capacitor. This is a useful feature of this circuit, since the charge on C_4 is the result of the average amplitude or strength of the incoming signal, and it may be used as an AVC voltage. At frequencies above or below center frequencies the charges on C_2 and C_3 are unequal, but they always equal C_4. The proportional charge between the two capacitors is taken as the audio output voltage since the proportion or division of the voltage depends upon the frequency deviation.

Other circuits are used in FM detection and more advanced texts should be consulted for detailed information.

DE-EMPHASIS

Higher audio frequencies usually have lower amplitudes because they may be harmonics of fundamental tones. The lower amplitudes will not produce sufficient frequency swing. It is common practice to pre-emphasize the higher frequencies of the audio signal before it is used to modulate the transmitter. At your FM receiver the higher audio frequencies must be de-emphasized to restore the audio signals to their original shape. A de-emphasis network is shown in Fig. 16-15 which is so designed that higher frequencies produce a lower response due to the shunting effect of the capacitor.

TELEVISION CONTROLS

There are a number of operating and servicing controls on your home television set. Some may be freely adjusted by the TV viewer, while others require the skill and knowledge of the technician. Some of these operating controls are listed in the following table together with information regarding their purposes

and circuits affected.

ON-OFF: Applies line power to the power supplies in the receiver.

VOLUME CONTROL: Controls the loudness of the sound by varying the amplitude of the audio signal fed to the audio amplifiers.

CHANNEL SELECTOR: A rotary switch which changes the inductors in the TUNER for station selection.

FINE TUNING: Controls the frequency of the local oscillator in the TUNER so that the IF will be correct for maximum response in IF amplifiers.

BRIGHTNESS CONTROL: Adjusts the overall brightness of the picture by moving the fixed bias on the CRT.

CONTRAST CONTROL: Changes the ratio between the black and white content in the picture by changing the gain of the video amplifiers.

HORIZONTAL HOLD: Provides slight adjustment of the horizontal frequency oscillator so that it will lock-in with horizontal sync pulse.

VERTICAL HOLD: Provides slight adjustment of vertical oscillator so that it will lock-in with vertical sync pulse.

The preceding controls are usually found on the front of the television. Other controls on the rear of the set require special tools and skills to adjust, and include height, width and linearity controls, plus positioning and focusing of the picture.

Fig. 16-16. A unitized custom TV chassis. Individual sections of a television may be independently serviced or replaced. (Setchell-Carlson)

HORIZONTAL OSCILLATOR AND HIGH VOLTAGE POWER SUPPLY

VIDEO AMP, AGC AND SYNC SEPARATOR

LOW VOLTAGE POWER SUPPLY

VERTICAL OSCILLATOR

AM OR FM TUNER

VIDEO IF AMP

FM SOUND PUSH-PULL AMP.

FRONT END TUNER

FOR DISCUSSION   (Use the library)

1. Name and discuss the function of each of the following controls in a TV receiver. State the circuit which is regulated by each control.

A. Horizontal Hold   G. Vertical Linearity
B. Brightness   H. Horizontal Linearity
C. Vertical Hold   I. Height Control
D. Fine Tuning   J. Contrast
E. Channel Selector   K. Width Control
F. Focus

2. Explain the meaning of negative transmission used in television in the U.S.
3. How does the vertical integration network separate the vertical sync pulse?
4. If DC amplifiers were used in the video section, would DC restoration be necessary?

TEST YOUR KNOWLEDGE

1. What is the frequency of the horizontal oscillator in a TV?
2. What is the frequency of the vertical oscillator?
3. What is meant by the interlace scanning system?
4. How many horizontal lines are in one field?
5. Which circuit and major components produce the high voltage for the picture tube?
6. In television, which methods of modulation are used for the video and sound transmission?
7. What information is contained in the composite video signal?
8. What is the purpose of the ion trap?
9. At center frequency or carrier frequency, what is the value of the audio voltage in a FM discriminator circuit?
10. Draw a block diagram of the television receiver.
11. What frequency is the PIX-IF in television?
12. What frequency is the sound IF?

Will tomorrow's cars be powered by the sun? The top photo shows an old time electric automobile which has been converted to use solar energy. Experimental model by International Rectifier Corp. Below. Electronic temperature controllers in a steel mill.

Chapter 17

TRANSISTORS

On July 1, 1948, an announcement of a new scientific discovery was made in the New York Herald Tribune:

"A tiny device that serves nearly all of the functions of a conventional vacuum tube, and holds wide promise for radio, telephone and electronics, was demonstrated yesterday by the Bell Telephone Laboratories scientists who developed it. Known as the transistor . . . ."

The tiny transistor has truly revolutionized the electronics industry. The transistor provides immediate circuit operation. No warm-up time is needed, as in the vacuum tube circuits. Power is not required for heaters. The transistor is characterized by small size, ruggedness, low power requirements, long life, reliability and lightweight.

In the study of transistors some entirely new concepts in electronic theory must be understood. Briefly, what do we know about conductors? We learned that a copper wire used for electrical connections is a good conductor. We learned also, that certain materials such as glass and rubber, are classified as insulators. Somewhere between the insulator and the conductor are many materials. These are classified as semiconductors. The transistor falls into this class; it is neither a good conductor nor a good insulator.

ATOMIC CHARACTERISTICS

A few minutes spent in review of Chapter 1 will materially aid your understanding of the atomic structure of materials. In Fig. 17-1, the atomic diagram of the elements of GERMANIUM (Ge) and SILICON (Si) are drawn. Note that the atomic number of Ge is 32 and Si is 14 which means that these ele-

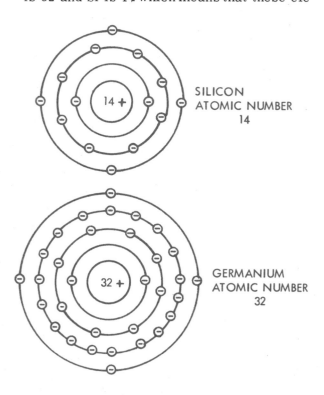

Fig. 17-1. The atomic structure of Germanium and Silicon.

ments have electrons in orbits in outer rings of 32 and 14 respectively. Note also that each has four electrons in its outer ring.

In the crystalline structure of pure Germanium shown in Fig. 17-2, the four electrons in the outer rings of each atom tend to join in what is called a covalent bond. These electrons seem to have a binding force which joins them together, yet each electron is bound to its own nucleus. This overlapping or sharing effect, resulting from the covalent bonds, presents a picture of Germanium called the LATTICE CRYSTALLINE STRUCTURE. Only the electrons in the outer orbit are illustrated.

Fig. 17-2. The crystalline structure of Germanium showing covalency between electrons in outer rings.

In this form the Germanium is a pure insulator and will not conduct electricity.

CONDUCTION OF ELECTRICITY

At this point in our studies, it has been well established that current flow in a conductor is a result of the transfer of energy by electrons. For emphasis, a copper conductor is sketched in Fig. 17-3. As an electron is added to one end of the conductor, an

Fig. 17-3. Electricity is conducted in a copper wire by the transfer of energy by electron movement.

electron leaves the opposite end. This chain reaction explains the conduction of electricity by ELECTRONS.

Assume now, in Fig. 17-4 that an electron is removed from one end of the conductor, leaving a vacancy or hole in which there should be an electron, but there is none. This hole has a strong attraction for an electron and can

be considered as positive. So the next electron fills up the hole and leaves a positive hole in its place. The positive holes are successively filled until the vacant hole appears at the other end of the conductor. Conduction has taken place by the movement of HOLES through the material. In the study of transistors we are concerned with both electrons and holes as conductors.

SEMICONDUCTORS

Returning now to the pure Germanium crystal, which is a good insulator, a minute amount of an impurity may be added which

Fig. 17-4. Conduction through a material as the result of holes.

will change its conduction characteristics. Impurities commonly used in transistors may be classified as:

TRIVALENTS: Aluminum, Gallium, Indium, Boron.

PENTAVALENTS: Arsenic, Bismuth, Antimony, Phosphorus.

The prefixes "TRI" and "PENTA" refer to the number of electrons in the outer ring of the atom. When a pentavalent, such as Arsenic, is added to the crystalline Germanium, four of the electrons in the outer ring of the Arsenic atom join in covalent bond with four electrons in the outer ring of the Germanium, leaving one electron from the Arsenic FREE. This is illustrated in Fig. 17-5. These free electrons change the characteristics of the Germanium from an insulator to a semiconductor. Conduction through the material will be by means of FREE-ELECTRONS. Since the pentavalent impurity contributed free electrons to the crystal, it is called a DONOR IMPURITY. Since conduction will be by negative electrons, the crystal now becomes an N TYPE crystal.

Consider now the addition of a trivalent impurity which has only three electrons to

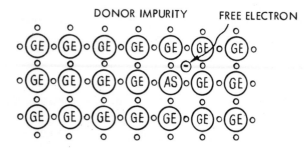

Fig. 17-5. A pentavalent impurity leaves free electrons. It is called a DONOR impurity.

join in covalent bond. One more electron is needed to complete the lattice structure, so therefore a HOLE is left, as illustrated in Fig. 17-6. Since the impurity has created a hole or vacancy, it is called an ACCEPTOR IMPURITY. Conduction through this crystal will be the result of POSITIVE HOLES and is named a P TYPE crystal. The simple cir-

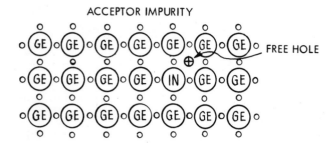

Fig. 17-6. A trivalent impurity leaves positive "holes." It is called an ACCEPTOR impurity.

cuit in Fig. 17-7 shows conduction through an N type crystal by means of free electrons. In Fig. 17-8 conduction is shown through a P type crystal. Notice that the hole movement is in the opposite direction to electron flow.

SEMICONDUCTOR DIODES

The semiconductor diode results from the fusion of a small N type crystal to a P type crystal. See Fig. 17-9. At the junction be-

Fig. 17-7. Conduction through an N type crystal by electrons.

tween the two crystals, the carriers, (electrons and holes) tend to diffuse. Some of the electrons move across the barrier to join the holes; some of the holes move across the barrier to join the electrons. This action is

Fig. 17-8. Conduction through a P type crystal by holes.

explained by the LAW OF CHARGES. Unlike charges attract each other. Due to the diffusion, the region around the junction in the P type crystal becomes negative, having collected electrons from the N crystal. Also, the region around the junction in the N type crys-

Fig. 17-9. A crystal diode made of N and P type crystals.

tal becomes positive, having lost electrons and gained holes. Therefore, a small voltage or potential exists between the regions close to the junction. This is called a POTENTIAL HILL or POTENTIAL BARRIER.

The barrier prevents the other electrons and holes in the crystal from combining.

A voltage or potential is connected across the diode in Fig. 17-10. In this case the positive terminal of the source is connected to the P crystal and the negative source to the N crystal. The negative electrons in the N crystal move toward the barrier and the positive holes in the P crystal move toward

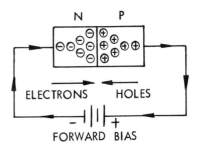

Fig. 17-10. Current conduction through the crystal diode when biased in the forward direction.

the barrier. The source voltage opposes the potential hill and reduces its barrier effect and allows the electrons and holes to join at the barrier. Therefore, current flows in the circuit. In the P crystal, by holes; in the N crystal, by electrons. The diode is BIASED IN A FORWARD DIRECTION.

A comparison to Fig. 17-11 shows the same junction diode connected with REVERSE BIAS, that is, the positive source to the N

Fig. 17-11. Conduction through the diode when biased in a reverse direction.

crystal and the negative source to the P crystal. In this case the source voltage aids the potential hill and limits the electron-hole combinations at the junction. The electrons in

the N crystal are attracted toward the positive terminal of the source. Very little current will flow in the circuit. The reverse voltage may be increased to a point where the diode will break down. This is similar to the inverse peak voltage rating of a vacuum tube.

CRYSTAL DIODE

The crystal diode has many applications in electronic circuits for detection and rectification. The point-contact diode consists of a small piece of N type Germanium crystal, against which is pressed a fine phosphor-bronze wire. During manufacture, a high current is run through the diode from wire to crystal which forms a P type region around the contact point in the Germanium crystal. The point-contact diode, therefore, has both the P and N type crystals and its operation is similar to the junction diode. A crystal diode used in a radio detector is shown in Fig. 17-12, together with its schematic

Fig. 17-12. A typical crystal diode. (Sylvania)

symbol. This diode is used in several projects in this text.

THE JUNCTION TRANSISTOR

The ability of a transistor to amplify is the key to its popularity in electronics. The JUNCTION TRANSISTOR consists of three layers of the impure Germanium crystals. There are two junctions. Transistors are illustrated by blocks and schematic symbols in Fig. 17-13. In the first case a thin layer of N type crystal is sandwiched between two P type crystals and is designated as a PNP transistor. In the second case a thin layer of P type crystal separates two N type crystals and is called an NPN transistor. In either case, the first crystal is called the EMITTER; the center section, the BASE; and the third crystal, the COLLECTOR. In the schematic symbols, notice the direction of the arrow-

Fig. 17-13. Block diagrams and symbols for NPN and PNP transistors.

head which signifies whether it is a PNP or NPN transistor. Popular transistors used in many of your projects are illustrated in Fig. 17-14.

Fig. 17-14. Typical transistors used in projects in this text. (Sylvania)

The theory of operation of an NPN transistor is illustrated in Fig. 17-15. For ease in understanding, two batteries are used. The negative terminal of the battery is connected to the N Emitter and the positive terminal of the same battery is connected to the P type Base. Therefore, the <u>Emitter-Base circuit is forward biased</u>. In the collector circuit, the N Collector is connected to the positive battery terminal and the P base to the negative terminal. The collector-base circuit is <u>reverse biased</u>.

Electrons enter the emitter from the nega-

tive battery source and flow toward the junction. The forward bias has reduced the potential hill of the first junction so the electrons combine with the hole carriers in the base to complete the emitter-base circuit. However, the base is a very thin section, approximately .001 in. and most of the electrons flow on through to the collector. This electron flow is aided by the low potential hill of the second PN junction. Approximately 95 to 98 per cent of the current through the transistor is from emitter to collector and about 2 to 5 per cent between emitter and base. A small change in emitter bias voltage

Fig. 17-15. The current flow in the NPN transistor.

will cause a relatively large change in emitter-collector current, while the emitter base current change is quite small. Although the current gain is less than one, the voltage gain can be many times. The current gain in a junction transistor is designated as ($\propto$) alpha. In the previous discussion, $\propto$ = .95 to .98.

The ability of the transistor to amplify is the result of the ratio between input and output resistance. Since the emitter-base is

Transistors

biased in a forward direction, its resistance is very low, (200-500 Ω). The collector-base circuit is biased in a reverse direction and has a very high resistance (100kΩ - 1 meg Ω). The voltage gain may be computed as,

$$A = \propto \frac{R_{output}}{R_{input}}$$

Example: A transistor has an alpha characteristic of .98. Its input resistance is 500 Ω and its output resistance is 500kΩ. What voltage gain may be expected?

$$A = .98 \times \frac{500,000}{500} = 980$$

The previous discussion has used a NPN transistor as an example. The theory of operation would be the same for a PNP, except that battery voltages must be reversed. In any case, the emitter is always biased in a forward direction and the collector in a reverse direction.

Now that we have inquired into the theory of transistor operation, a comparison to the familiar vacuum tube is desirable. They are alike in many respects. In Fig. 17-16, the emitter may be compared to the cathode which

Fig. 17-16. A comparison between the transistor and the triode vacuum tube.

emits electrons. The plate and collector receive the electrons. In the case of the vacuum tube a negative bias on the grid limits the electron flow through the tube. In most cases the grid is not driven positive. Therefore, the tube has a high input impedance. In the transistor, due to forward bias, current does flow from emitter to base and this circuit has a low impedance. The vacuum tube is considered as a VOLTAGE OPERATED device, whereas the transistor is CURRENT OPERATED.

TRANSISTOR CIRCUIT CONFIGURATIONS

The transistor may be connected in three circuit configurations, depending on which element is common to both input and output circuits. Usually the common element is at ground potential. In Fig. 17-17 the COMMON BASE amplifier circuit is drawn and it is

Fig. 17-17. The common base or grounded base configuration and its vacuum tube counterpart.

compared to the grounded-grid vacuum tube circuit. The AC input signal between the emitter and base will vary the forward bias by alternately adding to and subtracting from the fixed bias. The increase and decrease in current in the emitter-collector circuit produces the amplified voltage across R_L. The input signal and the output signal are in phase. There is no signal inversion.

Fig. 17-18. The common emitter circuit compared to the triode vacuum tube.

In Fig. 17-18, the COMMON EMITTER circuit is drawn. This is by far the more common transistor circuit and will be studied in more detail later in this chapter. Again the comparative vacuum tube circuit is drawn.

Notice that this circuit conforms very closely to the conventional vacuum tube amplifier. In the common emitter circuit a positive input signal would make the base more positive or less negative with respect to the emitter, thus reducing the forward bias of the circuit. A negative input signal would make the base more negative and increase the forward bias. As a result, the voltage across R_L in the output circuit is 180 deg. out of phase. The signal has been inverted in the same manner that signals are inverted in a vacuum tube circuit.

In the common emitter circuit the gain is computed as the ratio between the change in collector current and the change in base current. The current gain is specified by the

COMMON COLLECTOR   CATHODE FOLLOWER

Fig. 17-19. The common collector circuit may be compared to the cathode follower vacuum tube circuit.

Greek letter β (beta) and may be mathematically stated as,

$$\beta = \frac{\Delta I_c}{\Delta I_b} \qquad V_c \text{ Constant}$$

where:

β (beta) equals current gain in common emitter circuit

ΔI_c equals the change in collector current

ΔI_b equals the change in base current

while holding V_c (collector voltage) constant.

Note: In transistor circuits, voltage is represented by the capital letter V instead of E

as used in vacuum tube circuits and electricity.

Fig. 17-19 represents a common collector circuit and its vacuum tube comparison. The signal is applied between the base and collector. The output is taken from the collector-emitter circuit. This circuit compares to the conventional CATHODE FOLLOWER vacuum tube circuit. It will have a very high input impedance and a low output impedance. It is useful as an impedance matching circuit. The input and output signals are in phase. The voltage gain in this circuit must always be less than one.

THE TRANSISTOR AMPLIFIER

In Fig. 17-20, the common emitter amplifier circuit is drawn and its vacuum tube comparison. Only one battery is used and its positive terminal is connected to ground for the PNP transistor. Follow the circuit and notice that the emitter-base circuit is forward biased and the collector base circuit is reverse biased. The resistor R_1 limits the emitter-base current and its value is selected for the desired operating point from the transistor specifications. R_L acts as the load re-

Fig. 17-20. A single stage transistor amplifier with common emitter configuration compared to the vacuum tube amplifier.

sistor for the transistor and the amplified signal voltage appears across this resistor.

Transistors differ from resistors in respect to temperature effects. As the operating temperature increases, there is greater thermal activity in the crystalline structure and there is a decrease in resistance. The

Fig. 17-21. Left. Common emitter stage with stabilizing resistor and bypass capacitor.
Fig. 17-22. Right. Two common emitter stages transformer coupled.

cumulative effect of decreasing resistance and increasing current may destroy the transistor by THERMAL RUNAWAY. In Fig. 17-21, the common emitter amplifier is drawn with a stabilizing resistor R_3. Any increase in current will make the emitter end of R_3 more negative in respect to ground and thereby decrease the forward bias of the emitter base circuit. This acts as a limiter to current increases resulting from thermal runaway. C_3 is a bypass capacitor and serves the same function as its counterpart in a vacuum tube amplifier. It prevents degeneration and loss of gain.

CASCADED AMPLIFIERS

As in vacuum tube circuits, several transistor stages may be connected in CASCADE to produce the desired amplification. There is a drawback which adds some expense to transistor amplifiers. This is the problem of matching the high impedance output of one transistor to the low input impedance of the following transistor without severe loss in gain. This may be accomplished by transformer coupling and many miniature transformers of the sub-ouncer and sub-sub-ouncer size are manufactured. They are relatively expensive and frequently do not produce the desired signal response without distortion. It may be more economical to use RC coupling and compensate for the reduction in gain by adding another stage of transistor amplification. Circuits using both transform-

er and RC coupling are drawn in Figs. 17-22 and 23. Many of the transistor projects described in this text use these types of amplifier circuits and you will recognize them and understand them as you build the projects. Projects may first be constructed experimentally on the breadboard and then assembled as finished and practical devices which will give you many hours of enjoyment.

POWER AMPLIFIERS

The power amplifier does not differ in any degree from the transistor voltage amplifier, except in its ability to dissipate heat.

Fig. 17-23. Two common emitter stages using RC coupling.

Various methods have been devised to aid heat dissipation. Some transistors have cooling fins similar to those on an air cooled engine, only much smaller. Others take advantage of direct mechanical connections to the chassis on which they are mounted, so that the chassis may be used as a HEAT SINK. A push-pull power amplifier circuit is drawn in Fig. 17-24. The grounded or common emitter configuration is used with transformer coupling. The amplifier may be operated either Class A or Class B, depending on the forward bias of the emitter-base circuits. Its operation is the same as the vacuum tube push-pull amplifier. This power amplifier circuit will be used in projects that you build as part of your instruction in electronics.

PRECAUTIONS IN THE USE OF TRANSISTORS

1. Do not remove or replace transistors in circuits when the power is on. Surge currents may destroy the transistor.

2. Be very careful with close connections such as those found in minature transistor circuits. A momentary short circuit can burn out a transistor.

3. When measuring resistances in a transistor circuit, bear in mind that your ohmmeter contains a battery and if improperly applied will burn out a transistor. It is also

Fig. 17-24. A push-pull power amplifier used to drive a speaker.

important to observe the correct polarity when measuring ohms for accurate readings.

4. Soldering the leads of transistors is a skill which you must develop. Heat will destroy the transistor. When soldering a transistor lead, grasp the lead between the transistor and the connection to be soldered with

a pair of long nose pliers. These pliers will act as a heat sink and absorb the heat from the soldering. Use a pencil type soldering iron of about 25 watts.

PRINTED CIRCUITRY

In recent years much research has been done in the minaturization and rapid fabrication of electronic circuits. Transistors lend themselves to this type of circuit, so a brief discussion of the printed circuit technique is in order.

The basic component of the etched or so-called printed circuit is a copper-clad plastic board. The circuit is produced on the copper clad board by several methods.

1. Painting. In this process the circuit is hand drawn on the board with acid resisting paint. When dry, the board is placed in an acid bath, which eats away uncoated sections and leaves only the copper clad required for connections to components.

2. For more rapid production of duplicate boards the circuit may be printed on the board by the silk screen process. The unwanted sections are etched away in the acid bath.

3. The photographic method is slightly more involved. The copper-clad is coated with a photo sensitive chemical which makes it similar to a negative film. A cut-out or mask of the desired circuit is placed on the sensitized board and it is exposed to light. In the developing process the exposed surfaces are etched away, leaving the circuit connections desired.

Many etched circuits are used in electronics equipment. Examples are illustrated in Fig. 17-25. Some companies manufacture complete basic circuits for use in a variety of equipment. Fig. 17-26 illustrates a minature amplifier circuit used in a hearing aid.

After the circuit board has been etched, small holes are drilled at the ends of the copper-clad conductors through which components, such as resistors, capacitors, sockets, etc., are mounted. The leads of the components are inserted through the holes

Fig. 17-25. An example of a printed circuit and special soldering iron.
(Ungar)

and quickly soldered to the copper conductors. Special soldering tools of the pencil type have been developed for servicing and repairing printed circuitry. Some of these

Fig. 17-26. Printed circuits are used to miniaturize equipment. These complete amplifiers are compared to a book of matches.
(Centralab)

tools are shown in Fig. 17-27. The procedure, in brief, for making an etched circuit board is as follows.

1. Cut your blank of copper clad board to exact size for your selected circuit.

2. Using carbon paper and a hard pencil

(4H), transfer your circuit design to the copper-clad. Mark holes to be drilled for all components.

3. Drill #40 pilot holes for all components. Enlarge holes by gradually increasing drill size until proper size is reached.

4. Carefully paint the transferred pattern with acid-resist paint and allow to dry.

Fig. 17-27. Some special soldering and desoldering tools developed for printed circuit work.

5. Etch in bath of Ferric Chloride ($FeCl_3$) for one to two hours. Remove from bath, wash with clear water and remove resist paint with cloth and solvent.

6. Holes for wires may now be drilled using a #54 drill.

7. Mount parts and solder. Avoid excess heat but be sure you have no rosin joints.

In your instructional projects, you will have opportunities to design and make an etched circuit. You may wish to adapt this method also to other projects included in this text. Experience is the best teacher. Work carefully, plan ahead, and analyze your circuit for a practical printed circuit layout.

Fig. 17-28. Safety flasher.

SAFETY FLASHER

PREVENT ACCIDENTS

A very practical and inexpensive project which involves electronic circuitry, transistors and the printed circuit method of construction is shown in Fig. 17-28 to 17-30 incl. You may wish to build one for your family car. It is used in case of car trouble or a flat tire and may be placed down the road fifty feet or more as a warning for oncoming motorists. It produces a bright flashing light which may be seen at some distance.

Its construction is quite simple and the suggested circuit layout on the copper-clad board is shown. You may wish to design your own board. The project case was made with galvanized iron and painted black. However, your own design may be more desirable. Some ingenious young man will probably use an ordinary tin can.

PARTS LIST FOR SAFETY FLASHER

C_1 - 100 μf - 10 volt Electrolytic
R_1 - 220 Ω, 1/2 w
R_2 - 6800 Ω, 1/2 w
R_3 - 8200 Ω, 1/2 w
R_4 - 3900 Ω, 1/2 w
Q_1 - 2N35 Sylvania Transistor
Q_2 - 2N363 Raytheon Transistor
#46 Pilot light and socket slide or toggle switch SPST
Red Auto Taillight Glass
6 volt Battery or 4 Flashlight Cells in Series

Fig. 17-29. Safety flasher wiring diagram.

Fig. 17-30. Safety flasher components mounted on back of board.

FOR DISCUSSION

1. Why should transistors be temperature controlled by heat sinks and ventilation?
2. Discuss transformer coupling vs. RC coupling in transistor circuitry.
3. Discuss precautions in the use of and servicing of transistor circuits.
4. Name several advantages of "printed circuits."

TEST YOUR KNOWLEDGE

1. What is meant by covalent bonds in a lattice crystalline structure?
2. Name three donor impurities. Why are they called donor impurities?
3. Name three acceptor impurities. Why are they called acceptors?
4. How is the potential barrier formed at the junction of a PN crystal?
5. Draw a block diagram of the crystal diode showing forward bias connections.
6. Draw the same diagram showing reverse bias.
7. Draw a block diagram of an NPN transistor, with bias batteries connected with proper polarity.
8. Draw the common emitter amplifier circuit.
9. How is the gain in the common emitter stage computed?
10. Name four advantages of transistors over vacuum tubes.
11. An N type crystal conducts by _____. A P type crystal conducts by _____

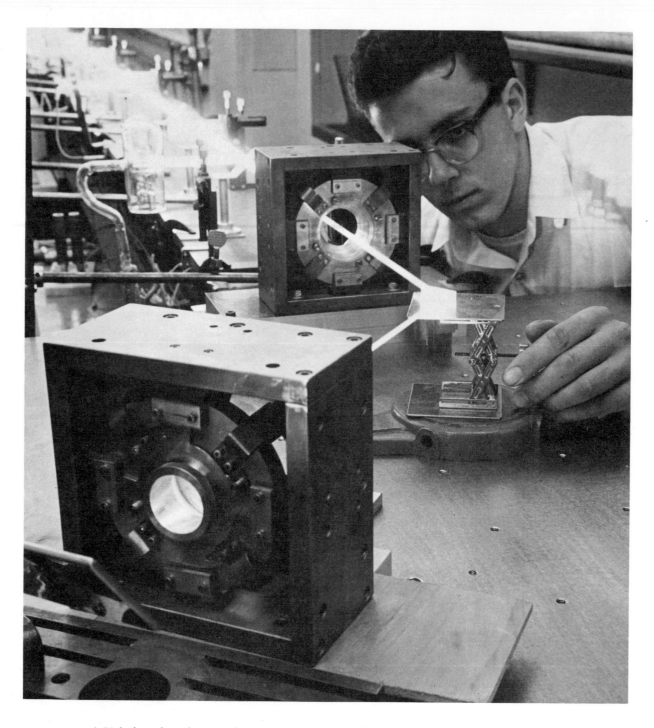

A 33 ft. laser beam being used in experimentation at Bell Laboratores. The laser opens the doors to the future in many areas.

Chapter 18

ELECTRONICS IN INDUSTRY

The visible evidence of progress in electronics technology is apparent in radio and television and in the developments of the space age.

Almost any manufactured product we use today has in some way been made better or more economically through the use of electronics. Automation in industry means electronic control of machine operation, grading and counting of products and inspection. Only a few years ago many men performed long and tedious operations which now may be accomplished with only a few highly skilled technicians. This means shorter working hours and more leisure time; higher wages and a bountiful supply of useful products for everyone to enjoy. Now, highly complex computers do the work of thousands of men involved in mathematical computations and accounting and the computer can complete work in a few minutes which previously required weeks and months of manpower. Yes, we do live in an electronic age. The average citizen would be amazed, if he did know, how involved his life has become in electronics and how dependent he is upon this science.

The purpose of this chapter is to acquaint the student with a few of the more common electronic applications in industry. Advanced studies in this specialized field will be rewarding. Opportunities for employment as a skilled technician seem almost unlimited in this technical age.

PHOTOELECTRIC CONTROLS

In our study of the principles of the vacu-um tube, we discovered that certain materials, when heated, would "boil out" or emit electrons. This type of material was used as the cathode in the vacuum tube. This type of emission was called THERMIONIC EMISSION.

Other materials exhibit a similar characteristic when exposed to light. Materials which are sensitive to light include Zinc, Potassium and other alkali metals. This type of emission has been named PHOTOELECTRIC EMISSION. When a light strikes a surface of these materials, the light energy, if sufficiently strong, will cause free electrons to be emitted from the surface. This is a very useful discovery. Circuits may be designed which will take advantage of the intensity of light to control certain industrial operations, counting, sorting and inspection.

There are three classes of light sensitive materials which are used in light control circuits:

1. PHOTO EMISSIVE CELLS OR PHOTO-TUBES. These are gas filled or high vacuum type tubes with two elements, i.e. cathode and anode. This tube is illustrated in Fig. 18-1 with its schematic symbol. Light shining

Fig. 18-1. The phototube and its schematic symbol.

281

on the cathode will cause electrons to be emitted. When a positive voltage is applied to the anode, it will attract the electrons and current will flow through the tube. This current may be used to control another vacuum tube and relay circuit.

2. PHOTOCONDUCTIVE CELLS. These materials show a decrease in resistance and consequently an increase in current when light shines on them. In Fig. 18-2 a photo transistor is diagramed. This is a PN junction photo diode connected with reverse bias. Only a small amount of reverse current will flow, in the order of a few microamperes. This is termed the DARK CURRENT. When a light

Fig. 18-2. The block diagram of a photo transistor.

strikes the surface of the transistor, the current will increase due to the diffusion of minority carriers across the junction. A minority carrier in a P crystal is an electron; in an N crystal, a hole.

3. PHOTOVOLTAIC CELLS. This cell has many uses. It will develop a voltage across its surfaces when exposed to light. This discovery came from the research on transistors by the Bell Telephone Laboratories. Walter H. Brattain, co-inventor of the transistor, remarked when he first observed this experiment:

"There was this man ...... and he had a little chunk of black stuff with a couple of contacts on it and when he shone a flashlight on it, he got a voltage .... I didn't believe it."

Contrast this relatively primitive experiment to the Bell System Communication Satellite shown in Fig. 18-3. An array of solar cells used to convert sunlight into electricity covers most of the surface. Such a satellite is used for relaying of telephone calls, television signals and overseas communication.

A very familiar application is the Light

Fig. 18-3. Left. Men installing solar cells on the surface of communications satellite. Fig. 18-4. Right. Sun cells used to power telephone communications system.
(Bell Telephone Laboratories)

Meter. Such an instrument is indispensable to the photographer, who uses the meter to determine the intensity of the light.

In Fig. 18-4 a bank of solar cells is used to power a telephone communications system for the Bell System.

In the project illustrated in Fig. 7-27, a photo cell is used in the automatic garage light. The headlights from your car pointed

tive bias to above cutoff and V_2 conducts. Current through V_2 activates relay K_1. The relay points may be used to switch machines on or off, ring bells, trigger counting devices, open doors, and perform many other tasks. R_2 is a potentiometer for a sensitivity control.

Another interesting application of the phototube is derived from the SPECTRAL SENSITIVITY of materials used as a cathode

Fig. 18-5. The basic photo control circuit.

toward this device will turn on your garage lights. Similar arrangements are used for automatic headlight dimming on some models of cars.

BASIC PHOTO CONTROL CIRCUITS

In the diagram, Fig. 18-5 the schematic of the basic photo control circuit is shown. In this circuit the cathode of V_2 is connected to a tap on the voltage divider in the power supply at 30 volts positive. The grid is at ground potential so therefore it is 30 volts more negative than the cathode. The tube is cutoff. The anode of V_1 is at a positive potential since it is connected to B+ through resistor R_1. When light strikes the phototube V_1, current will flow from ground, through R_2, through V_1 to B+. A voltage drop appears across R_2 with its grid end positive. This positive voltage subtracts from the nega-

for the tube. A tube may be sensitive to red light and not to blue light, as well as different shades of colors. Some sensitive circuits approach the color vision properties of the human eye.

TIME CONTROL CIRCUITS

In industry there are many needs for precise timing operations. In many cases the timing is done by mechanical devices and switches. The electronic timer is a very useful device, whether used to control a photo enlarger in a photographic laboratory, or a huge welding machine in industry. Basically, an RC time constant circuit is used as the timing components which control a vacuum tube and relay. A review of Chapter 7 at this point in our studies is advisable. The basic time control circuit is shown in Fig. 18-6. The cathode of V_1 is connected to a 30 volt positive tap on the voltage divider in the power supply. Since the grid of V_1 is connected to ground, the cathode is 30 volts more positive than the grid or the grid is 30 volts more negative than the cathode. The tube is cutoff. When switch S_1 is momentarily closed, the grid and cathode are at the same voltage, which removes the bias and V_1 conducts and activates the relay. Also C_1 charges immedi-

Fig. 18-6. The basic timer circuit.

ately when S_1 is closed. After S_1 is open, the charge on C_1 holds the tube V_1 in conduction, until the charge bleeds off through potentiometer R_1. When the voltage across C_1 decreases to cutoff, tube V_1 stops conducting and the relay opens. R_1 may be adjusted for selected time intervals.

AC TIME CONTROL CIRCUITS

It is often more convenient to operate a time control circuit directly from the AC line, rather than use a power supply for DC voltages. Before examining this circuit, a few words should be said about the THYRATRON tube, which has not been mentioned in our previous studies. The thyratron is a gas filled tube, which conducts by ionization of the gas. No conduction takes place until a certain plate voltage is reached which causes ionization. This is called the FIRING OR IGNITION VOLTAGE. Thyratrons are grid controlled. However, the bias on the grid only changes the ignition voltage. The more negative the grid,

the higher ignition voltage required. After the tube fires and starts conduction, the grid no longer has any effect on the conduction of the tube. The tube will stop conduction only when the plate voltage is lowered to a point called the EXTINGUISHING VOLTAGE. Thyratrons are excellent tubes for switching and control operations. A thyratron tube is used in the time control circuit in Fig. 18-7. Note the black dot within the tube symbol which means that-it is a gas filled tube.

In this circuit, first assume switch S_1 is open. During the positive AC half cycle, A is positive in respect to B. Since S_1 is open, there is no potential between the cathode and plate of V_1. However, the grid will have a positive voltage depending on the setting of R_2. The grid will collect electrons and C_1

Fig. 18-7. The timer control circuit using AC power and a thyratron tube.

will become charged. During the negative half cycle C_1 will try to discharge through R_3, but the time constant is too long so it does not discharge completely. After several cycles the charge on C_1 levels off to a constant value depending on the setting of R_2. Tube V_1 remains cutoff. The timing circuit is activated by closing S_1. Now the total AC voltage appears across V_1. The tube is still held at cutoff by the negative charge on C_1, but C_1 gradually discharges through R_3 until the cutoff point is reached. V_1 then "fires" and conduction takes place which activates relay K_1. By opening switch S_1 the circuit may be reset.

Fig. 18-8. This garage door opener is radio controlled.
(Perma-Power)

Fig. 18-8A. Radio controlled miniature aircraft used to determine the shape of the Space Shuttle Re-entry vehicle.
(NASA)

RADIO CONTROL

The use of radio frequency waves to control machinery and devices in distant locations is becoming increasingly more popular. A radio-controlled garage door opener is illustrated in Fig. 18-8. The car is equipped with a small radio transmitter. When keyed by the driver, the transmitter sends out a modulated RF wave to the garage receiver, which activates a relay and starts the door opening mechanism.

The aerospace industry uses radio frequency waves to control the flight pattern of new aircraft ideas in model form before going to the tremendous expense of building and testing full size aircraft, Fig. 18-8A. The aircraft can be tested to the complete limits of their capability without endangering the life of a test pilot.

Military applications of remotely piloted vehicles (RPVs) is developing into a new technology. Radio control provides adequate command and control of unpiloted aircraft over hostile environments at altitudes up to 70,000 ft. for reconnaissance purposes. RPVs, Fig. 18-9, equipped with miniature TV cameras, can accurately deliver weapons on ground targets with the control pilot safely located many miles away.

The hobby of controlling boats, planes and cars, Fig. 18-10, is followed enthusiastically

Fig. 18-9. One of the newest RPV (Remotely Piloted Vehicle). This craft permits the reconnaissance of enemy territory with the pilot safely located many hundreds of miles away.

Fig. 18-10. The interior of radio controlled model aircraft. Control surfaces are actuated by servos triggered through the receiver by commands from the pilot on the ground.
(Heath Company)

by millions of persons. These hobbyists are able to put their craft through intricate maneuvers, on command, by using radio equipment that can be purchased fully assembled or in kit form, Fig. 18-11.

The Federal Communications Commission (FCC) has set aside specific frequencies on the 27MHz, 53MHz and 72MHz bands for exclusive use of radio controlled models.

NOTE: *It is necessary to have a CLASS C operator's license from the FCC before radio control equipment can be operated on the 27 and 72MHz bands. A technician class or higher amateur radio operator's license is required to operate on the 53MHz band.*

THEORY OF OPERATION

The radio control unit shown in Fig. 18-11, was constructed from a kit, and can be constructed as either a 3- or 4-channel unit. That is, it can be used for the remote control

Fig. 18-11. *Radio control units can be purchased already assembled or constructed from well-designed kits. Shown are 3- and 4-channel Digital Proportional Systems. Units with up to 8-channels are available.* (Heath Company)

of three or four devices (usually servos) depending upon the type of circuit constructed. It is a Digital Guidance System that operates on a pulse-width comparison principle. Pulse modulation of the RF carrier is crystal controlled.

When all controls are in neutral, the transmitter sends out a frame of five pulses that are repeated continuously every 16,000 microseconds. See Fig. 18-12, WAVEFORM A. Each pulse in the frame is 350 microseconds wide, and all pulses in the frame, except the first one, normally start 1500 microseconds after the start of the previous pulse. This is called a "fixed frame rate" because the time interval between the first pulse in one frame and the first pulse in the next frame is always 16,000 microseconds. This cannot be changed.

The time frame between pulses is 1500 microseconds and can be increased or decreased as much as 500 microseconds. The infinitely (immeasureable) variable width between individual pulses controls the amount of servo travel (how far the control surface will move). A tiny change in pulse width, wider or narrower, produces a small amount of servo travel in the appropriate direction. A large movement of the control stick will produce a large change in pulse width and gives a correspondingly greater amount of servo travel. Other channels are not affected, Fig. 18-12, WAVEFORM B.

Fig. 18-12. *Typical waveform of a 3- or 4-channel RC unit.* (Heath Company)

The modulated RF carrier can be seen in Fig. 18-13. It shows that the RF carrier is turned off during the 350 microsecond pauses,

ONE FRAME

RF CARRIER

FRAME STARTING
PULSE

CONTROLLING PULSES

MODULATED RF CARRIER

SYNC PAUSE

Fig. 18-13. Modulated RF Carrier of a 4-channel RC unit.
(Heath Company)

but is on all other times. Off time is minimized to reduce the possibility of interference that will cause erratic and unwanted
servo movement (called "glitches" by the RC
hobbyist). The schematic for the 3-channel
Digital Proportional Transmitter is shown
in Fig. 18-14.

The pulse train, upon being detected by
the receiver, is amplifed. It triggers the
decoder circuits which "read-out" the individual pulses to the appropriate servos.
For example: The pilot wants his model
plane to make a climbing right turn. The

elevator control (channel #1) is pulled down
slightly for a gradual climb and the rudder
control (channel #2) is moved to the right.
The control stick movements change the
pulse lengths of channels #1 and #2. Pulse
length of the other channel is not affected.
The decoder circuit in the receiver notes
the change in the pulse length of channel #1
and instructs the elevator servo how far up
it must move the plane's elevator. Almost
instantaneously, the decoder is also telling
the rudder servo how far it is to move the
rudder to the right. Control surface movement is proportional to the stick movement.

Fig. 18-14. Schematic for the 3-channel Digital Proportional
Transmitter shown in Fig. 18-11.   (Heath Company)

Control movements are held until the control stick is returned to neutral or moved to a new position. The decoder circuits are reset in synchronism with the transmitter signal by the long sync pause.

ELECTRONIC HEATING

In recent years industry has discovered many methods of heating both conductive and non-conductive materials by using high frequency alternating currents. These methods have provided a means to quickly heat, to a controlled temperature and depth, many materials for specific industrial applications.

INDUCTIVE HEATING

Induction heating is used for materials which conduct electricity. In its more simple form it consists of only a transformer with a single turn or short circuited secondary winding as drawn in Fig. 18-15. The alternating current in the primary winding induces

Fig. 18-15. The short circuit secondary winding demonstrates the principle of induction heating.

a current in the secondary. In earlier studies we learned about the I^2R power loss in a transformer, generator or motor. In the induction heater the power loss, as a result of the high currents, serves a useful function of heating the material. More specifically, the secondary of the transformer may be the material to be heated, and the induced currents are the eddy currents within the material. See Fig. 18-16. As the frequency of the alternating current is increased, the eddy currents have a tendency to flow on the surface of the material. This phenomena is known as SKIN EFFECT. It is useful in industrial processes. In many cases it is necessary to heat the sur-

face of a material for surface hardening, yet leaving the interior of the material softer and stronger. In induction heaters, vacuum tube oscillators are used for the generation of high frequency currents. These oscillators do not differ, circuitwise, from oscillators used in radio transmitters, except in their

Fig. 18-16. Heat is produced in the material when it is inserted in the work coil.

ability to produce high power. In some industrial applications thousands of watts of power are required. A conventional oscillator circuit used in an induction heating circuit is drawn in Fig. 18-17.

The tuned circuit $L_1 C_1$ determines the frequency of the oscillator. Energy is fed back to the grid of tube V_1 from the tickler coil L_2. Even though this circuit appears like a conventional oscillator used in radio communications, it must handle high voltages and

Fig. 18-17. A basic oscillator circuit used in induction heating.

frequently many thousands of watts in power. All parts must be rugged and well insulated.

Examples of induction heating may be found in heat treating processes, brazing, tin plating and other applications requiring a high degree of temperature control and heat penetration, as well as cleanliness and economy.

An induction furnace for the heat treating of steel is illustrated in Fig. 18-18. The photos show front and rear view of a 10 KW Induction Heating Unit. Work to be heated is

electronics serves us. Improved methods in manufacturing bring to the consumer better products at lower prices. Improved methods in industry provide more healthful and satisfying working conditions, plus higher wages and shorter working hours.

DIELECTRIC HEATING

When non-conductive materials must be heated, they may be placed between plates as a dielectric material used in the familiar capacitor. Fig. 18-19 illustrates this type of heating. When a high AC voltage is applied to

Fig. 18-18. An induction furnace used in heat-treating steel in industry.

placed in the work coil, as seen in the front view, which acts as a primary winding of a transformer. The resulting eddy currents in the work produce heat as they overcome the resistance of the work. The depth of the heating may also be controlled by changing the frequency of the induction heating. Lower frequencies produce greater depth of heat; surface heating is accomplished by higher frequencies. This is one other way by which

Fig. 18-19. In dielectric heating the material serves as the dielectric of a capacitor.

the plates, the heating within the insulating material or dielectric is the result of molecular distortion and friction. The high frequency voltage applied to the plates causes the molecules of the dielectric to vibrate and rub together and heat is produced by intermolecular friction. This may be compared to hysteresis loss in the iron core of a transformer, and is termed dielectric hysteresis. This type of heating requires higher frequencies than the induction heating, usually from 1 mc to 50 mc.

Interesting applications of dielectric heating are in the electronic oven for cooking, electronic gluing of plywoods and furniture, heating and shaping of plastics, and medical treatments requiring deep heat and the producing of artificial fever in patients.

MAGNETIC AMPLIFIERS AND REACTORS

The term magnetic amplifier and saturable reactor are sometimes used interchangeably, but actually the magnetic amplifier consists of the saturable reactor plus other associated components such as rectifiers, resistors and transformers. Before actually looking at the saturable reactor, a

Fig. 18-20. The basic circuit of the saturable reactor.

brief review of magnetism and inductive reactance should be made. Repeat the experiments as illustrated in Fig. 7-3. The student must realize that the reactance of a coil varies according to the permeability of the core. In the case of the dimmer circuit in this experiment the core was changed from air to iron by inserting the iron core in the coil. It is, therefore, a correct assumption that the impedance of a coil may be varied

by varying the permeability of the core. Also the permeability as stated in Chapter 4, is

$$\mu = \frac{B}{H}$$

where,

μ = Permeability

B = Flux density

H = Magnetizing force

These are the principles on which the saturable reactor is based.

The basic circuit of the saturable reactor shown in Fig. 18-20, requires some explanation. To one side of the transformer is connected a variable DC voltage. The load, AC power source and the other side of the reactor are connected in series. When no DC voltage is applied to the control side, the impedance of the load windings is maximum and the current through the load is minimum. As the DC control voltage is increased, the magnetic flux density of the core increases and its permeability decreases. This reduces the impedance of the load windings and the current through the load increases. This is a very useful device and has many industrial applications. Its advantage lies in the fact that a small direct current may be used to control a relatively large AC power circuit. Theaters use a device of this sort for dimming the lights. Otherwise, large rheostats would be necessary which would be cumbersome and wasteful of power.

This basic circuit is not practical for an obvious reason. The AC in the load circuit would induce a voltage in the DC control side through transformer action. One common solution to this problem is found in the three-legged saturable reactor illustrated in Fig. 18-21. The DC control produces a magnetic field as indicated by the solid arrows. The AC load circuit produces magnetic fields as indicated by the dashed lines. Note that in the center core the AC fields are opposite and equal and therefore cancel each other. The fields in the two outside cores are the resultant between the AC and DC fields. (On one side the fields are opposing, on the other side the fields are additive.) The resulting impedance of the two series load windings is the sum of the impedance. Since impedance is a function of "rate of change" in flux density, a low DC control current permits maximum change and

VARIABLE DC

LOAD   **AC**

SX MEANS
SATURABLE REACTOR

DC

Fig. 18-21. *The three-legged or tertiary wound reactor diagram.*

therefore maximum impedance. A high DC control current permits a minimum change and minimum impedance.

MAGNETIC AMPLIFIER

A detailed study of magnetic amplifiers is beyond the scope of this text. Only a simple explanation will be included, such as the circuit illustrated in Fig. 18-22. The amplifier includes other parts, such as the saturable reactor, rectifier and load resistor. This circuit produces a controllable DC voltage across the load R_L. It is a simple half-wave rectifier circuit. The magnitude of the voltage appearing across the load is a function of the impedance of the load windings, which in turn is varied by the DC control windings. This circuit may be converted to a controlled full-

wave rectifier output by using the bridge type rectifier in Fig. 18-23.

The amplifying characteristic of the magnetic amplifier has already been mentioned. Further amplification may be achieved by a feedback system whereby part of the load cur-

LOAD

AC

Fig. 18-22. *The magnetic amplifier circuit.*

rent change may be inductively coupled to the control circuit in the proper phase. This is commonly called regenerative feedback. In this case windings are included on the saturable reactor for feedback as shown in the symbol in Fig. 18-24.

VARIABLE DC

DC LOAD

AC

Fig. 18-23. *The magnetic amplifier using a full-wave bridge rectifier for controlled DC voltage.*

CONTROL   **FEEDBACK**

Fig. 18-24. *The schematic diagram of the reactor with control and feedback windings.*

Interested students should refer to the bibliography in the Appendices of this text for a list of books on Magnetic Amplifiers and Applications.

ULTRASONIC CLEANING

An ultrasonic dishwasher is shown in Fig. 18-25. Sound waves, generated by an oscillator, are transmitted to the water by a

Fig. 18-25. Ultrasonic dishwasher featured in the House of the Future.
(Westinghouse)

transducer that invisibly agitates the water and cleans without the use of soap, detergents or hot water.

The principle involved has already found many applications in industry for cleaning small and intricate mechanisms and parts.

THERMOELECTRIC COOLING

Your home of the future will probably contain a refrigerator which freezes or cools your food in absolute and mysterious silence.

No motors or refrigerants will be required. Cooling will be by "thermoelectric refrigeration." This phenomenon is produced when an electric current is passed through the proper kinds of semiconductor materials. Thermoelectric refrigeration is characterized by simplicity, ruggedness and freedom from

Fig. 18-26. Thermo electric refrigeration featured in the House of the Future.

maintenance. Your "Home of the Future" refrigerator may consist of a series of cabinets and drawers as illustrated in Fig. 18-26. These amazing futuristic appliances will be another electronic contribution to better living.

FOR DISCUSSION

1. List all the ways that you can think of by which electronic circuits have improved our way of living.
2. Suggest some applications for the photo electric control system.
3. Suggest some applications for the electronic timing circuits.

TEST YOUR KNOWLEDGE

1. Name three types of photo sensitive materials used in light control circuits.
2. What is meant by "spectral sensitivity?"
3. What is a Thyratron?
4. Name two types of electronic heating.
5. Draw the basic magnetic amplifier circuit using half-wave rectification.
6. Draw the basic oscillator circuit used in induction heating. How does it differ from the oscillator in a radio transmitter?

Lunar surface magnetometer containing more than 4,000 separate electrical parts, connected by 40,000 welds. It is expected this will be placed on the moon by Project Appolo astronauts.
(Space Div., Philco-Ford Corp.)

Chapter 19

TEST INSTRUMENTS

The basic instrument meter movement used in the measurement of voltage, current and resistance was discussed in detail in Chapter 10. Actual measurement problems were used to show some of the disadvantages of these meters. Among these disadvantages is that by nature the meter will load a circuit. Increasing the sensitivity of the meter in ohms/volt reduces the error resulting from loading to a tolerable amount. An improvement upon the basic meter is the Vacuum Tube Voltmeter (VTVM) which has an input resistance of 10 megohms and higher and the current drawn from the circuit under test is negligible. The D'Arsonaval rectifier type meter, when used for measuring high frequency alternating currents also has a shunting effect due to the capacitance of the rectifiers. In the VTVM the shunting effect is eliminated and voltages at frequencies up to 100 mc may be measured.

THE VTVM

The basic circuitry of the vacuum tube voltmeter is drawn in Fig. 19-1. The tube V_1 is biased to cutoff and the meter in the plate circuit reads "zero." When a positive voltage is applied to the grid, the tube starts conduction and the meter in the plate circuit is calibrated to read in volts. This plate circuit meter is really an ammeter, but its deflection is the result of voltage applied to the grid.

The same type of circuit may be used for measuring AC. Since the tube is biased to cutoff, only the positive half of the AC cycle causes current to flow in the plate circuit. The negative half cycle drives the grid more

negative beyond cutoff. The meter actually measures the average value of the AC wave, but may be calibrated to indicate average, rms or peak voltages applied to the grid.

A more sophisticated VTVM employs multiplier resistors to increase its range and

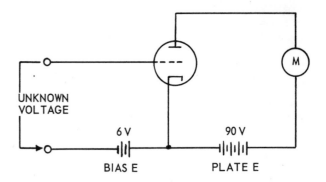

Fig. 19-1. Theory of the VTVM may be compared to a simple vacuum tube circuit.

a balanced DC amplifier. This circuit is shown in Fig. 19-2. Consider the circuit first with no voltage applied to the grid of V_1. The bridge may be balanced by adjusting R_1 until the meter reads "zero." A negative voltage applied through the voltage divider network to the grid of V_1 upsets the balanced condition of the bridge since V_1 would be conducting less than V_2. The unbalanced state creates a difference in voltage drop between R_2 and R_3 which causes current to flow through the meter. The meter is calibrated to read in volts. The switching arrangement permits the measurement of either negative or positive voltages.

In order to measure AC voltages with this VTVM a diode rectifier probe must be used,

Fig. 19-2. Practical VTVM circuit used in many commercial meters.

Fig. 19-3. Another type of probe uses a series resistor with a value between 1 and 5 megohms. This resistor prevents detuning or loading of circuits to be measured. Another probe, used in the measurement of AC voltages, employs a small series capacitor which reduces the input capacitance of the meter. It also reduces detuning effects when making AC

ages, both negative and positive DC voltages and resistances. The right hand switch sets the meter on its proper function and the left hand switch selects the range. Potentiometers are provided for "Ohm's Adjust" and "Zero Adjust" for bridge balancing.

THE OSCILLOSCOPE

The oscilloscope permits the technician to observe the wave forms in an electronic cir-

CONTAINED IN PROBE

Fig. 19-3. Circuit diagram of an AC probe used with a VTVM when measuring AC voltages.

measurements. Still another probe uses a crystal diode which extends the high frequency response of the meter.

The VTVM is a useful service and test instrument. Its advantages include its high sensitivity and high impedance input. It may be used to measure voltages in high impedance circuits, amplifier gains and signal tracing. A typical instrument is illustrated in Fig. 19-4. This instrument measures AC volt-

Fig. 19-4. Typical VTVM used by technicians.
(EICO)

cuit. It is a valuable service instrument. Although a detailed description of the oscilloscope is beyond the scope of this text, the student should be familiar with some of the basic principles and the operating controls.

The display of wave forms is produced upon the face of the cathode ray tube (CRT) in a fashion similar to your television. An electron beam from the gun in the CRT is made to sweep from left to right by the saw-tooth voltages produced by the sweep oscillator. Review Chapter 16. This produces a single line (usually green) on the face of the tube. If an AC voltage is applied to the vertical deflection circuit, then a wave is produced on the CRT. This wave represents the instantaneous voltage during the cycles of the AC input.

The horizontal sweep oscillator is adjustable through a wide range of frequencies. Assume that it is adjusted at 60 cps. It is then producing 60 straight lines per second across the face of the CRT. The time for one sweep would be 1/60 of a second.

Now a 60 cps AC voltage is applied to the vertical input terminals. This wave starts at zero, rises to maximum positive and returns to zero, then decreases to maximum negative and returns to zero. This all occurs during one cycle and the period of this cycle is 1/60 second. Therefore the horizontal sweep and the input signal voltage are synchronized. One wave appears on the screen. If the horizontal sweep were set at 30 cps, which is only one half as fast as the 60 cps input signal, then two complete waves would appear on the screen. The horizontal frequency may be adjusted so that the wave forms appear stationary.

OSCILLOSCOPE FAMILIARIZATION

The function of the basic oscilloscope controls will be described, using the illustration in Fig. 19-5.

INTENSITY: This controls the brightness of the trace on the screen. It is combined with the on-off switch.

FOCUS: Use to adjust the electronic focusing of the electron beam in order to make a sharp trace on the screen.

V-CENTERING: To move the beam up or down, so that it can be located in the center of the screen.

H-CENTERING: To move the beam right or left so that the wave pattern may be centered on the screen.

Fig. 19-5. *Typical oscilloscope used in electronic laboratories.* (RCA)

BAND RESPONSE SWITCH: This switch provides either a wide or narrow band response.

V-POLARITY: The pattern may be inverted by this switch.

SWEEP VERNIER: Fine frequency adjustment for horizontal sweep oscillator.

H-GAIN: Increases the length of pattern by expanding it horizontally.

V-RANGE: Selects the voltage range for measurement.

V-CAL: To make calibration adjustments

so that peak voltages may be read directly on the scope. Set wave form peaks to the required height.

SWEEP: Selects the range of frequencies for the sweep oscillator.

SYNC: Switch for either internal or external synchronization pulses. These pulses are used to lock input signal and horizontal sweep for a stationary pattern.

V-INPUT: Terminal for input to vertical response circuits.

GND: Ground.

Z-AXIS: A signal may be applied to this terminal to modulate the intensity of the trace.

PHASE: Used in conjunction with "line sync" so that sweep oscillator will be synchronized correctly.

SYNC TERMINAL: To this terminal an external sync pulse may be applied.

H-INPUT: The horizontal sweep may be switched from the selective internal oscillator, to 60 cps line or to an external oscillator by this switch.

CALIBRATION SCALE: This is a plastic scale which fits over the face of the CRT. The instrument is calibrated so that these scales may be used for direct measurements of the peak value of wave forms.

Complete the activity with the "scope" outlined at the end of this chapter. Experience is the best teacher.

THE SIGNAL GENERATOR

Signal generators may be described as instruments which produce an electrical wave at a given amplitude and frequency. The generator employs electronic circuitry and vacuum tubes or transistors in the conventional oscillator circuits which you have studied. They may be classified according to their range of

frequencies, such as audio and radio frequency generators. In either case the generator produces a signal of known frequency and amplitude which may be used by the technician in the service and adjustment of circuits. An rf generator set at the intermediate frequency 455 kc is used to align the superheterodyne radio. The generated signal is fed through the if stages and the transformers are tuned to give maximum response. The audio generator may be used to check the audio sections of radios and TVs as well as the response of the now popular Hi-Fi sound systems.

These two generators are combined in the instrument illustrated in Fig. 19-6. To use a generator of this type, and all types are similar, the output cable is connected to the

Fig. 19-6. Combination audio and radio frequency generator used in service work.

desired output jack, - RF or AF. The band switch is set to the band which includes the desired frequency. The tuning dial is adjusted to that frequency. The Multiplier switch must be considered on this instrument. The amplitude of the output will depend upon the multiplier factor selected. The ATTENUATOR varies the amplitude of the signal. The signal selector switch is set to the desired

AF or RF output. When in the modulation (MOD) position, the RF wave is modulated with a 400 cps audio sine wave. This instrument will be used in "Activities with the Oscilloscope" at the end of this chapter.

TUBE CHECKERS

An instrument to test the condition of vacuum tubes and transistors is a "must" in every electronics laboratory. With the possible exception of the multimeter, it will be the most used piece of equipment. Tube failures in radios and televisions account for the major share of service problems. Considering the vacuum tube, there are three general faults which may develop and a good checker should provide a means of checking them.

1. The emission of the cathode. As tubes age in service, the ability of the cathode to emit electrons deteriorates. Most tube checkers employ a meter which reads, "Good," "Doubtful," "Bad" and the condition may be quickly determined.

2. Interelectrode short circuits between the elements in the tube must be discovered.

3. The transconductance of the tube which is a measurement of the electron flow through the grid type tube.

Provisions for checking rectifiers and diodes must also be included in the instrument.

Tube checkers vary over a wide range of quality and price. The determining factor is the accuracy and dependability required for specific applications. Checks on tubes may be static tests or dynamic tests. In static tests constant voltages are applied to the elements of the tube and the DC plate current is measured. The information secured from this test is not particularly valuable since the tube is not performing under simulated operating conditions. A more meaningful test is the dynamic test, during which an actual signal is applied to the grid of the tube. In the dynamic test a comparison is made between the change in plate current as a result of a change in grid voltage. This quotient reads directly on the meter in "micromhos" of transconductance.

A popular type of electron Tube Tester is shown in Fig. 19-7. This particular tester is automatic in many respects. A card is selected from the file representing the tube to be checked. The card is inserted in the instrument and all proper connections and voltages are made to the tube when the lever on the left is placed in testing position. Other testers require the manual setting of several levers and dials for each tube to be checked. There are many variations to the basic tube checker

Fig. 19-7. A tube tester which uses a card index for automatic setting. (RCA)

and the operator should become thoroughly acquainted with the particular instrument in use. Detailed instructions will always be found in the manual supplied with the tester.

THE SWEEP GENERATOR

The primary function of any generator is to simulate an actual signal, which may be applied to a circuit for measurements of performance and the location of malfunctions. The sweep generator is another valuable instrument for servicing FM radios and TVs. This generator consists of two oscillators:

1.) A fixed oscillator, the frequency of which is set by the manually controlled dial. 2.) A variable frequency oscillator which Frequency Modulates the fixed rf signal. As a result the signal "sweeps" back and forth between the limits of the modulation. This sweep width is set by the amplitude of the control voltage.

When this instrument is connected to the if stages of an FM receiver, the output may be observed on an oscilloscope which will show the response pattern of the stages over the band of frequencies used in the modulated signal.

In the sweep generator a part of the modulating voltage is brought out to a terminal, which may be connected to the EXTERNAL SYNC terminal of the oscilloscope. This is done to synchronize the sweep circuits of the scope with the generator.

FREQUENCY METERS

The frequency meter is discussed at this point to reinforce some of the lessons learned in the earlier studies of basic electronics. In discussions of tuning your radio, you will recall that it was necessary to tune the tank circuit of the radio to the frequency of the incoming signal. The tuning circuit provided a

Fig. 19-8. Circuit for an absorption frequency meter.

means of selecting the desired broadcasting station to be received. The ABSORPTION FREQUENCY METER operates on the same principle and is represented in its basic form in Fig. 19-8. A commercial type is illustrated in Fig. 19-9. During operation coil L is loosely coupled to the oscillating circuit under measurement. Capacitor C is adjusted for maximum response or absorption of energy. This point is indicated by the brilliance of the lamp in series with the circuit. The dial for capacitor C is calibrated in frequency and may be read directly. An instrument of this type is made to cover a limited range of frequencies. The range is fixed by the values of L and C. Usually the technician has a set of these absorption meters to cover the radio frequency spectrum.

ACTIVITIES

The following is presented so that you may become familiar with the oscilloscope and signal generators.

1. Connect the output terminals of an AF signal generator to the V-input terminals of an oscilloscope.
2. Turn on scope. Adjust intensity and focus to produce a sharp visible line.
3. Adjust H and V positioning control until line is in center of screen.

Fig. 19-9. A commercial absorption frequency meter. (Millen Mfg. Co.)

4. Adjust H gain control to produce a line about two inches long in center of screen.
5. Set V gain to lowest position and Sync switch to "Internal Sync."
6. Set sweep frequency range to lowest range.
7. Set audio generator to 100 cps. Turn generator on and observe pattern on screen.
8. Turn fine frequency control on scope until one sine wave pattern appears stationary.
9. Adjust V gain and notice the change in amplitude of the wave form.
10. Adjust output of generator and notice change in amplitude.
11. Adjust fine frequency control so that two complete sine waves appear on the screen.

AUDIO GENERATOR

1. Return to the single sine wave pattern and then increase audio generator to 200 cps.

Two sine waves should appear on screen. Slight frequency adjustment may be necessary.

2. Increase generator to 400 cps. Change frequency range on scope and adjust frequency control to a single sine wave pattern.

RF GENERATOR

1. Connect output of rf generator to the V terminals of the scope. Set frequency range of scope to include 400 cps. Set rf generator to 1000 kc.

2. Turn instruments on and adjust gains and positioning until a rectangular green pattern about 2 inches wide and 1-1/2 inches high appears on the screen. (This is the pattern of the rf wave. The frequency is so high that individual waves cannot be distinguished.)

3. Turn rf generator to MOD position and notice that the amplitude of the rf wave now follows a 400 cps wave pattern.

NOTICE: If your scope has a Sync control, increase in a clockwise direction sufficiently to obtain a stable stationary pattern. This will probably be between 25 to 35 per cent of the maximum Sync.

Chapter 20

CAREER OPPORTUNITIES

IN ELECTRONICS

What do you want to do when your education is completed? What vocation will you choose to assure an interesting and rewarding future for you and your family? What type of education should you acquire in preparation for your selected future? Are you qualified by interest, desire and capacity to take advantage of the educational opportunities within your reach today? These questions can only be answered by you. To help you make an intelligent decision your parents, your school guidance counselors, your teachers and friends in business and industry stand ready to give you information gained from years of experience. Do not hesitate to ask questions.

Newspaper headlines and editorials indicate the explosive discoveries and developments in science and technology. Without question, ELECTRONICS, together with other fields of science, will continue to play a major role in our modern civilization. In the field of communications the familiar telephone, radio and TV are supplemented with the advanced techniques of the TELSTAR satellite, the LASER and MASER and moon bounce signals. Ships and aircraft arrive safely at their destinations when such navigational aids as LORAN, SONAR, and RADAR constantly supply needed information to their captains. The defense of our nation depends upon the great research and development of our space and rocket program. Tomorrow's industry will be electronically controlled. Automation is displacing thousands of pro-

duction workers each year. Electronic computers now do work in business and ac-

Engineers of the Philco Corporation designed this intricate communications and control system for the Discoverer program. Skilled technicians must operate and maintain such equipment.

counting, and in mathematical and scientific calculations in only a few minutes, which previously required months of work. Electronics has entered the field of medicine and has become an important instrument in the hands of your physician and hospital. And as each new electronic miracle is born and given to our people, thousands of highly skilled technicians must be trained to maintain and service it.

A brief look at YOUR OPPORTUNITY, Chart 1, will be a guidepost for your future. Here is the prediction of the National Science Foundation on the Long Range Demand for Scientific and Technical Personnel. Notice these significant figures! Since 1954 there has been an increase in graduate engineers to approximately 82,000; by 1970 we will need 183,000. The need for supporting and service technicians will correspondingly increase to over 150,000. Our country's need for highly trained scientists must also double

in the next decade. Associated with this phenomenal growth in the electrical and electronics industries will be thousands of additional opportunities in management, administration and sales representation.

YOUR EDUCATION

A wise philosopher once stated, "There are many roads to the top of the mountain." This is true also at technical levels of employment in electronics. A high school education is required as a foundation on which to build further skills and knowledge. Your specialized training may come from a two year Junior or Community College offering an associate degree in technology. You may wish to enroll in one of the many fine residence schools in electronic technology located throughout our country. Some high school graduates have entered industry directly and received their specialized education in the training facilities maintained by

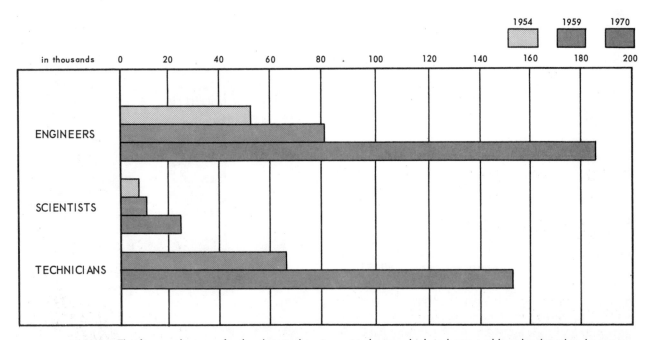

Note: The figures above are for the electrical equipment industry, which is larger and broader than the electronics industry, but includes it. It is estimated by authoritative industry sources that the electronic industry segment should enjoy an even faster rate of growth. Obviously, opportunities exist for managerial, administrative, sales and other professional categories in an industry with such a high rate of growth.

Chart 1. Employment of scientists, engineers and technicians in the electrical equipment industry.

larger companies. Employment is not an end in itself. One must constantly read and study to keep abreast with this rapidly changing industry. Advancement and security will come through self improvement.

In the fields of science and engineering a college degree is almost a necessity, with advanced degrees becoming increasingly important. There are many state and private universities offering engineering degrees. Consult your school counselor for locations and entrance requirements. A new job classification is presently emerging, frequently called an engineering assistant or technologist. This classification requires the skills of the technician and a B.S. degree from an approved institution. Undergraduate studies sometimes include some business administration.

Military electronic technicians will be trained to operate this Radar control console. This unit automatically tracks a space vehicle and communicates with it.

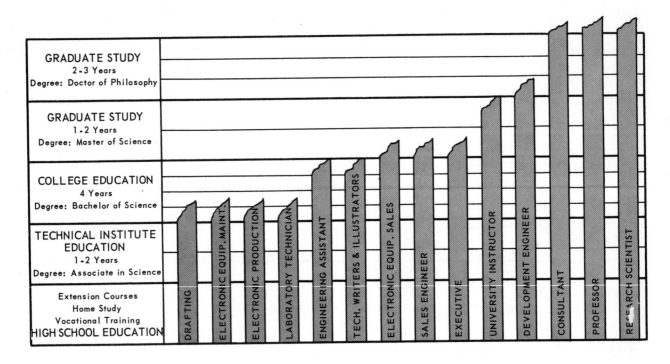

GRADUATE STUDY 2-3 Years Degree: Doctor of Philosophy												CONSULTANT	PROFESSOR	RESEARCH SCIENTIST
GRADUATE STUDY 1-2 Years Degree: Master of Science									UNIVERSITY INSTRUCTOR	DEVELOPMENT ENGINEER				
COLLEGE EDUCATION 4 Years Degree: Bachelor of Science				ENGINEERING ASSISTANT	TECH. WRITERS & ILLUSTRATORS	ELECTRONIC EQUIP. SALES	SALES ENGINEER	EXECUTIVE						
TECHNICAL INSTITUTE EDUCATION 1-2 Years Degree: Associate in Science	DRAFTING	ELECTRONIC EQUIP. MAINT.	ELECTRONIC PRODUCTION	LABORATORY TECHNICIAN											
Extension Courses Home Study Vocational Training HIGH SCHOOL EDUCATION															

Chart 2. Educational requirements for careers in electronics. (Reprinted from "Electronics Your Chance to Shape the Future," published by Electronics Industry Association and the IEEE.)

Chart 2, shows in graphical form, some of the major job categories and the usual educational requirements. Careful study of Chart 2, will help you plan your high school and college courses.

YOUR DECISION

The electronics industry offers many employment opportunities. You have reviewed the educational requirements and technical skills demanded. Will you be successful in reaching your goal? Really, no one can accurately predict your personal success and fulfillment of your personal satisfactions. There are, however, some guide lines which may influence your decision:

1. Since electronics is a science, a healthy interest in scientific subjects during your high school career will give you direction.

2. Mathematics is the tool of the scientist and engineer. If you like these subjects and do well with them, a career in electronics may be a wise choice.

3. Many able scientists and engineers started with an early interest in electronics

as a hobby. Experimentation with electronics and amateur radio are leisure time educational activities which will point toward success in this chosen vocation.

4. Discuss your abilities with your counselor. There are a number of valid interest inventory tests which you may take to discover your interests and capacity for learning this scientific field.

5. The fact that you are now reading and studying this text is a fairly accurate indication of your interest in electronics.

6. Have you elected some courses in Electronics in high school? Did you like them? Did you do well?

The choice is your choice in the final analysis. Study hard and prepare yourself well. Do not study only electronics, for your contacts with industry and fellow workers demand an understanding of languages of communication, social studies, how to get along well with your co-workers, and your ability to contribute to the success of your company. Remember that many of the greatest discoveries in recent years have resulted from team effort.

APPENDICES

Appendix 1

SCIENTIFIC NOTATION

In the study of Electronics it is necessary to work with extremely small quantities. As a student of mathematics you will realize that the multiplication and division of numbers involving many zeros and decimal points will cause errors unless caution is exercised at all times. The use of "powers of ten" or Scientific Notation is a rapid and easy method. Let's see how it works:

$$1 \times 10^0 = 1$$

$$1 \times 10^1 = 10$$

$$1 \times 10^2 = 100$$

$$1 \times 10^3 = 1,000$$

$$1 \times 10^4 = 10,000$$

$$1 \times 10^5 = 100,000$$

$$1 \times 10^6 = 1,000,000$$

$$1 \times 10^{-1} = .1$$

$$1 \times 10^{-2} = .01$$

$$1 \times 10^{-3} = .001$$

$$1 \times 10^{-4} = .0001$$

$$1 \times 10^{-5} = .00001$$

$$1 \times 10^{-6} = .000001$$

Follow these examples and you will learn to use the scientific notation method.

To express a number:

$$47,000 = 47 \times 10^3$$

$$.000100 = 100 \times 10^{-6}$$

$$.0025 = 25 \times 10^{-4}$$

$$3,500,000 = 3.5 \times 10^6$$

To multiply, add the exponents of ten.

$$47 \times 10^3 \times 25 \times 10^{-4}$$
$$= 47 \times 25 \times 10^{-1}$$

$$100 \times 10^{-6} \times 3.5 \times 10^6$$
$$= 100 \times 3.5$$

To divide, subtract exponents

$$\frac{3.5 \times 10^6}{25 \times 10^{-4}} = \frac{3.5 \times 10^{10}}{25}$$

$$\frac{100 \times 10^{-6}}{25 \times 10^{-4}} = \frac{100 \times 10^{-2}}{25}$$

$$6 - (-4) = +10$$

$$-6 - (-4) = -2$$

To square, multiply exponent by 2.

$$(25 \times 10^2)^2 = 25^2 \times 10^4$$

$$(9 \times 10^{-3})^2 = 81 \times 10^{-6}$$

To extract square root, divide exponent by 2.

$$\sqrt{81 \times 10^4} = 9 \times 10^2$$

$$\sqrt{225 \times 10^{-8}} = 15 \times 10^{-4}$$

See Appendix 3 for using Powers of Ten in Conversions.

Appendix 2

COLOR CODES

RESISTORS: For your convenience, a standard Color Code has been adopted to determine the values of resistors and capacitors. The following table has been supplied through the courtesy of the Radio-Television Manufacturer's Association. (RETMA)

The silver band tells us that it is within the limits of $\pm$ 10% of the color coded value.

Follow these examples for further experience:

Yel-vio-brn-sil
Brn-blk-red-gold
Orn-orn-red-none
Grn-blue-red-none
Red-red-grn-sil
470 Ω $\pm$ 10%
1,000 Ω $\pm$ 5%
3,300 Ω $\pm$ 20%
5,600 Ω $\pm$ 20%
2,200,000 Ω $\pm$ 10%

CAPACITORS: Recent practices include the numerical marking of capacitors. Their values may be read directly. However, there are many coded capacitors in use. The current standard JAN and RETMA code will only be

COLOR	NUMERICAL FIGURE	DECIMAL MULTIPLIER		VALUE TOLERANCE
		Power of 10	Multiplier Value	
Blk	0	10^0	1	
Brn	1	10^1	10	
Red	2	10^2	100	
Orn	3	10^3	1,000	
Yel	4	10^4	10,000	
Grn	5	10^5	100,000	
Blu	6	10^6	1 Million	
Vio	7	10^7	10 Million	
Gra	8	10^{-2} (alternate)	0.01 *	
Wht	9	10^{-1} (alternate)	0.1 *	
Sil	—	10^{-2} (preferred)	0.01	$\pm$10%
Gld	—	10^{-1} (preferred)	0.1	$\pm$5%
None	—	—	—	$\pm$20%

Color code for resistors and capacitors.

HOW TO READ THE CODE

Secure several resistors from stock. Hold a resistor so that the color bands are to the left as illustrated in Fig. A2-1. Let's assume the band colors are (from left to right) brown, black, green, silver.

The brown band is <u>1</u>. The black band is <u>0</u>. The green band is the multiplier, x 10^5.

Fig. A2-1. When reading color code, resistor should be held with bands at left.

described. There are many special marking systems and a detailed manual describing all codes should be consulted when necessary.

In Fig. A2-2. Let's assume that the upper left hand dot is WHITE. WE WILL USE THE RETMA CODE. The next dot is RED. We will read 2. The third dot is GREEN. We will

Fig. A2-2. Capacitor codes.

read 5. Our first two significant figures are 25. Going to the Multiplier we see that it is BROWN which means x 10^1. Our value then is 250 mmfds. The tolerance value and the class may also be found but their meanings will not be discussed in this basic text.

Appendix 3

CONVERSIONS

When using formulas to determine unknown values in a circuit, you will find the formula may be given in basic units, but the quantities you wish to use are given in larger or smaller units. A conversion must be made. For example: Ohm's Law states that:

$$I \text{ (in amperes)} = \frac{E \text{ (in volts)}}{R \text{ (in ohms)}}$$

If R were given in megohms such as 2.2 megohms, it would be necessary to change it to 2,200,000 ohms. If E were given in mi-crovolts, such as 500 μv, it would be necessary to change it to .0005 volts.

Powers of Ten offer a simple solution to making conversions, but first, let's look at the common prefixes used in electronics.

kilo = 1,000 times

mega = 1,000,000 times

milli = $\frac{1}{1000}$ of

micro = $\frac{1}{1,000,000}$ of

micromicro = $\frac{1}{1,000,000,000,000}$ of

The prefix "PICO" has now been adopted for "micromicro." Compare the meaning of these prefixes to powers of ten in Appendix 1 and you will discover that:

10,000 ohms	=	10,000 x 10^{-3} kilohms
47 kilohms	=	47 x 10^3 ohms
950 kilocycles	=	950 x 10^3 cycles or
		950 x 10^{-3} megacycles
100 milliamperes	=	100 x 10^{-3} amperes or
		100 x 10^3 microamperes
.01 microfarads	=	.01 x 10^{-6} farads or
		.01 x 10^6 $\mu\mu$f
250 $\mu\mu$f	=	250 x 10^{-6} μf or
		250 x 10^{-12} f
8 μf	=	8 x 10^{-6} f or
		8 x 10^6 $\mu\mu$f
75 milliwatts	=	75 x 10^{-3} watts

A simple rule will also help you:

If the exponent of ten is negative, the

decimal point is moved to the left in the answer.

$$447 \times 10^{-3} = .447$$

$$250 \times 10^{-6} = .00025$$

If the exponent is positive, the decimal point is moved to the right.

$$447 \times 10^{3} = 447,000$$

$$250 \times 10^{6} = 250,000,000$$

Here is a problem: What is the reactance of a 2.5 mh choke at 1000 kc?

$$X_L = 2\pi fL$$

$$= 2\pi f \text{ (in cps) } xL \text{ (in henrys)}$$

Two conversions must be made:

$$1000 \text{ kc} = 1000 \times 10^{3} \text{ cps}$$

$$2.5 \text{ mh} = 2.5 \times 10^{-3} \text{ henrys}$$

Then:

$$X_L = 2 \times 3.14 \times 1000 \times 10^{3}$$

$$\times 2.5 \times 10^{-3}$$

$$= 6.28 \times 2.5 \times 10^{3}$$

(1000 changed to 10^3)

$$= 15.7 \times 10^{3} = 15,600 \text{ ohms}$$

NATURAL TRIGONOMETRIC FUNCTIONS

Angle	Sine	Cosine	Tangent	Angle	Sine	Cosine	Tangent
1°	.0175	.9998	.0175	34°	.5592	.8290	.6745
2°	.0349	.9994	.0349	35°	.5736	.8192	.7002
3°	.0523	.9986	.0524	36°	.5878	.8090	.7265
4°	.0698	.9976	.0699	37°	.6018	.7986	.7536
5°	.0872	.9962	.0875	38°	.6157	.7880	.7813
6°	.1045	.9945	.1051	39°	.6293	.7771	.8098
7°	.1219	.9925	.1228	40°	.6428	.7660	.8391
8°	.1392	.9903	.1405	41°	.6561	.7547	.8693
9°	.1564	.9877	.1584	42°	.6691	.7431	.9004
10°	.1736	.9848	.1763	43°	.6820	.7314	.9325
11°.	.1908	.9816	.1944	44°	.6947	.7193	.9657
12°	.2079	.9781	.2126	45°	.7071	.7071	1.0000
13°	.2250	.9744	.2309	46°	.7193	.6947	1.0355
14°	.2419	.9703	.2493	47°	.7314	.6820	1.0724
15°	.2588	.9659	.2679	48°	.7431	.6691	1.1106
16°	.2756	.9613	.2867	49°	.7547	.6561	1.1504
17°	.2924	.9563	.3057	50°	.7660	.6428	1.1918
18°	.3090	.9511	.3249	51°	.7771	.6293	1.2349
19°	.3256	.9455	.3443	52°	.7880	.6157	1.2799
20°	.3420	.9397	.3640	53°	.7986	.6018	1.3270
21°	.3584	.9336	.3839	54°	.8090	.5878	1.3764
22°	.3746	.9272	.4040	55°	.8192	.5736	1.4281
23°	.3907	.9205	.4245	56°	.8290	.5592	1.4826
24°	.4067	.9135	.4452	57°	.8387	.5446	1.5399
25°	.4226	.9063	.4663	58°	.8480	.5299	1.6003
26°	.4384	.8988	.4877	59°	.8572	.5150	1.6643
27°	.4540	.8910	.5095	60°	.8660	.5000	1.7321
28°	.4695	.8829	.5317	61°	.8746	.4848	1.8040
29°	.4848	.8746	.5543	62°	.8829	.4695	1.8807
30°	.5000	.8660	.5774	63°	.8910	.4540	1.9626
31°	.5150	.8572	.6009	64°	.8988	.4384	2.0503
32°	.5299	.8480	.6249	65°	.9063	.4226	2.1445
33°	.5446	.8387	.6494	66°	.9135	.4067	2.2460

Angle	Sine	Cosine	Tangent	Angle	Sine	Cosine	Tangent
67°	.9205	.3907	2.3559	79°	.9816	.1908	5.1446
68°	.9272	.3746	2.4751	80°	.9848	.1736	5.6713
69°	.9336	.3584	2.6051	81°	.9877	.1564	6.3138
70°	.9397	.3420	2.7475	82°	.9903	.1392	7.1154
71°	.9455	.3256	2.9042	83°	.9925	.1219	8.1443
72°	.9511	.3090	3.0777	84°	.9945	.1045	9.5144
73°	.9563	.2924	3.2709	85°	.9962	.0872	11.4301
74°	.9613	.2756	3.4874	86°	.9976	.0698	14.3006
75°	.9659	.2588	3.7321	87°	.9986	.0523	19.0811
76°	.9703	.2419	4.0108	88°	.9994	.0349	28.6363
77°	.9744	.2250	4.3315	89°	.9998	.0175	57.2900
78°	.9781	.2079	4.7046	90°	1.0000	.0000	

Appendix 4

TRIGONOMETRY

Skill in using trigonometry is a part of the "kit of tools" of the electronic technician. It simplifies the solution of alternating current problems. It finds many applications in the designing and understanding of electronic circuits. Basically, trigonometry is the relationship between the angles and sides of a triangle. These relationships are called functions and represent numerically the ratio between two sides of the right triangle.

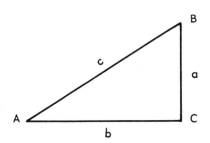

Sine of angle A $= \dfrac{\text{a opposite side}}{\text{c hypotenuse}}$

Cosine of angle A $= \dfrac{\text{b adjacent side}}{\text{c hypotenuse}}$

Tangent of angle A$= \dfrac{\text{a opposite side}}{\text{b adjacent side}}$

There are other functions, but these three are widely used in solving problems in electronics. By the above equations, if two values are known, the third may be found.

EXAMPLE: In a triangle, side a = 6 and b = 10. Find angle A. The tangent equation is used.

$$\text{Tan } A = \frac{a}{b} = \frac{6}{10} = .6$$

Now look at the table of Natural Functions and find the angle whose tangent is .6. It is 31° (answer)

EXAMPLE: Angle A = 45°, a = 6. What is the value of side c? Use sine equation.

$$\text{Sine } 45° = \frac{6}{c}$$

Look up the sine of 45°. It is .707. Then,

$$c = \frac{6}{.707} = 8.5 \text{ (approx.)}$$

In electronics, the right triangle used in the above example is labeled other ways, but the problems are worked out in exactly the same manner.

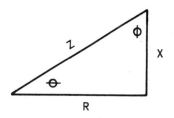

EXAMPLE: A circuit contains $40\,\Omega$ resistance (R) and $50\,\Omega$ reactance (X). What is the circuit impedance Z in ohms?

Find angle θ:

$$\text{Tan } \theta = \frac{X}{R}$$

$$= \frac{50}{40} = 1.25$$

Look up in Tables: $\theta = 51^{\circ}$ approx.

Find Z:

$$\text{Sine } \theta = \frac{X}{Z}$$

Look up in Tables: $.777 = \dfrac{50}{Z}$

$$Z = \frac{50}{.777} = 64.3\,\Omega$$

These applications of trigonometry must be thoroughly understood. The best way to realize this is by practice. Problems have been included in the text for this purpose.

Appendix 5

STANDARD SYMBOLS
AND
ABBREVIATIONS

LETTER SYMBOLS

I current
E voltage
R resistance
X reactance
X_L inductive reactance
X_C capacitive reactance
Z impedance
L inductance
C capacitor
M mutual inductance

f frequency
f_r resonant frequency
λ wave length
θ phase displacement
Δ a change in
Ω ohms
Φ phi-magnetic flux
G conductance
Q Q factor
r_p plate resistance
gm transconductance
μ amplification factor, permeability, micro.
A voltage gain
t time
ϕ phase angle
ω angular velocity
V vacuum tube or volts in transistor circuits
P watts

Symbols and abbreviations used in this text conform to Military Abbreviations and Contractions and IRE STANDARDS 54 IRE 21S1 and represent accepted practice in trade and industry.

Appendices

CIRCUIT SYMBOLS
(ASA – Y32.2)

GROUND

WIRES CROSSING
NOT CONNECTED

WIRES CROSSING
CONNECTED

RELAY

ANTENNA

METALLIC RECTIFIER
CRYSTAL DIODE

METER (INSERT LETTER)
A–AMMETER
V–VOLTMETER
MA–MILLIAMMETER

SWITCH SPST

SWITCH SPDT

CHASSIS
CONNECTION

TRANSISTOR NPN

RESISTOR

POTENTIOMETER

BASIC COIL – AIR CORE
RADIO FREQUENCY CHOKE

COIL – IRON CORE
CHOKE

TRANSFORMER
IRON CORE

TRANSFORMER
AIR CORE

FIXED CAPACITOR

VARIABLE CAPACITOR

BATTERY

CRYSTAL

SPEAKER

311

Electricity - Electronics

TRANSISTOR PNP

TRIODE

TETRODE

PENTODE

PENTAGRID
CONVERTER

DIODE

VR TUBE

MICROPHONE

HEADPHONES

LAMP

PILOT LIGHT

JACK

TERMINAL

FUSE

AC PLUG

MALE

FEMALE

STANDARD ABBREVIATIONS

ac	alternating current
AWG	American Wire Gage
amp	ampere
AM	Amplitude Modulation
af	audio frequency
afc	automatic frequency control
avc	automatic volume control
bfo	beat-frequency-oscillator
CRT	Cathode Ray Tube
cw	continuous wave
cps	cycles per second

db	decibel
dc	direct current
dpst	double pole, single throw
dpdt	double pole, double throw
emf	electromotive force
FM	Frequency modulation
gnd	ground
H	Henrys
hf	high frequency
hp	horsepower
if	intermediate frequency
JAN	Joint-Army-Navy
kc	kilocycle

k	kilohm		min	minimum
kv	kilovolt		osc	oscillator
kwh	kilowatt hour		pot	potentiometer
lf	low frequency		PF	power factor
mmf	magnetomotive force		rf	radio frequency
max	maximum		rpm	revolutions per minute
mc	megacycle		rms	root mean square
meg	megohm		spdt	single pole, double throw
μ	micro		spst	single pole, single throw
μa	microampere		spkr	speaker
μh	microhenry		sw	switch
$\mu\mu$f	micromicrofarad		TR	Transmit-receive
mike	microphone		uhf	ultra high frequency
μv	microvolt		vtvm	vacuum tube voltmeter
mh	millihenry		vhf	very high frequency
ma	milliampere		vf	video frequency
mv	millivolt		E	volts
mw	milliwatt		w	watts

Appendix 6

ELECTRODEMONSTRATOR KIT

The Electrodemonstrator kit contains parts needed to build quickly and inexpensively, sixteen projects illustrated and described in preceding chapters of this text.

Projects which may be built from the parts include:

1. Permanent Magnetic Fields
2. Electromagnetic Fields
3. Electromagnet
4. Relay
5. Circuit Breaker
6. Door Chime
7. Buzzer
8. Series DC Motor
9. Shunt DC Motor
10. AC Motor
11. Faraday's Experiment
12. Solenoid Sucking Coil
13. Reactance Dimmer
14. Induction Coil
15. Series Circuits
16. Parallel Circuits

Each project is assembled on a peg-board base. After the project has been built and tested, and has served the purpose for which it was intended, it is then disassembled, and the parts reused to make other projects.

Items in the Electrodemonstrator kit are listed below. This includes items like sockets, leads, bolts and nuts, which are purchased; and student-made parts such as

THE ELECTRODEMONSTRATOR PARTS LIST

Quan.	Part	Material
1	Base	1/8 x 7 1/2 x 10 Masonite Peg-Board
4	Base Feet	Rubber 3/8, (Allied 44N763)
4	Feet Bolts	3/8 x 8-32 Rd Hd with Nuts
1	Base Support	Wood (See Plan, Detail M)
2	Coils	(Plan, Detail F)
4	Coil Brackets	Brass 1/32" (Plan, Detail G)
2	Coil Cores	1/2 x 2 1/2 Mild Steel (plan,Detail E)
1	Solenoid Core	Mild Steel (Plan, Detail H)
2	Magnets	1/2 x 2 1/2 Round (Miami Magnet Co.)
1	Armature Bracket	Brass 1/32" (Plan, Detail J)
1	DC Armature	(Plan, Detail A)
1	AC Armature	(Plan, Detail B)
1	Brush Support	(Plan, Detail L)

1	Relay Armature	(Plan, Detail N)
1	Armature Plate	(Plan, Detail K)
1	Circuit Breaker	
	Stop	(Plan, Detail P)
2	Contact Brackets	(Plan, Detail R)
1	Induction Coil	(Plan, Detail D)
1	.01 Paper	Sprague 4TM-S10 - Mount on sub-
	Capacitor	bases
1	Push Button	
	Switch	Philmore 2234
1	Toggle Switch	Philmore 219 - Mount on sub-bases
3	Sub-base	Science Electronics MA2
6	Jiffy Leads 8"	Science Electronics JC8
3	Miniature Sockets with bulbs 6 V	
1	Door Bell Transformer	
1	50 Ω Poten-	
	tiometer	Allied 29M405 - Mount on base
1	Sub-base for Po-	
	tentiometer	Science Electronics MD3
1	Terminal Base	Science Electronics TP1
3	Battery Holders	
	#2 cell	Allied 54J040
3	Battery Holder	
	Bases	Science Electronics MC2
1	Chime	Hard Steel Tube or Bar
1	Galvanometer,	
	500-0-500 μa	Allied 67F591
1	Meter Case	Allied 88P542
12	Bolts	3/8 x 8-32 Rd Head
12	Nuts, Hex.	8-32
4	Stove Bolts	3/16 x 2 1/2
8	Nuts	3/16"

brackets, coils, etc. Constructional details on the student-made parts are given in the drawings, Fig. A6-1.

TO THE TEACHER: The construction of Electrodemonstrator kits will make a good mass production activity for your shop. A kit should be made for each two students. The kits will become a valued part of your standard laboratory equipment. It is suggested that a pilot model be constructed first, so that variations to the plan may be made to use materials on hand. It is not necessary to follow exact specifications given by the drawings.

Construction Hints:

1. The Masonite peg-board base with attached rubber feet at each corner is used as a base for all projects.

2. The two coils F are interchangeable in all projects. The coil brackets are bolted to the Masonite base. The saw kerf at each end of coil fits snugly into bracket.

3. The permanent magnets are interchangeable with the iron cores, when used for magnetic field demonstrations or in the DC motor.

4. The induction coil D is made to slide over coil F. It may be wound with many more than 8 layers of #30 wire if higher voltages are desired. The capacitor is connected across the breaker points.

5. If difficulty is experienced with the AC motor, try starting it by winding a string around the armature shaft and pulling on it. Its speed must be synchronized with the 60-cycle line voltage for operation.

6. All motors are constructed by placing armatures between plate R, bolted to base, and armature bracket as the top bearing.

7. The brush support L is constructed so that it may be locked in several positions to demonstrate a change in commutation angle.

LOCKNUT

DRILL & TAP 1/4-20

BRASS

PLASTIC WASHER
7/8 DIA. × 1/4 THICK

WIRES TO COIL

DC
COMMUTATOR

SEE DETAIL **C**
FOR DIMENSIONS

DC ARMATURE
A

ARMATURE REQUIRES APPROX.
6 LAYERS #21 ENAMEL WIRE

DRILL & TAP 1/4-20

3/4 DIA.

1/4 DIA.

2 3/16

1/16

7/8

7/8

1/16

DC ARMATURE
MILD STEEL
C

15/32 DIA.

2 1/2

CORE
2 REQ'D. MILD STEEL
E

1/4

2 3/8 DIA.

TO FIT TUBE

2

COIL FORM
PLASTIC
D

1/8 WALL THICKNESS

1 1/4 ID

NOTE: ASSEMBLE COIL FORM
WITH PLASTIC CEMENT
WIND COIL WITH 6-8
LAYERS OF #30 ENAMELED
MAGNET WIRE
SOLDER COIL ENDS TO TERMINALS

DRILL FOR
TERMINAL
TAP 8-32

TERMINAL
PIN-THREAD 8-32

1/4-20 HEX
LOCKNUT

3/4 DIA.

DRILL & TAP
1/4-20

AC ARMATURE
3/4 DIA. × 2 1/4 LONG
MILD STEEL

2 3/4

5/8

AC ARMATURE
B

TERMINAL PINS 1/8 BRASS RODS

DRILL &
TAP 6-32

1 3/16 DIA.
PLASTIC RING

3/8

1/2 ID
PLASTIC
TUBE

2 3/8

COIL FORM
2 REQ'D.
F

NOTE: COIL FORM ASSEMBLED
WITH PLASTIC CEMENT
WIND COIL WITH 6 LAYERS
#21 ENAMEL WIRE
SOLDER COIL ENDS TO TERMINALS

DRILL
TO FIT TUBE

SAW KERF
1/2 DP.

3/4

1 1/16

3/8 R.

1/32

3/4

1/4

1

1 1/2

1/4 R.

3/16 DIA.

BRACKET
4 REQ'D.
BRASS 1/32"
G

*Fig. A6-1. Constructional details on electrodem-
onstrator parts.*

7/8

1/8 DIA. x 1/4 BRASS PIN SOLDER ON

3/16 DIA.

7/16

4 3/16

2 3/32

3/16 DIA.

1/4 R.

CENTER PUNCH FROM BELOW

2 3/4

5/8

1/4

7/16

ARMATURE BRACKET
1 REQ'D. BRASS 1/32
J

2 1/2 DIA.

1/8 DIA.

3/8 x 8-32 BOLT, WASHER & THUMBSCREW

BRUSHES

2" DIA. BOLT CENTERS

1/2

1/8 MASONITE OR PLASTIC

ARMATURE BRACKET

BRUSH SUPPORT BRASS 20 GA.

BRUSHES BRASS .005 SOLDER TO SUPPORTS

BRUSH SUPPORT - DC MOTOR
L

1/8 DIA.

1/4 DIA.

3/8

7/16 DIA.

2 11/16

3 1/16

CENTER PUNCH

1

1/2

21/32

1/4 R.

3/16 DIA.

5/32

1

1 5/16

SOLENOID PLUNGER
1 REQ'D. SAE 1010 STEEL
H

ARMATURE PLATE
1 REQ'D. BRASS
K

1/4

1/2

3/16 DIA.

1/4 R.

7/8

SPRING BRASS .005

1 3/4

3/16

BRUSH
2 REQ'D. R. H. & L. H.
ASSEMBLE ON SUPPORT L

1/8 x 3/8 GROOVE

7 1/2

2 1/2

BASE SUPPORT
USE WITH DOOR CHIME
3/4" WOOD
M

TERMINAL

3 3/4

IRON

SOLDER

1 1/2

SPRING BRASS

3/16 DIA.

3/8

1/4 R.

RELAY & BUZZER ARMATURE
BRASS 20 GA.
N

Fig. A6-1. (Con.) Constructional details on electrodemonstrator parts.

CIRCUIT BREAKER STOP
1/8" MASONITE OR PLASTIC

P

BRACKET FOR
RELAY CONTACTS
2 REQ'D. BRASS 1/32

R

Fig. A6-1. (Con.) Constructional details on electrodemonstrator parts.

AUTHOR'S ACKNOWLEDGMENTS

I would like to acknowledge and express my appreciation and thanks to these associates who so willingly supplied their assistance and knowledge in the preparation of this text:

Robert Mathison, Gary Van, James Collins, Leon Pearson, and John Lienhart, Electronic technicians at Chico State College. Bobbie Fikes, and Moore Smalley, Graduate students in electronics at San Jose State College. Virtue B. Gerrish (wife of the author) for typing the manuscript.

And also to the many industries for their generous supply of illustration and product information, without which this text could not have been written. Special credit is due:

Allied Radio Corporation
Babcock Models
Barley and Dexter Laboratories
Centralab, Globe Union, Inc.
Cincinnati Milling Machine Co.
Daystrom, Inc.
Delco Products, General Motors
Delco Remy, General Motors
DeVilbiss Co.
Eastman Kodak Co.
Electronic Industries Association
Electronic Instrument Co.
Fosdick Machine Tool Co.
General Electric Co.
Gulton Industries, Inc.
Hammarlund Mfg. Co., Inc.
International Rectifier Corp.
James Millen Co.
J. W. Miller Co.
Lindberg Engineering Co.
Minneapolis-Honeywell Regulator Co.
Montgomery Ward
National Automatic Tool Co.
Ohmite Mfg. Co.
Pacific Telephone Co.

Philco Corp.
Plastoid Corp.
Potter & Brumfield
Radio Corporation of America
Raytheon Company
Science-Electronics, Inc.
Shure Bros., Inc.
Simpson Electric Co.
Sprague Products Co.
Sylvania Electric Products, Inc.
The American Radio Relay League
The Electric Storage Battery Co.
The Johnson Co.
The Murdock Corp.
The Superior Electric Co.
Triad Transformer Corp.
Ungar Electric Tools
Union Carbide Consumer Products Co.
Union Switch & Signal Co.
United Transformer Corp.
Westinghouse Electric Corp.
Welch Scientific Co.

Illustrations by Charles Tyler,
San Jose City College.

BIBLIOGRAPHY

Bartee, Thomas C.   DIGITAL COMPUTER FUNDAMENTALS.   New York City: McGraw-Hill Book Co., Inc.

Buban, Peter and Schmitt, Marshall L.   UNDERSTANDING ELECTRICITY AND ELECTRONICS.   New York City: McGraw-Hill Book Co., Inc.

Chute, George M.   ELECTRONICS IN INDUSTRY.   New York City: McGraw-Hill Book Co., Inc.

Gillie, Angelo C.   TRANSISTORS.   Englewood Cliffs, N. J., Prentice-Hall Inc.

Grob, Bernard.   BASIC ELECTRONICS.   New York City: McGraw-Hill Book Co., Inc.

Grob, Bernard.   BASIC TELEVISION.   New York City: McGraw-Hill Book Co., Inc.

Grob, Bernard and Kiver, Milton S.   APPLICATIONS OF ELECTRONICS.   New York City: McGraw-Hill Book Co., Inc.

Headquarter's Staff, The American Radio Relay League. THE RADIO AMATEUR'S HANDBOOK.   West Hartford, Conn. American Radio Relay League.

Hickey and Villines.   ELEMENTS OF ELECTRONICS.   New York City: McGraw-Hill Book Co., Inc.

Marcus, Abraham.   BASIC ELECTRICITY.   Englewood Cliffs, New Jersey, Prentice-Hall, Inc.

Marcus, Abraham and Marcus, William.   ELEMENTS OF RADIO.   Englewood Cliffs, New Jersey, Prentice-Hall, Inc.

Oldfield, R. L.   RADIO-TELEVISION AND BASIC ELECTRONICS.   Chicago, Ill. American Technical Society.

Philco Corporation Staff.   ELECTRONIC AND ELECTRICAL FUNDAMENTALS. VOLUME I. BASIC CONCEPTS AND DC CIRCUITS.   Philadelphia, Pa., Philco Tech. Rep. Division.

Philco Corporation Staff.   ELECTRONIC AND ELECTRICAL FUNDAMENTALS. VOLUME II. FUNDAMENTALS OF AC AND A-C CIRCUIT ANALYSIS.   Philadelphia, Pa., Philco Tech. Rep. Division.

Philco Corporation Staff.   ELECTRONIC AND ELECTRICAL FUNDAMENTALS. VOLUME III. VACUUM TUBE AND SEMI-CONDUCTOR FUNDAMENTALS.   Philadelphia, Pa., Philco Tech. Rep. Division.

Philco Corporation Staff.   ELECTRONIC AND ELECTRICAL FUNDAMENTALS. VOLUME IV. BASIC ELECTRONIC CIRCUITS AND SYSTEMS.   Philadelphia, Pa., Philco Tech. Rep. Division.

Platt, Sidney.   MAGNETIC AMPLIFIERS - THEORY AND APPLICATION.   Englewood Cliffs, N. J., Prentice-Hall Inc.

Shrader, Robert L.   ELECTRONIC COMMUNICATION.   New York City: McGraw-Hill Book Co., Inc.

Slurzberg, Morris and Osterheld, William.   ESSENTIALS OF RADIO-ELECTRONICS.   New York City: McGraw-Hill Book Co., Inc.

Turner, Rufus P.   BASIC ELECTRONIC TEST INSTRUMENTS.   New York City: Holt Rinehart and Winston.

DICTIONARY OF TERMS

A-BATTERY: Battery used to supply heater voltage for electron tubes.

AC: Alternating current.

ACCEPTOR CIRCUIT: Series tuned circuit at resonance. Accepts signals at resonant frequency.

ACCEPTOR IMPURITY: Impurity added to semiconductor material which creates holes for current carriers.

AC GENERATOR: Generator using slip rings and brushes to connect armature to external circuit. Output is alternating current.

AC PLATE RESISTANCE (symbol r_p): Variational characteristic of vacuum tube representing ratio of change of plate voltage to change in plate current, while grid voltage is constant.

AERIAL: An antenna.

AGC: Abbreviation for AUTOMATIC GAIN CONTROL. Circuit employed to vary gain of amplifier in proportion to input signal strength so output remains at constant level.

AGC: Automatic gain control.

AIR-CORE INDUCTOR: Inductor wound on insulated form without metallic core. Self-supporting coil without core.

ALNICO: Special alloy used to make small permanent magnets.

ALPHA: Greek letter α, represents current gain of a transistor. It is equal to change in collector current caused by change in emitter current for constant collector voltage.

ALPHA CUT-OFF FREQUENCY: Frequency at which current gain drops to .707 of its maximum gain.

ALTERNATOR: An AC generator.

ALTERNATING CURRENT (AC): Current of electrons that moves first in one direction and then in the other.

ALMALGAM: Compound or mixture containing mercury.

ALMALGAMATION: Process of adding small quantity of mercury to zinc during manufacture.

AM MODULATION, Types of: GRID. Audio signal is applied in series with grid of power amplifier.

PLATE. Audio signal is injected into plate circuit of modulated stage.

AMMETER: Meter used to measure current.

AMPERE (Symbol I): Electron or current flow representing flow of one coulomb per second past given point in circuit.

AMPERE-HOUR: Capacity rating measurement of batteries. A 100 ampere-hour battery will produce, theoretically, 100 amperes for one hour.

AMPERE TURN (IN): Unit of measurement of magnetomotive force. Represents product of amperes times number of turns in coil of electromagnet.
F = 1.257 IN.

AMPLIFICATION: Ability to control a relatively large force by a small force. In a vacuum tube, relatively small variation in grid input signal is accompanied by relatively large variation in output signal.

AMPLIFICATION FACTOR: Expressed as π (mu). Characteristic of vacuum tube to amplify a voltage. Mu is equal to change in plate voltage as result of change in grid voltage while plate current is constant.

AMPLIFIERS: POWER. Electron tube used to increase power output. Sometimes called a current amplifier.

VOLTAGE. An electron tube used to amplify a voltage.

CLASS A. An amplifier, so biased that plate current flows during entire cycle of input signal.

CLASS B. An amplifier, so biased that plate current flows for approximately one half the cycle of input signal.

CLASS C. An amplifier, so biased that plate current flows for appreciably less than half of each cycle of applied signal.

CLASS AB. A compromise between class A and class B.

CLASS AB_1. Same as class AB, only grid is never driven positive and no grid current flows.

CLASS AB_2. Same as AB except that signal drives grid positive and grid current does flow.

DC AMPLIFIER. Directly coupled amplifiers. Amplifies without loss of dc component.

AF AMPLIFIER. Used to amplify audio frequencies.

IF AMPLIFIER. Used to amplify intermediate frequencies.

RF AMPLIFIER. Used to amplify radio frequencies.

VIDEO AMPLIFIER. Used to amplify video frequencies.

PULSE AMPLIFIER. Used to amplify pulses.

AMPLITUDE: Extreme range of varying quantity. Size, height of.

AMPLITUDE MODULATION (AM): Modulating a transmitter by varying strength of r-f carrier at audio rate.

ANGLE OF COMPENSATION: Correcting angle applied to compass reading to compensate for local magnetic influence.

ANGLE OF DECLINATION: See DECLINATION.

ANGULAR PHASE: Position of rotating vector in respect to reference line.

ANGULAR VELOCITY (ω): Speed of rotating vector in radians per second. ω (omega) = $2\pi f$.

ANODE: Positive terminal, such as plate in electron tube.

ANTENNA: Device for radiating or receiving radio waves.

APPARENT POWER: Power apparently used in circuit as product of current times voltage.

ARCBACK: Current flowing opposite direction in a diode, when plate has a high negative voltage.

ARMATURE: Revolving part in generator or motor. Vibrating or moving part of relay or buzzer.

ARMATURE REACTION: Effect on main field of generator by armature acting as electromagnet.

ARRL: American Radio Relay League. The association of radio amateurs.

ARTIFICIAL MAGNETS: Man-made magnets.

ASPECT RATIO: Ratio of width to height of TV picture. This is standarized as 4:3.

A-SUPPLY: Voltages supplied for heater circuits of electron tubes.

AT-CUT CRYSTAL: Crystal cut at approximately a 35 deg. angle with Z axis.

Electricity - Electronics

ATOM: Smallest particle that makes up a type of material, called an element.

ATOMIC NUMBER: Number of protons in nucleus of a given atom.

ATOMIC WEIGHT: Mass of nucleus of atom in reference to oxygen, which has a weight of 16.

ATTENUATION: Decrease in amplitude or intensity.

ATTENUATOR: Networks of resistance used to reduce voltage, power or current to a load.

AUTOTRANSFORMER: Transformer with common primary and secondary winding. Step-up or step-down action is accomplished by taps on common winding.

AVC: Automatic volume control.

AVERAGE VALUE: Value of alternating current or voltage of sine wave form that is found by dividing area under one alternation by distance along X axis between 0 and 180 deg. $E_{avg} = .637 E_{max}$

AWG: American Wire Gauge - used in sizing wire by numbers.

BAND: Group of adjacent frequencies in frequency spectrum.

BAND PASS FILTER: Filter circuit designed to pass currents of frequencies within continuous band and reject or attenuate frequencies above or below the band.

BAND REJECT FILTER: Filter circuit designed to reject currents in continuous band of frequencies, but pass frequencies above or below the band.

BAND SWITCHING: Receiver employing switch to change frequency range of reception.

BANDWIDTH: Band of frequencies allowed for transmitting modulated signal.

BARRIER REGION: Potential difference across a PN junction due to diffusion of electrons and holes across junction.

BASE: Semiconductor between emitter and collector of transistor.

BASS: Low frequency sounds in audio range.

BATTERY: Several voltaic cells connected in series or parallel. Usually contained in one case.

B-BATTERY: Group of series cells in one container producing high voltage for plate circuits of electronic devices. Popular batteries include 22-1/2, 45 and 90 volts.

BACK EMF: See COUNTER EMF.

BEAM POWER TUBE: Tube so constructed that electrons flow in concentrated beams from cathode through grids to plate.

BEAT FREQUENCY: The resultant frequency obtained by combining two frequencies.

BEAT FREQUENCY OSCILLATOR: Oscillator whose output is beat with continuous wave to produce beat frequency in audio range. Used in C-W reception.

BEL: Unit of measurement of gain equivalent to 10 to 1 ratio of power gain.

BETA: Greek letter β, represents current gain of common-emitter connected transistor. It is equal to ratio of change in collector current to change in base current, while collector voltage is constant.

BIAS: CATHODE SELF-BIAS. Bias created by voltage drop across cathode resistor.
FIXED. Voltage supplied by fixed source.
GRID LEAK. Bias created by charging capacitor in grid circuit. Bias level is maintained by leak resistor.

BIAS, FORWARD: Connection of potential to produce current across PN junction. Source potential connected so it opposes potential hill and reduces it.

BIAS, REVERSE: Connection of potential so little or no current will flow across PN junction. Source potential has same polarity as potential hill and adds to it.

BINARY: Number system having base of 2, using only the symbols 0 and 1.

BLACK BOX: Box containing unknown and possibly complicated circuit.

BLANKING PULSE: Pulses transmitted by TV transmitter, which are used in receiver to cut off scanning beam during retrace time.

BLEEDER: Resistor connected across power supply to discharge filter capacitors.

BRIDGE CIRCUIT: Circuit with series-parallel groups of components that are connected by common bridge. Bridge frequently is meter in measuring devices.

BRIDGE RECTIFIER: Full-wave rectifier circuit employing four rectifiers in bridge configuration.

BRIGHTNESS: In television. Overall intensity of illumination of picture.

BRUSH: Sliding contact, usually carbon, between commutator and external circuit in DC generator.

B-SUPPLY: Voltages supplied for plate circuits of electron tubes.

BUFFER: Type of amplifier placed between oscillator and power amplifier to isolate oscillator from load.

BYPASS CAPACITOR: Fixed capacitor which bypasses unwanted AC to ground.

BX CABLE: Cable sheathed in metallic armor.

CABLE: May be stranded conductor or group of single conductors insulated from each other.

CAPACITANCE: Inherent property of electric circuit that opposes change in voltage. Property of circuit whereby energy may be stored in electrostatic field.

CAPACITIVE COUPLING: Coupling resulting from capacitive effect between components or elements in electron tube.

CAPACITIVE REACTANCE (X_C): Opposition to AC as a result of capacitance.

CAPACITOR: Device which possesses capacitance. Simple capacitor consists of two metal plates separated by insulator.

CAPACITOR INPUT FILTER: Filter employing capacitor as its input.

CAPACITOR MOTOR: Modified version of split-phase motor, employing capacitor in series with its starting winding, to produce phase displacement for starting.

CAPACITY: Ability of battery to produce current over given length of time. Capacity is measured in ampere-hours.

CARRIER: Usually radio frequency continuous wave to which modulation is applied. Frequency of transmitting station.

CARRIER (in a semiconductor): Conducting hole or electron.

CASCADE: Arrangement of amplifiers where output of one stage becomes input of next, throughout series of stages.

CASCODE: Electron tubes connected so second tube acts as plate load for first. Used to obtain higher input resistance and retain low noise factor.

CATHODE: Emitter in electron tube.

CATHODE FOLLOWER: Single-stage Class-A amplifier, output of which is taken from across unbypassed cathode resistor.

CATHODE RAY TUBE: Vacuum tube in which electrons emitted from cathode are shaped into narrow beam and accelerated to high velocity before striking phosphor-coated viewing screen.

CAT WHISKER: Fine wire used to contact a crystal.

C-BATTERY: Battery used to supply grid bias voltages.

CENTER FREQUENCY: Frequency of transmitted carrier wave in FM when no modulation is applied.

CENTER TAP: Connection made to center of coil.

CHARACTERISTIC CURVE: Graphical representation of characteristics of component, circuit or device.

CHOKE INPUT FILTER: Filter employing choke as its input.

CIRCUIT BREAKER: Safety device which automatically opens circuit if overloaded.

CIRCULAR MIL: Cross sectional area of conductor one mil in diameter.

CIRCULAR-MIL-FOOT: Unit conductor one foot long with cross sectional area of one circular mil.

CIRCULATING CURRENT: Inductive and capacitive currents flowing around parallel circuit.

COAXIAL LINE: Concentric transmission line in which inner conductor is insulated from tubular outer conductor.

COEFFICIENT OF COUPLING (K): Percentage of coupling between coils, expressed as a decimal.

COLLECTOR: The electrode that collects electrons in a tube after they have performed their function.

COMMON BASE: Transistor circuit, in which base is common to input and output circuits.

COMMON COLLECTOR: Transistor circuit in which collector is common to input and output circuits.

COMMON EMITTER: Transistor circuit in which emitter is common to input and output circuits.

COMMUTATION: Process of reversing current in armature coils and conducting direct current to external circuit by means of commutator segments and brushes.

COMMUTATOR: Group of bars providing connections between armature coils and brushes. Mechanical switch to maintain current in one direction in external circuit.

COMPOUND GENERATORS, Degree of: FLAT. When no-load and full-load voltages have same value.

OVER. Full-load voltage is higher than no-load voltage.

UNDER. Full-load voltage is less than no-load voltage.

CONDENSER: Older name for a capacitor.

CONDUCTANCE (symbol G): Ability of circuit to conduct current. It is equal to amperes per volt and is measured in mhos. $G = \dfrac{1}{R}$

CONDUCTION BAND: Outermost energy level of atom.

CONDUCTIVITY, N type: Conduction by electrons in N-type crystal.

CONDUCTIVITY, P type: Conduction by holes in a P-type crystal.

CONDUCTOR: Material which permits free motion of large number of electrons.

CONTINUOUS WAVE (cw): Uninterrupted sinusoidal rf wave radiated into space, with all wave peaks equal in amplitude and evenly spaced along time axis.

CONTRAST: In television. Relative difference in intensity between blacks and whites in reproduced picture.

CONTROL GRID: Grid in vacuum tube closest to cathode. Grid to which input signal is fed to tube.

CONVERTER: Electromechanical system for changing alternating current to direct current.

CO-ORDINATES: Horizontal and vertical distances to locate point on graph.

COPPER LOSSES: Heat losses in motors, generators and transformers as result of resistance of wire. Sometimes called the I^2R loss.

COULOMB: Quantity of electrons representing 6.28×10^{18} electrons.

COUNTER EMF (cemf): Voltage induced in conductor moving through magnetic field which opposes source voltage.

COUPLING: Percentage of mutual inductance between coils. LINKAGE.

COVALENT BOND: Atoms joined together, sharing each other's electrons to form stable molecule.

CROSSOVER FREQUENCY: Frequency in crossover network at which equal amount of energy is delivered to each of two loudspeakers.

CROSSOVER NETWORK: Network designed to divide audio frequencies into bands for distribution to loudspeakers.

CROSS NEUTRALIZATION: Method of neutralization used with push-pull amplifiers, where part of output from each tube is fed back to grid circuit of each opposite tube through capacitor.

CROSS TALK: Leakage from one audio line to another which produces objectionable background noise.

CRYSTAL DIODE: Diode formed by small semiconductor crystal and cat whisker.

CRYSTAL LATTICE: Structure of material when outer electrons are joined in covalent bond.

C-SUPPLY: Voltages supplied for grid bias of electron tubes, usually negative voltage.

CURRENT: Transfer of electrical energy in conductor by means of electrons moving constantly and changing positions in vibrating manner.

CUTOFF BIAS: Value of negative voltage applied to grid of tube which will cut off current flow through tube.

CW: Abbreviation for Continuous Wave.

CYCLE: Set of events occurring in sequence. One complete reversal of an alternating current from positive to negative and back to starting point.

DAMPER: Tube used in television set as half-wave rectifier to prevent oscillations in horizontal output transformer.

DAMPING: Gradual decrease in amplitude of oscillations in tuned circuit, due to energy dissipated in resistance.

D'ARSONVAL METER: Stationary-magnet moving coil meter.

DBM: Loss or gain in reference to arbitrary power level of one milliwatt.

DC: Direct current.

DC COMPONENT: DC value of AC wave which has axis other than zero.

DC GENERATOR: Generator with connections to armature through a commutator. Output is direct current.

DECAY: Term used to express gradual decrease in values of current and voltage.

DECIBEL: One-tenth of a Bel.

DECLINATION: Angle between true north and magnetic north.

DEFLECTION: Deviation from zero of needle in meter. Movement or bending of an electron beam.

DEFLECTION ANGLE: Maximum angle of deflection of electron beam in TV picture tube.

DEGENERATIVE FEEDBACK: Feedback 180 deg. out of phase with input signal so it subtracts from input.

DEMODULATION: Process of removing modulating signal intelligence from carrier wave in radio receiver.

DEPLETION LAYER (in a semiconductor): Region in

which mobile carrier charge density is insufficient to neutralize net fixed charge of donors and acceptors. (IRE).

DEPOLARIZER: Chemical agent, rich in oxygen, introduced into cell to minimize polarization.

DETECTION: See DEMODULATION.

DIAPHRAGM: Thin disk, used in an earphone for producing sound.

DIELECTRIC: Insulating material between plates of capacitor.

DIELECTRIC CONSTANT: Numerical figure representing ability of dielectric or insulator to support electric flux. Dry air is assigned number 1.

DIELECTRIC FIELD OF FORCE: See ELECTROSTATIC FIELD.

DIFFUSION: Movement of carriers across semiconductor junction in absence of external force.

DIODE: Two-element tube containing cathode and plate.

DIODE DETECTOR: Detector circuit utilizing unilateral conduction characteristics of diode.

DIRECT CURRENT (dc): Flow of electrons in one direction.

DISTORTION: The deviations in amplitude, phase and frequency between input and output signals of amplifier or system.

AMPLITUDE. Distortion resulting from non-linear operation of electron tube when peaks of input signals are reduced or cut off by either excessive input signal or incorrect bias.

FREQUENCY. Distortion resulting from signals of some frequencies being amplified more than others or when some frequencies are excluded.

PHASE. Distortion resulting from shift of phase of some signal frequencies.

DOMAIN THEORY: Theory concerning magnetism, assuming that atomic magnets produced by movement of planetary electrons around nucleus have strong tendency to line up together in groups. These groups are called "domains."

DONOR IMPURITY: Impurity added to semiconductor material which causes negative electron carriers.

DOPING: Adding impurity to semiconductor material.

DRY CELL: Non-liquid cell, which is composed of zinc case, carbon positive electrode and paste of ground carbon, manganese dioxide and ammonium chloride as electrolyte.

DYNAMIC CHARACTERISTICS: Characteristics of tube describing the actual control of grid voltage over plate current when tube is operating as an amplifier.

DYNAMIC PLATE RESISTANCE: See AC PLATE RESISTANCE.

DYNAMIC SPEAKER: Loudspeaker which produces sound as result of reaction between fixed magnetic field and fluctuating field of voice coil.

DYNAMOMETER: Measuring instrument based on opposing torque developed between two sets of current-carrying coils.

DYNAMOTOR: Motor-generator combination using two windings on single armature. Used to convert AC to DC.

EDISON CELL: Cell using positive electrodes of nickel oxide and negative electrodes of powdered iron. The electrolyte is dilute solution of sodium hydroxide.

EDISON EFFECT: Effect, first noticed by Thomas Edison, that emitted electrons were attracted to positive plate in vacuum tube.

EDDY CURRENT LOSS: Heat loss resulting from eddy currents flowing through resistance of core.

EDDY CURRENTS: Induced currents flowing in rotating core.

EFFECTIVE RESISTANCE: Ratio between true power absorbed in circuit to square of effective current flowing in circuit.

EFFECTIVE VALUE: That value of alternating current of sine wave form that has equivalent heating effect of a direct current. ($.707 \times E_{peak}$)

EFFICIENCY: Ratio between output power and input power.

ELECTRIC FIELD OF FORCE: See ELECTROSTATIC FIELD.

ELECTRODE: Elements in a cell.

ELECTRODYNAMIC SPEAKER: Dynamic speaker that uses electro-magnetic fixed field.

ELECTROLYTE: Acid solution in a cell.

ELECTROLYTIC CAPACITOR: Capacitor with positive plate of aluminum and dry paste or liquid forms negative plate. Dielectric is thin coat of oxide on aluminum plate.

ELECTROMAGNET: Coil wound on soft iron core. When current runs through coil, core becomes magnetized.

ELECTROMOTIVE FORCE (emf): Force that causes free electrons to move in conductor. Unit of measurement is the volt.

ELECTRON: Negatively charged particle.

ELECTROSTRICTION: Piezoelectric property of some elements of undergoing changes in shape and size when voltage is applied and conversely, of producing voltage when subjected to pressure or stress.

ELECTRON TUBE: Highly evacuated metal or glass shell which encloses several elements.

ELECTROSTATIC FIELD: Space around charged body in which its influence is felt.

ELEMENT: One of the distinct kinds of substances which either singly or in combination with other elements, makes up all matter in the universe.

EMISSION: Escape of electrons from a surface.

EMISSION, COLD CATHODE: Phenomena of electrons leaving surface of a material caused by high potential field.

EMISSION, Types of: A0 - Continuous wave, no modution.

A1 - Continuous wave, keyed.

A2 - Telegraphy by keying modulating audio frequency.

A3 - Telephony.

A4 - Facsimile.

A5 - Television.

F0 - Continuous wave, no FM.

F1 - Telegraphy by frequency shift keying.

F2 - Telegraphy by keying modulating audio frequency.

F3 - Telephone - FM.

F4 - Facsimile.

F5 - Television.

EMISSION, Types of: PHOTOELECTRIC. Emission of electrons as result of light striking surface of certain materials.

SECONDARY. Emission caused by impact of other electrons striking surface.

THERMIONIC. Process where heat produces energy for release of electrons from surface of emitter.

EMITTER: In transistor, semiconductor section, either P or N, which emits minority carriers.

EMITTER: Element in a vacuum tube from which electrons are emitted. The CATHODE.

ENERGY: That which is capable of producing work.

Dictionary of Terms

ENVELOPE: Enclosed wave form made by outlining peaks of modulated r-f wave.

EXCITER: Small DC generator used to excite or energize field windings of large alternator.

FARAD: Unit of measurement of capacitance. A capacitor has a capacitance of one farad when charge of one coulomb raises its potential one volt. $C = \dfrac{Q}{E}$

FEEDBACK: Transferring voltage from output of circuit back to its input.

FIELD MAGNETS: Electromagnets which make field of motor or generator.

FILAMENT: Heating element in vacuum tube coated with emitting material so it acts also as cathode.

FILTER: Circuit used to attenuate specific band or bands of frequencies.

FLUORESCENT: Property of a phosphor which indicates that radiated light will be extinguished when electron bombardment ceases.

FLUX DENSITY (symbol B): Number of lines of flux per cross sectional area of magnetic circuit.

FREQUENCY: Number of complete cycles per second measured in cycles per second. (cps).

FREQUENCY BANDS: VLF - Very low frequencies 10-30 kc.

LF - Low frequencies 30-300 kc.

MF - Medium frequencies 300-3,000 kc.

HF - High frequencies 3-30 mc.

VHF - Very high frequencies 30-300 mc.

UHF - Ultra high frequencies 300-3,000 mc.

SHF - Super high frequencies 3,000-30,000 mc.

EHF - Extremely high frequencies 30,000-300,000 mc.

FREQUENCY DEPARTURE: Instantaneous change from center frequency in FM as result of modulation.

FREQUENCY DOUBLER: Amplifier stage in which plate circuit is tuned to twice the frequency of grid tank circuit.

FREQUENCY METER: Meter used to measure frequency of an AC source.

FREQUENCY MODULATION (FM): Modulating transmitter by varying frequency of r-f carrier wave at an audio rate.

FREQUENCY RESPONSE: Rating of device indicating its ability to operate over specified range of frequencies.

FREQUENCY TRIPLER: Amplifier stage in which plate circuit is tuned to three times the frequency (2d. harmonic) of grid circuit.

FULL-WAVE RECTIFIER: Rectifier circuit which produces a DC pulse output for each half cycle of applied alternating current.

FUNDAMENTAL: A sine wave that has same frequency as complex periodic wave. Component tone of lowest pitch in complex tone. Reciprocal of period of wave.

FUSE: Safety protective device which opens an electric circuit if overloaded. Current above rating of fuse will melt fusible link and open circuit.

GAIN: Ratio of output AC voltage to input AC voltage.

GALVANOMETER: Meter which indicates very small amounts of current and voltage.

GAS FILLED TUBE: Tubes designed to contain a specific gas in place of air, usually nitrogen, neon, argon or mercury vapor.

GAUSS: Measurement of flux density in lines per square centimeter.

GENERATOR: Rotating electric machine which provides a source of electrical energy. A generator converts mechanical energy to electric energy.

GENERATORS, Types of: COMPOUND. Uses both series and shunt winding.

INDEPENDENTLY EXCITED. Field windings are excited by separate DC source.

SERIES. Field windings are connected in series with armature and load.

SHUNT. Field windings are connected across armature in shunt with load

GHOST: In TV. Duplicate image of reproduced picture, caused by multipath reception of reflected signals.

GILBERT: Unit of measurement of magneto motive force. Represents force required to establish one maxwell in circuit with one Rel of reluctance.

GRID: Grid of fine wire placed between cathode and plate of an electron tube.

GRID BIAS: Voltage between the grid and cathode, usually negative.

GRID CURRENT: Current flowing in grid circuit of electron tube, when grid is driven positive.

GRID DIP METER: A test instrument for measuring resonant frequencies, detecting harmonics and checking relative field strength of signals.

GRID LEAK DETECTOR: Triode amplifier connected so it functions like a diode detector and an amplifier. Detection takes place in grid circuit.

GRID MODULATION: Modulation circuit where modulating signal is fed to grid of modulated stage.

GRID VOLTAGE: Bias or C voltage applied to grid of a vacuum tube.

HALF-WAVE RECTIFIER: Rectifier which permits one half of an alternating current cycle to pass and rejects reverse current of remaining half cycle. Its output is pulsating DC.

HARMONIC FREQUENCY: Frequency which is multiple of fundamental frequency. Example: If fundamental frequency is 1000 kc, then second harmonic is 2 x 1000 kc or 2000 kc; third harmonic is 3 x 1000 kc or 3000 kc, and so on.

HEATER: Resistance heating element used to heat cathode in vacuum tube.

HEAT SINK: Mass of metal used to carry heat away from component.

HENRY (h): Unit of measurement of inductance. A coil has one henry of inductance if an emf of one volt is induced when current through inductor is changing at rate of one ampere per second.

HETERODYNE: Process of combining two signals of different frequencies to obtain different frequency.

HOLE: Positive charge. A space left by removed electron.

HOLE INJECTION: Creation of holes in semiconductor material by removal of electrons by strong electric field around point contact.

HORIZONTAL POLARIZATION: An antenna positioned horizontally, so its electric field is parallel to earth's surface.

HORSEPOWER: 33,000 ft. lbs. of work per minute or 550 ft. lbs. of work per second equals one horsepower. Also 746 watts = 1 HP.

HUM: Form of distortion introduced in an amplifier as result of coupling to stray electromagnetic and electrostatic fields or insufficient filtering.

HYDROMETER: Bulb-type instrument used to measure specific gravity of a liquid.

HYSTERESIS: Property of magnetic substance that causes magnetization to lag behind force that produces it.

HYSTERESIS LOOP: Graph showing density of magnetic field as magnetizing force is varied uniformly through one cycle of alternating current.

HYSTERESIS LOSS: Energy loss in substance as molecules or domains move through cycle of magnetization. Loss due to molecular friction.

IMPEDANCE (Z): Total resistance to flow of an alternating current as a result of resistance and reactance.

INDIRECTLY HEATED: Electron tube employing separate heater for its cathode.

INDUCED CURRENT: Current that flows as result of an induced emf.

INDUCED EMF: Voltage induced in conductor as it moves through magnetic field.

INDUCTANCE: Inherent property of electric circuit that opposes a change in current. Property of circuit whereby energy may be stored in magnetic field.

INDUCTION MOTOR: AC motor operating on principle of rotating magnetic field produced by out-of-phase currents. Rotor has no electrical connections, but receives energy by transformer action from field windings. Motor torque is developed by interaction of rotor current and rotating field.

INDUCTIVE CIRCUIT: Circuit in which an appreciable emf is induced while current is changing.

INDUCTIVE REACTANCE (X_L): Opposition to an AC current as a result of inductance.

INSTANTANEOUS VALUE: Any value between zero and maximum depending upon instant selected.

INSULATION RESISTANCE: Resistance to current leakage through and over surface of insulating material.

INSULATORS: Substances containing very few free electrons and requiring large amounts of energy to break electrons loose from influence of nucleus.

INTENSITY (H): Magnetizing force per unit length of magnetic circuit.

INTERELECTRODE CAPACITANCE: Capacitance between metal elements in an electron tube.

INTERLACE SCANNING: Process in television of scanning all odd lines and then all even lines to reproduce picture. Used in U. S.

INTERNAL RESISTANCE: Refers to internal resistance of source of voltage or emf. A battery or generator has internal resistance which may be represented as a resistor in series with source.

INTERPOLES: Auxillary poles located midway between main poles of generator to establish flux for satisfactory commutation.

INTERRUPTED CONTINUOUS WAVE (ICW): Continuous wave radiated by keying transmitter into long and short pulses of energy, (dashes and dots), conforming to code such as Morse Code.

INTERSTAGE: Existing between stages, such as an interstage transformer between two stages of amplifiers.

INTRINSIC SEMICONDUCTOR: Semiconductor with electrical characteristics similar to a pure crystal.

IONIZATION: An atom is said to be ionized when it has lost or gained one or more electrons.

IONIZATION POTENTIAL: Voltage applied to a gas-filled tube at which ionization occurs.

IONOSPHERE: Atmospheric layer from 40 to 350 miles above the earth, containing a high number of positive and negative ions.

IR DROP: See VOLTAGE DROP.

IRON VANE METER: Meter based on principle of repulsion between two concentric vanes placed inside a solenoid.

JOULE: Unit of energy equal to one watt-second.

JUNCTION DIODE: PN junction, having unidirectional current characteristics.

JUNCTION TRANSISTOR: Transistor consisting of thin layer of N or P type crystal between P or N type crystals. Designated as NPN or PNP.

KEY: Manually-operated switch used to interrupt r-f radiation of transmitter.

KEY CLICK FILTER: Filter in keying circuit of a transmitter to prevent surges of current and prevent sparking at key contacts.

KEYING: Process of causing c-w transmitter to radiate an r-f signal when key contacts are closed.

KEYING, SYSTEMS OF: CATHODE. Key is inserted in grid and cathode circuits of keyed stage.

GRID-BLOCK. Keying stage by applying high negative voltage on grid of tube.

PLATE. Key is inserted in plate circuit of stage to be keyed.

KILO: Prefix meaning one thousand times.

KILOGAUSS: One thousand gausses.

KILOWATT-HOUR (Kwh): Means 1,000 watts per hour. Common unit of measurement of electrical energy for home and industrial use. Power is priced by the Kwh.

KIRCHHOFF'S CURRENT LAW: At any junction of conductors in a circuit, algebraic sum of currents is zero.

KIRCHHOFF'S LAW OF VOLTAGES: In simple circuit, algebraic sum of voltages around circuit is equal to zero.

LAGGING ANGLE: Angle current lags voltage in inductive circuit.

LAMBDA: Greek letter λ. Symbol for wavelength.

LAMINATIONS: Thin sheets of steel used in cores of transformers, motors and generators.

LAWS OF MAGNETISM: Like poles repel; Unlike poles attract.

L/C RATIO: Ratio of inductance to capacitance.

LEAD ACID CELL: Secondary cell which uses lead peroxide and sponge lead for plates, and sulfuric acid and water for electrolyte.

LEADING ANGLE: Angle current leads voltage in capacitive circuit.

LECLANCHE CELL: Scientific name for common dry cell.

LEFT-HAND RULE: A method, using your left hand, to determine polarity of an electromagnetic field or direction of electron flow.

LENZ'S LAW: Induced emf in any circuit is always in such a direction as to oppose effect that produces it.

LINEAR AMPLIFIER: An amplifier whose output is in exact proportion to its input.

LINEAR DETECTOR: Detector using linear portions of characteristic curve on both sides of knee. Output is proportional to input signal.

LINEAR DEVICE: Electronic device or component whose current-voltage relation is a straight line.

LINEARITY: Velocity of the scanning beam. It must be uniform for good linearity.

LINES OF FORCE: Graphic representation of electrostatic and magnetic fields showing direction and intensity.

LOAD: Resistance connected across circuit which determines current flow and energy used.

LOADING A CIRCUIT: Effect of connecting voltmeter across circuit. Meter will draw current and effective resistance of circuit is lowered.

LOAD LINE: Line drawn on characteristic family of

curves of electron tube, when used with specified load resistor, representing plate current at zero and maximum plate voltage.

LOCAL ACTION: Defect in voltaic cells caused by impurities in zinc, such as carbon, iron and lead. Impurities form many small internal cells which contribute nothing to external circuit. Zinc is wasted away, even when cell is not in use.

LOCAL OSCILLATOR: Oscillator in superheterodyne receiver, output of which is mixed with incoming signal to produce intermediate frequency.

LODESTONE: Natural magnet, so called a "leading stone" or lodestone because early navigators used it to determine directions.

LOUDSPEAKER: Device to convert electrical energy into sound energy.

L-SECTION FILTER: Filter consisting of capacitor and an inductor connected in an inverted L configuration.

MAGNET: Substance that has the property of magnetism.

MAGNETIC AMPLIFIER: Transformer type device employing a DC control winding. Control current produces more or less magnetic core saturation, thus varying output voltage of amplifier.

MAGNETIC CIRCUIT: Complete path through which magnetic lines of force may be established under influence of magnetizing force.

MAGNETIC FIELD: Imaginary lines along which magnetic force acts. These lines emanate from N pole and enter S pole, forming closed loops.

MAGNETIC FLUX (symbol Φ phi): Entire quantity of magnetic lines surrounding a magnet.

MAGNETIC LINE OF FORCE: Magnetic line along which compass needle aligns itself.

MAGNETIC MATERIALS: Materials such as iron, steel, nickel and cobalt which are attracted to magnet.

MAGNETIC PICKUP: Phono cartridge which produces an electrical output from armature in magnetic field. Armature is mechanically connected to reproducing stylus.

MAGNETIC SATURATION: This condition exists in magnetic material when further increase in magnetizing force produces very little increase in flux density. Saturation point has been reached.

MAGNETOMOTIVE FORCE (F) (mmf): Force that produces flux in magnetic circuit.

MAGNETIZATION: Graph produced by plotting intensity of magnetizing force on X axis and relative magnetism on Y axis.

MAGNETIZING CURRENT: Current used in transformer to produce transformer core flux.

MAGNET POLES: Points of maximum attraction on a magnet; designated as North and South poles.

MAJOR CARRIER: Conduction through semi-conductor as result of majority of electrons or holes.

MATTER: Physical substance of common experience. Everything about us is made up of matter.

MAXIMUM POWER TRANSFER: This condition exists when resistance of load equals internal resistance of source.

MAXIMUM VALUE: Peak value of sine wave either in positive or negative direction.

MAXWELL: One single line of magnetic flux.

MEGA: Prefix meaning one million times.

MERCURY VAPOR RECTIFIER: Hot cathode diode tube which uses mercury vapor instead of high vacuum.

METALLIC RECTIFIER: Rectifier made of copper oxide, based on principle that electrons flow from copper to copper oxide but not from copper oxide to copper. It is unidirectional conductor.

MHO: Unit of measurement of conductance.

MICA CAPACITOR: Capacitor made of metal foil plates separated by sheets of mica.

MICRO: Prefix meaning one millionth of.

MICROFARAD (μf): One millionth of a farad.

MICROHENRY (μh): One millionth of a henry.

MICROMHO: One millionth of a mho.

MICROMICRO: Prefix meaning one millionth of one millionth of.

MICROMICROFARAD ($\mu\mu$f): One millionth of one millionth of a farad.

MICROPHONE: Energy converter that changes sound energy into corresponding electrical energy.

MICROSECOND: One millionth of a second.

MIL: One thousandth of an inch. (.001 inches).

MIL-FOOT: A wire which is one mil in diameter and one foot long.

MILLI: Prefix meaning one thousandth of.

MILLIAMMETER: Meter which measures in milliammeter range of currents.

MILLIHENRY (mh): One thousandth of a henry.

MINOR CARRIER: Conduction through semiconductor opposite to major carrier. Ex: If electrons are major carrier, then holes are minor carrier.

MINUS (symbol -): Negative terminal or junction of circuit.

MISMATCH: Incorrect matching of load to source.

MIXER: Multi-grid tube used to combine several input signals.

MODULATED CONTINUOUS WAVE (mcw): Carrier wave amplitude modulated by tone signal of constant frequency.

MODULATION: Process by which amplitude or frequency of sine-wave voltage is made to vary according to variations of another voltage or current called modulation signal.

MOLECULE: Smallest division of matter. If further subdivision is made, matter will lose its identity.

MOTOR: Device which converts electrical energy into mechanical energy.

MOTOR REACTION: Opposing force to rotation developed in generator, created by load current.

MOTORS, Types of DC: COMPOUND. Uses both series and parallel field coils.

SERIES. Field coils are connected in series with armature circuit.

SHUNT. Field coils are connected in parallel with armature circuit.

MU (μ): Greek letter representing the amplification factor of a tube.

MULTIELEMENT TUBE: Electron tube with more elements than cathode, plate and grid.

MULTIGRID TUBE: Special tube with 4, 5 or 6 grids.

MULTIMETER: Combination volt,ampere and ohm meter.

MULTIPLIER: Resistance connected in series with meter movement to increase its voltage range.

MULTIUNIT TUBES: HEXODE. Six elements with four grids.

HEPTODE. Seven elements with five grids.

OCTODE. Eight elements with six grids.

TWIN DIODE. Two diodes in one envelope.

TWIN DIODE-TRIODE. Diode and triode in one envelope.

TWIN DIODE TETRODE. Diode and tetrode in one envelope.

TWIN PENTODE: Two pentodes in one envelope.

MULTIVIBRATORS, Types of: ASTABLE. A free-running multivibrator.

BISTABLE. A single trigger pulse switches conduction from one tube to the other.

CATHODE COUPLED. Both tubes have a common cathode resistor.

FREE RUNNING. Frequency of oscillation depending upon value of circuit components. Continuous oscillation.

MONOSTABLE. One trigger pulse is required to complete one cycle of operation.

ONE SHOT. Same as MONOSTABLE.

PLATE COUPLED. The plates of the tubes and grids are connected by RC networks.

MUTUAL INDUCTANCE (M): When two coils are so located that magnetic flux of one coil can link with turns of other coil so change in flux of one coil will cause an emf in other, there is mutual inductance.

NATURAL MAGNET: Magnets found in natural state in form of mineral called Magnetite.

NEGATIVE ION: Atom which has gained electrons and is negatively charged.

NETWORK: Two or more components connected in either series or parallel.

NEUTRALIZATION: Process of feeding back voltage from plate of amplifier to grid, 180 deg. out of phase, to prevent self-oscillation.

NEUTRON: Particle which is electrically neutral.

NICKEL CADMIUM CELL: Alkaline cell with paste electrolyte hermetically sealed. Used in aircraft.

NO LOAD VOLTAGE: Terminal voltage of battery or supply when no current is flowing in external circuit.

NONLINEAR DEVICE: Electronic device or component whose current-voltage relation is not a straight line.

NUCLEUS: Core of the atom.

OERSTED: Unit of magnetic intensity equal to one gilbert per centimeter.

OHM (symbol Ω): Unit of measurement of resistance.

OHMMETER: Meter used to measure resistance in ohms.

OHM'S LAW: Mathematical relationship between current, voltage and resistance discovered by George Simon Ohm. $I = \dfrac{E}{R}$ $E = IR$ $R = \dfrac{E}{I}$

OHMS PER VOLT: Unit of measurement of sensitivity of a meter.

OPEN CIRCUIT: Circuit broken or load removed. Load resistance equals infinity.

OSCILLATOR: An electron tube generator of alternating current voltages.

OSCILLATORS, Types of: ARMSTRONG. An oscillator using tickler coil for feedback.

COLPITTS. An oscillator using split tank capacitor as feedback circuit.

CRYSTAL-CONTROLLED. Oscillator controlled by piezoelectric effect.

ELECTRON COUPLED OSCILLATOR (ECO): Combination oscillator and power amplifier utilizing electron stream as coupling medium between grid and plate tank circuits.

HARTLEY. Oscillator using inductive coupling of tapped tank coil for feedback.

PUSH-PULL. Push-pull circuit utilizing interelectrode capacitance of each tube to feed back energy to grid circuit to sustain oscillations.

RC OSCILLATORS. Oscillators depending upon charge and discharge of capacitor in series with resistance.

TRANSITRON. Oscillator utilizing negative transconductance.

TUNED-GRID TUNED-PLATE. Oscillator utilizing tuned circuits in both grid and plate circuits.

ULTRAUDION. Oscillator, similar to Colpitts, but employing grid-to-cathode and plate-to-cathode interelectrode capacitances for feedback.

OSCILLOSCOPE: Test instrument, using cathode ray tube, permitting observation of signal.

OVERMODULATION: Condition when modulating wave exceeds amplitude of continuous carrier wave, resulting in distortion.

PARALLEL CIRCUIT: Circuit which contains two or more paths for electrons supplied by common voltage source.

PARALLEL RESONANCE: Parallel circuit of an inductor and capacitor at frequency when inductive and capacitive reactances are equal. Current in capacitive branch is 180 deg. out of phase with inductive current and their vector sum is zero.

PARASITIC OSCILLATION: Oscillations in circuit resulting from circuit components or conditions, occuring at frequencies other than that desired.

PEAK: Maximum value of sine wave.

PEAK INVERSE VOLTAGE: Value of voltage applied in reverse direction across diode.

PEAK INVERSE VOLTAGE RATING: Inverse voltage diode will withstand without arcback.

PEAK TO PEAK: Measured value of sine wave from peak in positive direction to peak in negative direction.

PEAK VALUE: Maximum value of an alternating current or voltage.

PENTAGRID CONVERTER: Tube with five grids.

PENTAVALENT: Semi-conductor impurity having five valence electrons. Donor impurities.

PENTODE: Electron tube with five elements including cathode, plate, control grid, screen grid and suppressor grid.

PERCENTAGE OF MODULATION: Maximum deviation from normal carrier value as result of modulation expressed as a percentage.

PERCENTAGE OF RIPPLE: Ratio of rms value of ripple voltage to average value of output voltage expressed as a percentage.

PERIOD: Time for one complete cycle.

PERMEANCE (P): Ability of a material to carry magnetic lines of force. The reciprocal of reluctance. $P = \dfrac{1}{R}$

PERMEABILITY (symbol μ): Relative ability of substance to conduct magnetic lines of force as compared with air.

PERMANENT MAGNET: Bars of steel and other substances which have been permanently magnetized.

PHASE: Relationship between two vectors in respect to angular displacement.

PHASE INVERTER: Device or circuit that changes phase of a signal 180 deg.

PHASE SPLITTER: Amplifier which produces two waves that have exactly opposite polarities from single input wave form.

PHOTOSENSITIVE: Characteristic of material which emits electrons from its surface when energized by light.

PHOTOTUBE: Vacuum tube employing photo sensitive material as its emitter or cathode.

PICOFARAD (pf): Same as micromicrofarad.

PICTURE ELEMENT: Small areas or dots of varying intensity from black to white which contain visual image of scene.

PIERCE OSCILLATOR: Crystal oscillator circuit in which crystal is placed between plate and grid circuit of tube.

PIEZOELECTRIC EFFECT: Property of certain crystalline substances of changing shape when an emf is impressed upon crystal. Action is also reversible.

PI-SECTION FILTER: Filter consisting of two capacitors and an inductor connected in a π configuration.

PITCH: Property of musical tone determined by its frequency.

PLATE: Anode of vacuum tube. Element in tube which attracts electrons.

PLATE DETECTOR: R-f signal is amplified and detected in plate circuit. Tube is biased to approximately cutoff by cathode resistor.

PLATE EFFICIENCY: Ratio between useful output power to DC input power to plate of electron tube.

PLATE MODULATION: Modulation circuit where modulating signal is fed to plate circuit of modulated stage.

PLUS (symbol +): Positive terminal or junction of circuit.

PM SPEAKER: Loudspeaker employing permanent magnet as its field.

PN JUNCTION: Piece of N-type and a piece of P-type semi-conductor material joined together.

POINT CONTACT DIODE: Diode consisting of point and a semi-conductor crystal.

POLARITY: Property of device or circuit to have poles such as North and South or positive and negative.

POLARIZATION: Defect in cell caused by hydrogen bubbles surrounding positive electrode and effectively insulating it from chemical reaction.

POLARIZATION: Producing magnetic poles or polarity.

POLES: Number of poles in motor or generator field.

POLYPHASE: Consisting of currents having two or more phases.

POSITIVE ION: Atom which has lost electrons and is positively charged.

POWER: Rate of doing work. In DC circuits $P = I \times E$.

POWER AMPLIFICATION: Ratio of output power to input grid driving power.

POWER DETECTOR: Detector designed to handle signal voltages having amplitudes greater than one volt.

POWER FACTOR: Relationship between true power and apparent power of circuit.

POWER SUPPLY: Electronic circuit designed to provide various AC and DC voltages for equipment operation. Circuit may include transformers, rectifiers, filters and regulators.

PREAMPLIFIER: Sensitive low-level amplifier with sufficient output to drive standard amplifier.

PREEMPHASIS: Process of increasing strength of signals of higher frequencies in FM at transmitter to produce greater frequency swing.

PRIMARY CELL: Cell that cannot be recharged.

PRIMARY WINDING: Coil of transformer which receives energy from AC source.

PROTON: Positively charged particle.

PULSE: Sudden rise and fall of a voltage or current.

PUSH-PULL AMPLIFIER: Two tubes used to amplify signal in such a manner that each tube amplifies one half cycle of signal. Tubes operate 180 deg. out of phase.

Q: Letter representation for quantity of electricity (coulomb).

Q: Quality, figure of merit; ratio between energy stored in inductor during time magnetic field is being established to losses during same time.

$$Q = \frac{X_L}{R}$$

QUANTA: Definite amount of energy required to move an electron to higher energy level.

QUIESCENT: At rest. Inactive.

RADIO FREQUENCY CHOKE (RFC): Coil which has high impedance to rf currents.

RADIO SPECTRUM: Division of electromagnetic spectrum used for radio.

RASTER: Area of light produced on screen of TV picture tube by electron beam. Contains no picture information.

RATIO DETECTOR: Type of FM detector.

REACTANCE (X): Opposition to alternating current as result of inductance or capacitance.

REACTIVE POWER: Power apparently used by reactive component of circuit.

RECIPROCAL: Reciprocal of number is one divided by the number.

RECTIFIER: Component or device used to convert AC into a pulsating DC.

REGENERATIVE FEEDBACK: Feedback in phase with input signal so it adds to input.

REGULATION: Voltage change that takes place in output of generator or power supply when load is changed.

REGULATION, PERCENTAGE OF: Percentage of change in voltage from no-load to full-load in respect to full-load voltage. Expressed as: $\dfrac{E \text{ no load} - E \text{ full load}}{E \text{ full load}} \times 100 = \%$

REJECT CIRCUIT: Parallel tuned circuit at resonance. Rejects signals at resonant frequency.

REL: Unit of measurement of Reluctance.

RELATIVE CONDUCTANCE: Relative conductance of material in reference to Silver which is considered as 100 per cent.

RELATIVE RESISTANCE: Numerical comparison of resistance of a material compared to Silver which is assigned value 1.0.

RELAY: Magnetic switch.

RELAXATION OSCILLATOR: Non-sinusoidal oscillator whose frequency depends upon time required to charge or discharge capacitor through resistor.

RELUCTANCE: Resistance to flow of magnetic lines of force.

REMOTE CUTOFF TUBE: Tube which gradually approaches its cutoff point at remote bias point, due to special grid construction.

REPULSION-START MOTOR: Motor which develops starting torque by interaction of rotor currents and single-phase stator field.

RESIDUAL MAGNETISM: Magnetism remaining in material after magnetizing force is removed.

RESISTANCE: Quality of electric circuit that opposes flow of current through it.

RESONANT FREQUENCY: Frequency at which tuned circuit oscillates. (See TUNED CIRCUIT.)

RETENTIVITY: Ability of material to retain magnetism after magnetizing force is removed.

RETMA: Radio Electronics Television Manufacturer's Association.

RETRACE: Process of returning scanning beam to starting point after one line is scanned.

REVERSE CURRENT CUTOUT: Relay which permits current to flow only in one direction.

RIPPLE VOLTAGE: AC component of DC output of power supply due to insufficient filtering.

RMS VALUE: ROOT-MEAN-SQUARE value. The same

Electricity - Electronics

as effective value. (.707 x E_{peak})

ROLL-OFF: Gradual attenuation with increase or decrease in frequency of signal.

ROTOR: Rotating part of an AC generator.

ROWLAND'S LAW: Law for magnetic circuits which states that number of lines of magnetic flux is in direct proportion to magnetomotive force and inversely proportional to reluctance of circuit. $\Phi = \dfrac{F}{R}$

RUBEN CELL (RM cell): Mercury cell employing mercuric oxide and zinc. Electrolyte is potassium hydroxide.

RUMBLE: Low-frequency mechanical vibration of a turntable which is transmitted to recorded sound.

SATURATION CURRENT: Current through electron tube when saturation voltage is applied to plate.

SATURATION VOLTAGE: Voltage applied to plate of vacuum tube so all emitted electrons are attracted to plate.

SAWTOOTH GENERATOR: Electron tube oscillator producing sawtooth wave form.

SAWTOOTH WAVE: Wave shaped like teeth of saw.

SCAN: Process of sweeping electron beam across each element of picture in successive order, to reproduce total picture in television.

SCHEMATIC: Diagram of electronic circuit showing electrical connections and identification of various components.

SCREEN GRID: Second grid in electron tube between control grid and plate, to reduce interelectrode capacitance.

SECONDARY CELL: Cell that can be recharged by reversing chemical action with electric current.

SECONDARY EMISSION: Emission of electrons as result of electrons striking plate of electron tube.

SECONDARY WINDING: Coil which receives energy from primary winding by mutual induction and delivers energy to load.

SECOND HARMONIC DISTORTION: Distortion of wave by addition of its second harmonic.

SELECTIVITY: Relative ability of receiver to select desired signal while rejecting all others.

SELF-INDUCTANCE: Emf is self-induced when it is induced in conductor carrying current.

SEMI-CONDUCTOR: Conductor with resistivity somewhere in range between conductors and insulators.

SEMI-CONDUCTOR, N type: Semi-conductor which uses electrons as major carrier.

SEMI-CONDUCTOR, P type: Semi-conductor which uses holes as major carrier.

SENSITIVITY: Ability of circuit to respond to small signal voltages.

SENSITIVITY OF METER: Indication of loading effect of meter. Resistance of moving coil and multiplier divided by voltage for full scale deflection. Sensitivity equals one divided by current required for full scale deflection. Ex: A 100 μa meter movement has sensitivity of $\dfrac{1}{.0001}$ or 10,000 ohms/volt.

SERIES CIRCUIT: Circuit which contains only one possible path for electrons through circuit.

SERIES PARALLEL: Groups of series cells with output terminals connected in parallel.

SERIES RESONANCE: Series circuit of inductor, a capacitor and resistor at a frequency when inductive and capacitive reactances are equal and cancelling. Circuit appears as pure resistance and has minimum impedance.

SHADED POLE MOTOR: Motor in which each of its field poles is split to accommodate a short-circuit copper strap called a shading coil. This coil produces a sweeping movement of field across pole face for starting.

SHIELD: Partition or enclosure around components in circuit to minimize effects of stray magnetic and radio frequency fields.

SHORT CIRCUIT: Direct connection across source which provides zero resistance path for current.

SHOT EFFECT: Noise produced in electron tube as a result of variation in rate of electron emission from the cathode.

SHUNT: To connect across or parallel with circuit or component.

SHUNT: Parallel resistor to conduct excess current around meter moving coil. Shunts are used to increase range of meter.

SIDEBANDS: Frequencies above and below carrier frequency as result of modulation.
LOWER. Frequencies equal to difference between carrier and modulating frequencies.
UPPER. Frequencies equal to carrier plus modulating frequencies.

SIDE CARRIER FREQUENCIES: Waves of frequencies equal to sum and difference between carrier wave frequency and modulating wave frequency.

SINE WAVE: A graphical representation of a wave whose strength is proportional to the sine of an angle that is a linear function of time or distance.

SINGLE PHASE MOTOR: Motor which operates on single phase alternating current.

SINUSOIDAL: Wave varying in proportion to sine of angle.

SKY WAVE: Waves emanating toward sky from radio antenna.

SLIP RINGS: Metal rings connected to rotating armature windings in generator. Brushes sliding on these rings provide connections for external circuit.

SOCKET: Device for holding lamp or electron tube.

SOFT TUBE: Gaseous tube.

SOLENOID: Coil of wire carrying electric current possessing characteristics of magnet.

SOURCE OF SUPPLY: The device attached to input of circuit which produces electromotive force. May be generator, battery or other device.

SPACE CHARGE: Cloud of electrons around cathode of an electron tube.

SPECIFIC GRAVITY: Weight of liquid in reference to water which is assigned value 1.0.

SPLIT PHASE MOTOR: Single-phase induction motor, which develops starting torque by phase displacement between field windings.

SQUARE LAW DETECTOR: Detector whose output voltage is proportional to square of effective input voltage.

SQUIRREL CAGE ROTOR: Rotor used in an induction motor made of bars placed in slots of rotor core and all joined together at ends.

STAGE: Section of an electronic circuit, usually containing one electron tube and associated components.

STANDING WAVE: Wave in which ratio of instantaneous value at one point to that at another point does not vary with time. Waves appearing on transmission line as a result of reflections from termination of line.

STANDING WAVE RATIO: Ratio of effective voltage at loop of standing wave to effective voltage at node. It may also be expressed by effective current. Also ratio of characteristic impedance to load impedance.

STATIC CHARACTERISTICS: Characteristics of tube

taken with constant plate voltage.

STATIC CHARGE: Charge on body either negatively or positively.

STATIC ELECTRICITY: Electricity at rest as opposed to electric current.

STATOR: Stationary coils of an AC generator.

STEADY STATE: Fixed non-varying condition.

STORAGE BATTERY: Common name for lead-acid battery used in automotive equipment.

STRATOSPHERE: Atmosphere above troposphere in which temperature is constant and there is no cloud formation.

STYLUS: Phonograph needle or jewel, which follows grooves in a record.

SUBHARMONIC: Frequency below harmonic, usually fractional part of fundamental frequency.

SULFATION: Undesirable condition of lead-acid battery caused by leaving it in discharged condition or by improper care. Sulfates forming on plates make battery partially inactive.

SUPERSONIC: Frequencies above audio frequency range.

SURFACE ALLOY TRANSISTOR: Silicon junction transistor, in which aluminum electrodes are deposited in shallow pits etched on both sides of thin silicon crystal, forming P regions.

SUPERHETERODYNE: Radio receiver in which incoming signal is converted to fixed intermediate frequency before detecting audio signal component.

SUPPRESSOR GRID: Third grid in electron tube, between screen grid and plate, to repel or suppress secondary electrons from plate.

SWEEP CIRCUIT: Periodic varying voltage applied to deflection circuits of cathode ray tube to move electron beam at linear rate.

SWITCH: Device for directing or controlling current flow in circuit.

SYNCHRO: Electromechanical device used to transmit angular position of shaft from one position to another without mechanical linkage.

SYNC PULSE: Abbreviation for synchronization pulse, used for triggering an oscillator or circuit.

SYNCHRONOUS: Having same period or frequency.

SYNCHRONOUS MOTOR: Type of AC motor which uses a separate DC source of power for its field. It runs at synchronous speed under varying load conditions.

SYNCHRONOUS VIBRATOR: Vibrator with additional contact points to switch output circuit so current is maintained in one direction through load.

TANK CIRCUIT: Parallel resonant circuit.

TAP: Connection made to coil at point other than its terminals.

TELEVISION: Method of transmitting and receiving visual scene by radio broadcasting.

TELEVISION CHANNEL: Allocation in frequency spectrum of 6 mc assigned to each television station for transmission of picture and sound information.

TETRODE: Electron tube with four elements including cathode, plate, control grid and screen grid.

THERMAL RUNAWAY: In transistor, regenerative increase in collector current and junction temperature.

THERMISTOR: Semi-conductor device which changes resistivity with change in temperature.

THERMOCOUPLE METER: Meter based on principle that if two dissimilar metals are welded together and junction is heated, a DC voltage will develop across open ends. Used for measuring radio frequency currents.

THETA (θ): Angle of rotation of vector representing selected instants at which sine wave is plotted. Angular displacement between two vectors.

THORIATED TUNGSTEN: Tungsten emitter coated with thin layer of Thorium.

THREE-PHASE ALTERNATING CURRENT: Combination of three alternating currents having their voltages displaced by 120 deg. or one third cycle.

THRESHOLD OF SOUND: Minimum sound at particular frequency which can be heard.

THYRATRON: Gas-filled tube in which grid is used to control firing potential.

TICKLER: Coil used to feed back energy from output to input circuit.

TIME CONSTANT (RC): Time period required for the voltage of a capacitor in an RC circuit to increase to 63.2% of maximum value or decrease to 36.7% of maximum value.

TONE CONTROL: Adjustable filter network to emphasize either high or low frequencies in output of audio amplifier.

TRANSCONDUCTANCE (Symbol g_m): Grid plate transconductance of vacuum tube expressed as ratio of small change in plate current to small change in grid voltage while plate voltage is held constant. Measured in mhos.

TRANSDUCER: Device by which one form of energy may be converted to another form, such as electrical, mechanical or acoustical.

TRANSFER CHARACTERISTIC: Relation between input and output characteristics of device.

TRANSFORMER: Device which transfers energy from one circuit to another by electromagnetic induction.

TRANSFORMERS, Types: ISOLATION. Transformer with one-to-one turns ratio.

STEP-DOWN. Transformer with turns ratio greater than one. The output voltage is less than input voltage.

STEP-UP. Transformer with turns ratio of less than one. Output voltage is greater than input voltage.

TRANSIENT RESPONSE: Response to momentary signal or force.

TRANSISTOR: Semi-conductor device derived from two words, transfer and resistor.

TRANSMISSION LINE: Wire or wires used to conduct or guide electrical energy.

TRANSMITTER: Device for converting intelligence into electrical impulses for transmission through lines or through space from radiating antenna.

TRF: Abbreviation for TUNED RADIO FREQUENCY.

TRIODE: Three-element vacuum tube, consisting of cathode, grid and plate.

TRIVALENT: Semi-conductor impurity having three valence electrons. Acceptor impurity.

TROPOSPHERE: Lower part of earth's atmosphere in which clouds form and temperature decreases with altitude.

TRUE POWER: Actual power absorbed in circuit.

TUNED AMPLIFIER: Amplifier employing tuned circuits for input and/or output coupling.

TUNED CIRCUIT: Circuit containing capacitance, inductance and resistance in series or parallel, which when energized at specific frequency known as its resonant frequency, an interchange of energy occurs between coil and capacitor.

TURNS RATIO: Ratio of number of turns of primary winding of transformer to number of turns of secondary winding.

Electricity - Electronics

UNITY COUPLING: If two coils are positioned so all lines of magnetic flux of one coil will cut across all turns of second coil, it is called UNITY COUPLING.

UNIVERSAL MOTOR: Series AC motor which operates also on DC. Fractional horsepower AC-DC motor.

UNIVERSAL TIME CONSTANT CHART: Graph with curves representing growth and decay of voltages and currents in RC and RL circuits.

VALVE: British name for vacuum tube.

VARIABLE MU TUBE: Tube with increased range of amplification due to its remote cutoff characteristics.

VECTOR: Straight line drawn to scale, showing direction and magnitude of a force.

VECTOR DIAGRAM: Diagram showing direction and magnitude of several forces, such as voltage and current, resistance, reactance and impedance.

VELOCITY FACTOR: Velocity of propagation of signal along transmission line compared to speed of light.

VERTICAL POLARIZATION: Antenna positioned vertically so its electric field is perpendicular to earth's surface.

VIBRATOR: Magnetically operated interrupter, similar to door bell or buzzer, to change steady state DC to a pulsating DC.

VIDEO SIGNAL: Electrical signal from studio camera used to modulate TV transmitter.

VOICE COIL: Small coil attached to speaker cone, to which signal is applied. Reaction between field of voice coil and fixed magnetic field causes mechanical movement of cone.

VOLT (symbol E in electricity, symbol V in semiconductor circuits): Unit of measurement of electromotive force or potential difference.

VOLTAGE DIVIDER: Tapped resistor or series resistors across source voltage to produce multiple voltages.

VOLTAGE DOUBLER: Rectifier circuit which produces double the input voltage.

VOLTAGE DROP: Voltage measured across resistor. Voltage drop is equal to product of current times resistance in ohms. E = IR.

VOLTAGE MULTIPLIER: Rectifier circuits which produce output voltage at multiple greater than input voltage, usually doubling, tripling or quadrupling.

VOLTAGE REGULATOR TUBE: Cold cathode gas-filled tube which maintains constant voltage drop independent of current, over its operating range.

VOLTAIC CELL: Cell produced by suspending two dissimilar elements in acid solution. Potential difference is developed by chemical action.

VOLTMETER: Meter used to measure voltage.

V-R TUBE: Gas-filled, cold cathode tube used for voltage regulation.

VTVM: Vacuum Tube Volt Meter.

VU: Number numerically equal to number of decibels above or below reference volume level. Zero Vu represents power level of one milliwatt dissipated in 600-ohm load or voltage of .7746 volts.

WATT: Unit of measurement of power.

WATT-HOUR: Unit of energy measurement, equal to one watt per hour.

WATT-HOUR METER: Meter which indicates instantaneous rate of power consumption of device or circuit.

WATTLESS POWER: Power not consumed in an AC circuit due to reactance.

WATTMETER: Meter used to measure power in watts.

WAVE LENGTH: Distance between point on loop of wave to corresponding point on adjacent wave.

WAVE METER: Meter used to measure frequency of wave.

WAVE TRAP: Type of band reject filter.

WEAK-SIGNAL DETECTOR: Detector designed to handle signal voltages having amplitudes of less than one volt.

WHEATSTONE BRIDGE: Bridge circuit used for precision measurement of resistors.

WORK: When a force moves through a distance, work is done. It is measured in foot-pounds and, Work = Force x Distance.

WORKING VOLTAGE: Maximum voltage that can be steadily applied to capacitor without danger of arc-over.

WOW: Low-frequency flutter resulting from variations in turntable speeds.

WWV and WWVH: National Bureau of Standards Radio Stations in Washington D.C. and Hawaii respectively.

X AXIS: Horizontal axis of a graph.

X AXIS: Axis drawn through corners of hexagonal crystal.

X-CUT CRYSTAL: Crystal cut perpendicular to X axis.

YAGI ANTENNA: Dipole with two or more director elements.

Y-AXIS: Vertical axis of graph.

Y-AXIS: Axis drawn perpendicular to faces of hexagonal crystal.

Y-CUT CRYSTAL: Crystal cut perpendicular to Y axis.

YOKE: Coils placed around neck of TV picture tube for magnetic deflection of beam.

Z AXIS: Optical axis of crystal.

ZERO REFERENCE LEVEL: Power level selected as reference for computing gain of amplifier or system.

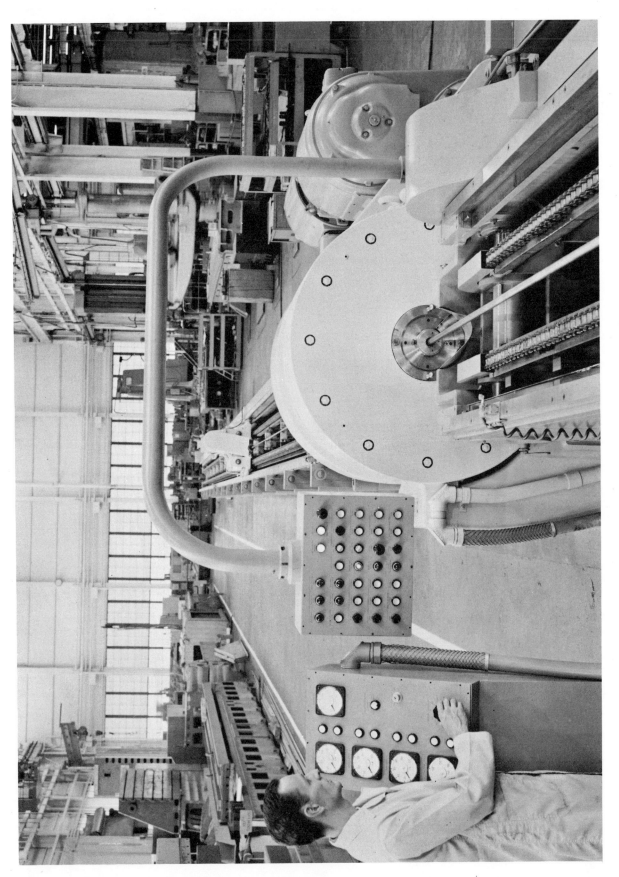

Controls of Cincinnati Intraform machine being operated by technician.

INDEX

Index

Index